AF528824

BEEKEEPING

EVERETT FRANKLIN PHILLIPS, Ph.D.
Professor of Apiculture,
New York State College of Agriculture,
Cornell University

AGROBIOS (INDIA)

Published by:
AGROBIOS (INDIA)
Agro House, Behind Nasrani Cinema
Chopasani Road, Jodhpur 342 002
Phone: 91-0291-2642319, Fax: 2643993
E. mail: agrobios@sify.com

AGROBIOS (INDIA)

First Indian Published 2003
Reprinted 2006
Reprinted 2010

ISBN (10): 81-7754-108-0
ISBN (13): 978-81-7754-108-3

Published by: Dr. Updesh Purohit for Agrobios (India), Jodhpur
Lasertypeset at: Yashee Computers and Printers, Jodhpur
Cover Design by: Reena
Printed at: Bharat Printing Press, Jodhpur

PREFACE TO SECOND EDITION

This book, first issued in 1915, is the result of an effort to present a logical discussion of various phases of the complex subject of beekeeping. It was not planned as a book of rules to which one may go for directions for each day's work, for beekeeping cannot be treated correctly in such a way. The activities of bees vary during the season and no two localities present to the bees and their owners exactly the same environmental conditions, so that the successful beekeeper is one who has a knowledge of the activities of bees, whereby he can interpret what he sees in the hives from day to day, and who can mold the instincts of the bees to his convenience and profit.

In the earlier chapters bees are discussed as they live and behave without man's interference, thus giving the foundations on which all sound practice rests. The beekeeper is not especially interested in the anatomy of the bee and, while it is necessary to use illustrations of various organs and to describe them briefly, an effort is made to treat the bee as a living animal (as something that happens) and to have the discussion deal with physiology and especially with activities, in so far as investigations have thrown light on these processes. In the preparation of the chapters devoted to apiary management, an effort is made to present the various systems of management in such a way that underlying principles shall be evident, rather than to attempt to describe each system as if it were separate.

For many years the author was in charge of the work in Bee Culture of the Bureau of Entomology and he is under lasting obligations to all his colleagues in that institution for assistance, not only in the preparation of this book but in a myriad of other ways. The more important published papers of these men are mentioned in the text. In the preparation of the portion on sources of honey in the first edition, valued help was received from F. V. Coville, of the Bureau of Plant Industry, and this part remains virtually unchanged in the present edition. In the earlier edition the author received help of incalculable value from his friend, the late Doctor C. C. Miller, and the present edition finds little need to change anything of which he approved earlier. After many years of work in association with the many persons who are working and who have worked for the advancement of American beekeeping, it becomes wholly impossible to mention all those whose efforts have helped to make this book possible, but for all these persons the author retains a sentiment of cordial thanks.

The illustrations used were drawn for the book by the late J. F. Strauss or were taken from publications of the Bureau of Entomology. A few illustrations are individually credited.

In presenting a book which aims to bring the more essential beekeeping knowledge down to date in a concise manner, the author would express the hope that it may be as helpful to his readers as the constant assistance and cooperation of many of them have been to him in his work.

E. F. PHILLIPS.

ITHACA, NEW YORK,
April, 1928.

CONTENTS

CHAPTER I

CHAPTER II

CHAPTER III

CHAPTER IV

CHAPTER V

CHAPTER VI

Contents

CHAPTER VII

CHAPTER VIII

CHAPTER IX

CHAPTER X

CHAPTER XI

CHAPTER XII

Contents

CHAPTER XIII

CHAPTER XIV

CHAPTER XV

CHAPTER XVI

CHAPTER XVII

CHAPTER XVIII

CHAPTER XIX

CHAPTER XX

CHAPTER XXI

CHAPTER XXII

Contents

LIST OF ILLUSTRATIONS

NOTE.—Illustrations taken from Farmers' Bulletins of the Department of Agriculture are not marked in cases in which the present author prepared the bulletins. Other illustrations are credited by authors individually.

List of Illustrations

List of Illustrations

BEEKEEPING

CHAPTER I

BEEKEEPING AS AN OCCUPATION

THE keeping of bees for the pleasure derived from their study and for the benefits and profits arising from their products has been an important vocation or avocation for many centuries, and there are now thousands who follow this pursuit. Aside from interest in the bees themselves, which is often adequate excuse for keeping them, their chief product, honey, is the most desirable form of sweet for human consumption, and, although many species of insects feed on nectar, the honeybee is the only agency for collecting for man's use the vast supply of sugar in the nectar which nature pours forth so lavishly.

An occupation as old as beekeeping, probably the oldest branch of agriculture, naturally has a thrilling history. There have been woven about the bee a vast folk-lore and many traditions and superstitions which find no place in modern beekeeping. There has also been written a vast literature on bees and their care, so vast that efforts to collect this literature are usually given up in despair. Bees were the basis for the founding of an ancient order of nobility and beekeeping is today the reason for many human organizations. Poets, philosophers, artists and artisans have found in bees an interesting subject, since the life of the bee colony is as unlike that of human society as one should expect the society of Mars to be, if such exists. Honey-production has been considered worthy of support from governmental agencies for centuries and is today moderately well supported from such sources in all parts of the civilized world. All this interest in bees arises from the fact that the bees themselves are enchanting and that their product, honey, is universally recognized as the highest form of natural food, unspoiled by man's manipulation. Beekeeping is, therefore, not living on its past but progresses steadily.

While bees have been studied for many centuries, within the past two or three decades knowledge of them has vastly increased. With the increased interest in biological study and with the improvement in technique and facilities for such work, the honeybee has attracted its share of biologists. The results of such investigations appear in books and scientific journals, but unfortunately most of the papers devoted to the more scientific phases of bee investigations usually fail to find mention in the journals devoted more especially to the practical part of apiary work. There has been a similar increase in knowledge of the best methods for managing bees from a more careful study of the requirements for colony prosperity and from the more intensive management demanded by modern commercial enterprises. There has also been considerable change in beekeeping methods due to a general change to the production of extracted honey. In this book an effort is made to present the more important results of these lines of change and advancement, although with such a wealth of material one finds difficulty in deciding which are the more important and what may be omitted without serious loss. The good beekeeper is one whose interest does not limit itself to the so-called practical methods of management, a fact well expressed by the noted German bee-master, von Berlepsch, who said: "Study theory or remain forever a bungler in practice." It is necessary that the informed beekeeper know the facts of bee behavior and physiology underlying practice, for beekeeping is not a matter of hives, honey-houses, extracting outfits and automobile trucks: it is applied bee behavior, and this is the theory which the beekeeper must know.

Coincident with the increase in knowledge of bees and beekeeping methods, there has been, especially in the United States and Canada, a corresponding advance in facilities for making these facts widely known. Thirty years ago the teaching of beekeeping was almost unknown, whereas today this subject finds a place in the curricula of a large number of colleges and universities. There has been an advance in opportunities for the practicing beekeeper to profit by the newer knowledge through extension teaching. The gospel of the "new beekeeping" is thus being spread and only the beekeeper who refuses to listen to these teachings fails to benefit thereby. This teaching of the more modern methods rests securely on the newer knowledge regarding the biological requirements of the bee colony, so that modern beekeeping owes its very existence to those who discover the scientific facts on which practice rests.

EXTENT OF BEEKEEPING IN THE UNITED STATES AND CANADA[1]

It is usually not known that beekeeping has so many followers. Unfortunately the data presented by the United States Census are quite unreliable, due partly to the fact that account is not taken of bees and beekeepers in towns

[1] For data on the extent of beekeeping in the United States, reference is made to the following sources of information:

Phillips, E. F., 1908. The status of apiculture in the United States. Bull. 75, part 5, Bur. Ent.

Root, E. R., 1923. Foreword *in* A B C and X Y Z of bee culture. Medina, Ohio: The A. I. Root Co.

Jones, S. A., 1915. Honeybees: wintering, yields, imports and exports of honey. Bull. 325, U. S. Dept. Agr., 12 pp.

Jones, S. A., 1918. Honeybees and honey production in the United States. Bull. 685, U. S. Dept. Agr., 61 pp.

Phillips, E. F., 1917. A wasted sugar supply. Yearbook of the U. S. Dept. Agr., 8 pp.

Data obtained by the Bureau of the Census appears in the various publications of that Bureau and may at times be of interest in making comparisons in various parts of the country. The data should never be accepted as exact. The data of the 1920 census for numbers of colonies of bees are presented graphically in Baker, O. E., 1921. A graphic summary of American agriculture, Yearbook of the U. S. Dept. Agr., pp. 407-506. The map on bees is on p. 488. *See also Fig. 99,* p. 229 of this book.

and cities, as a result of which omission most of the apiaries in the hands of commercial beekeepers are not included in the census figures. It is variously estimated that there are from 800,000 to 1,000,000 persons in the United States owning bees, and the Census reports over 500,000 farms alone on which bees were kept in 1919. The average number of colonies is small, perhaps not over ten to a beekeeper for the country as a whole. Certain definite trends are observable over a period of years, namely that the number of beekeepers is gradually decreasing, while the number of colonies of bees to a beekeeper is increasing, resulting in an actual increase in the total number of colonies and in their value. During the period of the World War, because of the greatly increased demand for honey, there was a marked increase in the number of colonies of bees in almost all parts of the country and during this period there was also an increase in the number of commercial beekeepers, thus bringing about a more rapid change along the lines which had previously been observed.

The aggregate crop of honey is also sufficiently great to cause surprise to one not familiar with beekeeping. The average value of the crop for the United States is at least $30,000,000, based on the present wholesale prices of the product. If this were calculated on the basis of retail prices, the amount would be considerably greater. The average value of the beeswax crop is probably about $2,000,000.

Census data for the Dominion of Canada seem to be almost as useless as are those of the United States in gauging the extent of beekeeping. Morley Pettit, formerly of the Ontario Agricultural College, is authority for the estimate that the Province of Ontario contains 300,000 colonies of bees. Ontario has long been the leading honey-producing province, but there is now a remarkable development in Quebec and in western provinces. As will be seen from later discussions, Canada has great advantages in honey-production, because of the more prolific yields of nectar at high latitudes, and apparently the present industry of beekeeping in Canada is only a promise of what is to come.

In addition to the financial value of the honey and wax crops, bees have a value to agriculture and to human economy that is doubtless far greater. Peculiarly the beekeeper is not the one who receives the greatest financial profit from the keeping of bees, for the honeybee is one of the most beneficial insects in cross-pollinating fruit and forage crops (Fig. 2) and is by far the most dependable of all insects which perform this necessary function. Bees may be taken to the orchard or field at the right time and in proper numbers to insure the setting of the crop which cannot be done with any other species of insect which is also capable of this work. In many orchards and in most commercial orchards honeybees are responsible for the setting of most of the crop, so that the honeybee is of far greater financial value in this function than as a honey-producer. In all matters pertaining to the advancement of beekeeping, the beekeeper should find a warm ally in the fruit-grower.

Fig. 2.—A bee and apple blossoms. Bees are valuable as agents of cross-pollination.

LIMITATIONS ON THE DEVELOPMENT OF BEEKEEPING

Beekeeping is from its very nature one of the minor branches of agriculture. A colony of bees requires a large supply of honey for its maintenance before it can provide any for human use, and the amount of nectar, although large, is limited by factors beyond human control. If too many persons were to keep bees or if too many colonies were placed in a limited region, there would be a reduction or loss of surplus honey, and for these reasons it is unwise to advocate beekeeping on every farm. The raw material of honey costs the beekeeper nothing and unless gathered by bees it is irrevocably and immediately lost. The labor of so managing the bees that they are able to gather a surplus of honey for human use takes time and study but if colonies of bees are wisely managed and properly located, the beekeeper is repaid for his labors. The supply of nectar secreted annually throughout the country is vast beyond human comprehension, but this does not indicate that beekeeping can be developed indefinitely. Bees require not only a large supply of nectar but a more or less regular supply, with periods of larger yields which the beekeeper calls a honey-flow, during which honey is produced beyond the needs of the bees. Usually not more than one hundred colonies may be kept with profit in one location, this being especially true of the clover region of the northeastern states. There should also usually be a distance of three to five miles between large apiaries, due allowance being made for numerous small apiaries scattered about the country. There is, therefore, a distinct limitation on the number of large apiaries which can be established in any region and beekeeping cannot with profit be expanded as widely as has sometimes been claimed. The problem in the expansion and development of beekeeping is so to distribute apiaries as to permit their management to return an adequate profit to the beekeeper and to gather the available supply of nectar economically and efficiently.

THE FUTURE OF BEEKEEPING

Unquestionably there is great opportunity for future development of beekeeping in the United States and Canada. Various writers have ventured estimates of the amount of nectar available without sufficient bees to gather it, these guesses varying greatly. It is doubtless a safe estimate that ten times the present crop of honey might be produced without exhausting the nectar resources or overstocking the country. In order that the vast store of sugar in this desirable form may be better conserved for human use, a careful planning of the location of competing apiaries would be necessary. As a rule, beekeepers are extremely careful and considerate of others in this regard and cooperate well in avoiding the territory of each other. There is naturally an element of selfishness in this cooperation—as there is in most cooperation, in fact.

The just fear is frequently expressed by beekeepers that if more of this vast store of nectar were made available to mankind as honey, the honey market would be so overstocked as to remove all profit from honey-production. If there should be a sudden marked increase in production, there would unquestionably be a drop in prices, and to that degree this fear is well grounded. There is, however, an increasing sale of honey throughout the year instead of in the autumn only, and this will provide an outlet for more honey than is now consumed. Furthermore an increase in production would doubtless result in the development of a real wholesale market, instead of the makeshift now known by that name. A larger supply of honey would induce larger and better firms to handle it, whereas now many good commercial houses refuse to handle honey because of the uncertainty of getting supplies. With increased production, more persons would be able to know what a good food honey is, whereas now there is such a small per capita production that the supply is soon exhausted in the average year. That the present crop is inadequate for present need is shown by the fact that there is rarely any appreciable amount of honey carried over to the following year, regardless of an unusual crop, and what carry-over there is may be attributed to poor distribution methods. In fact, the greater part of the annual crop is consumed before the holiday season and those who fail to provide for their needs before that time must usually go without honey until a new crop is marketed.

It must be recognized that with the present small production, many families never use honey, and many children grow to adults without ever tasting it. There can be an increase in the use of honey in baking, in cooking and in the making of confectionery, offering an excellent outlet for the darker grades. The use of honey in the making of anti-freeze mixture for automobiles, a form of sacrilege, will give an outlet for all the honey now produced if this use continues to develop. With such a condition of the possibilities of the honey market, there is no reason for the beekeeper to be pessimistic about the future, even though in some years he has difficulty in selling some of his crop or some kinds of honey. Honey is an advantageous product, for it keeps indefinitely, being far better in this regard than any other farm product, no cold storage being necessary except for a few types of honey.

TWO CLASSES OF BEEKEEPERS

Since the beginning of commercial honey-production to supply the larger markets, beekeepers may be classed broadly in two groups, so-called amateur beekeepers and commercial or professional beekeepers. The amateurs roughly include those who keep only a few colonies of bees for study or to provide their families with honey, perhaps selling a little locally. They are found in towns, villages, suburbs and cities throughout the country and constitute the great majority of those owning bees. The commercial beekeepers are those who make a real business of honey-production and on whom the supplying of the wholesale honey markets chiefly rests. Various conditions make it desirable, from the standpoint both of beekeeping and the honey market, that the number of commercial beekeepers be increased and that every possible aid be given to this phase of beekeeping, and this is definitely the trend in America today. No other course is possible if honey is to be provided regularly for more tables. Because of their higher skill, the beekeepers owning large numbers of colonies are able to obtain better crops to a colony, thus making their colonies of more economic value and likewise serving better to conserve the available nectar.[1]

The amateur beekeeper is, however, an important factor in beekeeping, for he is a most enthusiastic advertiser of honey and helps materially in the sale of the products of the commercial beekeeper. Furthermore it is usually from the ranks of the enthusiastic amateurs that commercial beekeepers are recruited. It often happens that the newer and better methods of beekeeping are accepted more quickly by the amateur than by the commerical producer, who has already developed his own methods, and without the amateurs it would often be difficult to advance beekeeping along the newer lines.

There is much to be said in favor of recruiting the ranks of commercial beekeepers from amateurs, for it is usually the best plan to begin beekeeping on a small scale and to increase the number of colonies as one's knowledge and experience increase. There are many details in beekeeping which make for success and these are rarely learned solely from reading or instruction. It is commendable to make the bees pay for themselves and for additional apparatus and colonies.

An additional reason for supporting amateur beekeepers is that they usually constitute the best support of bee-

[1] This is well shown from data obtained by B. F. Kindig in summarizing data obtained from 787 beekeepers of Michigan, as a result of an inquiry sent to 1600 beekeepers.

No. colonies	*Avg. No. colonies*	*No. beekeepers reporting*	*Avg. yields per colony*	*Money returns per colony*
1-9	4.33	295	22.9	$7.25
10-24	16	186	28.5	8.55
25-49	34	132	36	10.25
50-99	65	89	45	12.27
100 plus	200	85	57	15.06

keepers' organizations, often being more willing to give time and labor to the associations than are busy commercial beekeepers. They, as well as commercial honey-producers, get much profit and pleasure from association with kindred souls, bound together by a common interest in bees. This bond of union finds expression in the fraternal tone of articles in bee-journals and in the intimacy of beekeepers in their associations and in private life. This sympathy arises from the fact that, perhaps unknowingly, all beekeepers recognize that there is a fascination in the study of bees, regardless of the financial benefits derived therefrom, and from the fact that they are engrossed in the study of an animal so foreign to the knowledge of the public at large.

WHO SHOULD BE A BEEKEEPER?

Beekeeping is a peculiar occupation in that it can be followed in town or country, by young or old, by rich or poor. Many women are numbered among the ranks of beekeepers. To the professional or business man, it offers a change from the confinement of office or laboratory. To the mechanic, it serves equally as well for recreation. Many teachers find it a desirable occupation during vacation, at which time it adds not a little to the meager incomes provided by parsimonious school-boards. Lawyers, artists, farmers, ministers, merchants, brokers, professors in universities and laborers are numbered among its devotees. Several old men known to the writer are kept mentally alert by their work and interest in the bees, while one boy friend of eight summers is a veteran in enthusiasm. Among the ranks of professional beekeepers are well-educated and uneducated men of all ages and with all the mental and physical defects or advantages in the category.

With such an array, it may seem fruitless to ask who should be beekeepers. The care of bees is not, however, equally well suited to all persons, and it would save much disappointment, both financial and otherwise, if this question were more frequently asked before embarking on this business. First of all should be excluded those persons who are seriously affected by the poison of bee-stings. To some this is a serious matter and, unless it is imperative that they care for bees, it is better for them not to undertake it. To practically all beginners the stings are annoying, and the experienced beekeeper, however much he may brag of his indifference to stings, still suffers as much pain from the prick as he did at first. With time and numerous stings, an immunity to the poison is developed which eliminates the after-swelling, which is the most annoying feature of the stinging. Nervous persons who cannot take stings without excitement would do better to keep away from bees, as there are times when the best of beekeepers will be punctured.

To keep bees with interest and profit requires an intimate study of the insects and a detailed knowledge of their needs. It further requires a knowledge of the plants from which they gather nectar so that the necessary steps may be taken to get the colonies in proper condition for the work required of them. To be a good beekeeper, one must read and re-read the books and journals pertaining to the subject, for each reading, accompanied by additional experience among the bees, brings out some new point which proves important in the practical work. Furthermore, the beekeeper cannot work by rule of thumb. Bees are living lively animals and may be "expected to do the unexpected," as beekeepers so often express it. For this reason, it is necessary for the beekeeper to know the behavior of bees in all phases and in so far as they have been determined, which is not far, the causes of their various activities. Obviously, the successful beekeeper is a naturalist and such persons are born, not made successfully. Patience, power of concentration and sympathetic understanding of the bees are essentials and, as a result, the bees become pets rather than beasts of burden to the true bee-crank. Persons who fail to appreciate bees from this point of view will probably find it more pleasant and profitable to let them alone. Like all general statements about bees, there are exceptions to this one. Some who are financially successful beekeepers are totally devoid of sympathetic interest in bees and have learned to handle them as it were by force. Such men are out of place as amateur beekeepers and indeed fail to reach the highest success as professionals.

The ardent bee-man finds pleasure in comparing experiences and observations with his co-workers, in conventions and out, and some of the best "conventions" are those in which two or three experienced beekeepers spend half or more of the night in talking over their latest ideas. They discuss new and supposedly improved apparatus and all the latest systems of manipulation, for there seem to be styles and fads in beekeeping as in clothes. The man who fails to find pleasure in such an interchange of views will find himself out of place among bee-enthusiasts.

Not only is a knowledge of what to do necessary for success with bees, but it is equally necessary that the right thing be done at the right time. To put on comb-honey supers too late, to delay the necessary steps in swarm control or to neglect the preparation of bees for winter, all mean loss in bees, honey and money. In the make-up of the beekeeper must be promptness to do the things which his experience teaches. In the hands of the wise, the bees need remarkably little attention. They should not be manipulated daily and the hive is better unopened unless some change is called for. The beginner errs almost universally in over-manipulation. It must not be forgotten, however, that the reduction in handling which comes with experience is not neglect, and the beekeeper must know daily whether the condition of the nectar-secreting plants or of his colonies calls for any manipulation. This requires experience and observation and finally promptness in doing what is necessary.

Instead then of being an occupation fitted for everyone, beekeeping is well fitted only to the minority. The array of human excellences here enumerated are not all necessarily present in perfection, but the nearer the approach of these qualities to that happy state, the more satisfactory will beekeeping be found as a vocation or avocation. It is to be hoped that these formidable requirements will not deter the potential bee-crank from making a beginning.

Beekeeping for women.

A question much discussed in books and journals on bees is that of beekeeping for women. Many women can and do handle bees with marked success. In those parts of the business which require delicacy of touch and minute attention, such as queen-rearing, women often surpass men in proficiency. As amateur beekeepers they are at home. The question which usually presents itself, however, is whether beekeeping is suitable for women as a means of livelihood and repeatedly has the writer been asked for advice on this subject. Professional beekeeping on a scale sufficiently large to supply an adequate income requires long hours of work in the hot sun, heavy lifting and unremitting physical endurance. On a small scale these obstacles may be overcome, but in a commercial apiary the work must be done promptly, for delay means loss. While some women have found pleasure and profit in commercial beekeeping, it emphatically cannot be recommended for the majority, and this should be made clear to avoid disappointment for those who may be attracted to it. Of course, this applies only to those women who have no man in the company to do the heavy work. Many a professional beekeeper has receive assistance of incalculable value from the women of the family. It should be made clear that the obstacles to the commercial success of women beekeepers are physical ones only.

Beekeeping for professional men.

In parts of Europe the rank and file of beekeepers are ministers, teachers and men of other professions, whereas in America a much smaller proportion of such men is engaged in beekeeping. This difference is reflected in the beekeeping literature of the different countries. The professional man who can spare the time will find much of interest in bees and if he takes the proper care they will be profitable. Beekeeping will give him a recreation which will probably constitute his greatest profit and give him an outside interest and another field of study throughout the year in which he will take much pleasure.

Without intended disparagement of those engaged in beekeeping, one of the men in the work for the advancement of American beekeeping has often said that what is most needed in American beekeeping today is an improvement of the personnel, meaning by this statement that beekeeping would profit by having in its ranks a larger proportion of men of good education and ability to think scientifically. If a large number of men of that calibre were engaged in beekeeping, there would be better support for the advancement of beekeeping along proper scientific lines, the current literature of beekeeping would be improved by their contributions and the beekeepers' associations would be strengthened. So many men engaged in teaching or in the ministry would make good beekeepers and would at the same time be helped by the added financial support that it seems strange that in North America their aid has not been obtained in the advancement of beekeeping. It is entirely proper to call the attention of men of these classes to the benefits which they would receive from beekeeping, if for no other reason than the benefit which beekeeping would in turn receive from their support.

ADVANTAGES OF EXTENSIVE BEEKEEPING

Several references have been made to the desirability of encouraging professional beekeeping, and this should be explained to avoid misunderstanding. Everyone who desires to keep bees, of course, has that privilege, so long as by so doing he does not interfere with the rights of others. By common consent, a man's bees are not considered as trespassing when they go outside his land for forage and consequently a beekeeper cannot legally or morally claim the exclusive right to keep bees in a locality. The beginner, therefore, is not considered as overstepping his rights in getting bees. Taking a broader view of the subject, however, the professional beekeeper by his knowledge of the subject is able to produce larger crops, thereby utilizing the available nectar more economically. By this same knowledge and his better equipment, he is able to produce a better quality of honey. It is, therefore, evident that from the standpoint of conserving a resource to the best advantage there is reason to encourage the extensive beekeeper.

In case a brood disease breaks out in a community, there is every reason for taking sides with the professional beekeeper. The man with a few colonies is not financially interested to an extent which will compel him to care for the disease, and in disease control it is usually necessary that there be some incentive to compel action, the financial incentive being most efficient. The small beekeeper usually becomes a menace to the industry in such an outbreak and not until most of these men lose all they have is much progress made against disease.

The most economical development of the larger honey markets for the beekeepers of any region can come only through cooperation in buying necessary supplies and in selling their products. So long as there are so many thousands of beekeepers with small financial interest in the industry, such cooperation is rendered virtually impossible and the industry is thereby retarded. In some of the western states, beekeeping is conducted chiefly by extensive beekeepers and they have found cooperation practical and profitable, while the beekeepers of the East still fight their battles individually, cooperation being made practically impossible by the thousands of beekeepers who could not be reached by such movement.

Similarly, it is difficult to bring about concerted effort

in passing desirable laws for the protection of the industry or in instituting any agency for the advancement of the industry unless there are a number of men whose financial interest is sufficient to induce them to spend time and money in working for the things they need as beekeepers. Beekeepers are very human, and "money talks" in this business as well as in other lines of human endeavor. There is, therefore, adequate reason in the view that the development of beekeeping to its true place in American agriculture depends on the making of a large number of professional beekeepers and this in turn implies the elimination of the beekeeper with a few colonies, little interest and still less of willingness to work for the industry.

While the number of professional beekeepers is increasing in a way to give satisfaction to those interested in the best development of the industry, a word of caution may not be amiss. Some beekeepers feel that as professionals they must engage in no other business, whereas for certain months they are not occupied for more than a small fraction of the time. Without entering into a moral discussion on the virtue of industry or the various things that Satan is said to find for idle hands to do, it is obvious that the professional beekeeper may use other occupations to add to his income just as the amateur beekeeper uses his bees. As the beekeeper becomes more proficient he eliminates all unnecessary manipulation so that the care of a goodly

Fig. 3.—Roof apiary in lower New York City.

number of colonies may take a relatively short time. When the crop is off and sold he has little to engage his attention until the next season, especially if his bees are wintered out-of-doors.

There are, however, certain parts of the country where commercial beekeeping has not proved profitable, or at any rate where there are now few if any extensive honey-

Fig. 4.—An apiary in the sage region of southern California.

producers, a fact which those who insist that beekeeping should be strictly commercial fail to appreciate. In order that nectar available in such places shall not be lost, the only plan is to encourage the better amateur beekeepers to do their best to get all the available honey. In the later discussion of beekeeping regions in the United States, it will be seen that the areas in which commercial beekeeping is profitable are more limited than usually supposed, and in the regions unsuited to commercial honey-production every effort should be made to aid the amateur beekeeper.

WHERE BEES MAY BE KEPT

It has been the pleasure of the writer to visit apiaries on the roofs of city buildings (Fig. 3) and in the almost desert valleys of California (Fig. 4), in city backyards (Fig. 5) and in the mountain wilds, in small towns, on farms, in Canada and in the tropics (Fig. 6). In diversity of location these apiaries are as varied as their owners. While recruits to the ranks of beekeepers may be found in all ages and conditions of men, so bees may be kept in places which would at first appear utterly unproductive, as well as in places which are obviously abundant in their nectar supply. The uninformed observer may fail utterly in his estimate of the value of a location from the standpoint of the bee. Most of the valuable nectar-secreting plants do not have large highly colored flowers, and the cultivated varieties of the flower-garden are of insignificant value. Bees fly for two or three miles for forage and may go even farther

Fig. 5.—Apiary on shed roof, to economize space.

Fig. 6.—Tropical apiary, San Sebastian, Porto Rico.

in emergency. In choosing a location, it is therefore necessary that in the range of flight there be an adequate supply of nectar-producing plants. The ideal location is obviously one in which the nectar supply is near so that it may be obtained without the loss of energy incident to long flights.

RESULTS TO BE EXPECTED

The stories sometimes told of honey crops obtained from single colonies or of rapidity of increase in number of colonies are likely to mislead the beginner and to cause him to believe that beekeeping offers opportunity to get rich rapidly. While it is true that several hundred pounds of honey have at times been obtained from a single colony in a season, this is by no means usual. In apiaries managed for comb-honey-production, it is perhaps fair to estimate the average annual crop at 25 to 30 sections. For extracted honey, larger averages are expected, perhaps from 40 to 60 pounds. In the hands of a good beekeeper there is less difference in the amount of honey of the two kinds harvested, and the good beekeeper also far exceeds these average yields, because of his better management. The financial returns depend on market conditions and on the methods of selling the crop. If sold by the beekeeper direct to a consumer, a pound of extracted honey brings 20 cents up, while a section of comb-honey at present sells to the consumer at 25 cents up. It will be understood that prices vary from year to year, depending on the available supply and on the demands of the market, both factors to a considerable degree outside the control of the individual beekeeper. If the crop is sold to wholesale dealers, the return is considerably less but there is usually less liability of financial loss and less time is consumed in selling. Naturally these estimates must be dependent on the quality of the product and on the neatness of the package. In addition to labor there are certain expenses for supplies, such as comb-foundation, sections, hives and other fixtures, not counting the apparatus used in increasing the apiary.

These may cost from 60 cents to $1.00 for each colony a season.

Estimates such as these are really of little value since the returns differ so greatly according to the kind of honey obtained and the facilities for marketing. For example, the white-clover honey of the North brings a higher wholesale price than do the amber honeys from most regions farther south, but on the other hand the southern beekeeper usually enjoys a longer nectar-secreting season and often obtains larger yields from each colony. Estimates are also greatly modified by the energy displayed by the beekeeper in the development of local markets, some beekeepers selling out their entire crops at good prices and finding it necessary to buy more honey than they produce to care for the demands of the trade which they develop.

Another factor which must not be overlooked is the beekeeper. Anyone may reap a heavy harvest in the season when nectar is abundant, but in the lean years, which come more often than desired, only the good beekeeper makes the most of the nectar at hand. And then come years of practically total dearth of nectar, when feeding is necessary to keep the colonies alive.

Taking all these factors into consideration, it may be justly concluded that a successful beekeeper is usually well repaid for the time he spends in his work, if he considers the return in the sense of wage. He may also consider that he has received the interest on his original relatively small investment. He usually averages little more than this, however, so that beekeeping is in no sense a "get-rich-quick" business. Its advantage as a recreation over most other occupations of a similar character is that it is a means of occupying time not otherwise engaged to a financial profit and the returns, therefore, often add that part to the income which brings comforts and pleasures.

Beekeeping yields a quick return on the investment, for frequently in a good year a colony will pay for itself. In fact, there are few branches of agriculture which on so small an investment will yield as great a return. It may at least be said for the person who decides to try out beekeeping that he does not stand to lose much. This chance calls to mind a conversation with a western friend. In recounting the present advantages and past glory of his beautiful city, he recalled the former gambling days when everything was "open." After a vivid description of those halcyon days and of some of the men of that time, he said, "I knew some of those men well. They were personal friends of mine and they saw nothing wrong in gambling. And I can appreciate their point of view—for I'm a beekeeper myself."

In discussing the financial results, it is far from wise to overlook the other benefits. Beekeeping, to an enthusiast, means out-of-doors and intimacy with these interesting insects which have been studied for centuries and still remain an unsolved riddle in many of their activities. It may mean health to the person confined to an office. It means to a congenial spirit association with bee-enthusiasts, than whom no more optimistic and warm-hearted people exist. If these things make an appeal, then may apiculture be classed as yielding the greatest profits that can be conceived.

If now one attempts to decide for the questioning prospective beekeeper whether he should take up bees, from the previous discussion the whole question is solved: if he will like beekeeping, he should take it up; if not, he would better never have considered it. And this is about as reliable and lucid a prophecy as is usually possible.

CHAPTER II

APPARATUS FOR BEEKEEPING

BEFORE discussing either the activities of bees or their care, it is necessary to have some information regarding the equipment of the apiary, so that in later discussions these items will be understood. This unfortunately gives to the mechanical equipment of beekeeping a prominence to which it is not entitled in the relative importance of apparatus and knowledge of bees as the essential equipment of the beekeeper. The present discussion will deal with the general apparatus, leaving for future chapters special pieces or implements used in certain manipulations and managements.

FIG. 7.—A primitive box-hive.

RELATION OF APPARATUS TO THE DEVELOPMENT OF BEEKEEPING

It may be considered characteristic of human endeavor that when a new piece of apparatus is invented it is first made as complex as possible, and if it becomes widely adopted and is used commercially, much of the later development is in the direction of simplification. This has certainly been true of beekeeping apparatus, and the stage of commercial development of the industry in any country may be judged safely by the complexity of its equipment.

Fig. 8.—Mud hives in Palestine.

Primitive beekeeping consisted simply of giving the bees some sort of cavity in which to live (Fig. 7). Such hives are today exemplified in the mud hives of Palestine (Fig. 8), the straw skeps of some European beekeepers (Fig. 9, 10) and the log hives of the southern states, which are today probably used to house nearly one-third of all colonies in the United States. With such equipment modern beekeeping is impossible.

Fig. 9.—Group of Caucasian hives.

The invention of the movable-frame hive by Langstroth (1851), around which modern beekeeping centers, was the first step in the development of the present apiculture. Some time before this invention, the great bee-master, Dzierzon, had devised a hive having bars on which combs were built by the bees, comparable to the ancient bar-frame hives of Greece (Fig. 11). The movable frame is now used throughout the the world, but the hives holding them vary greatly in various countries and within each country.

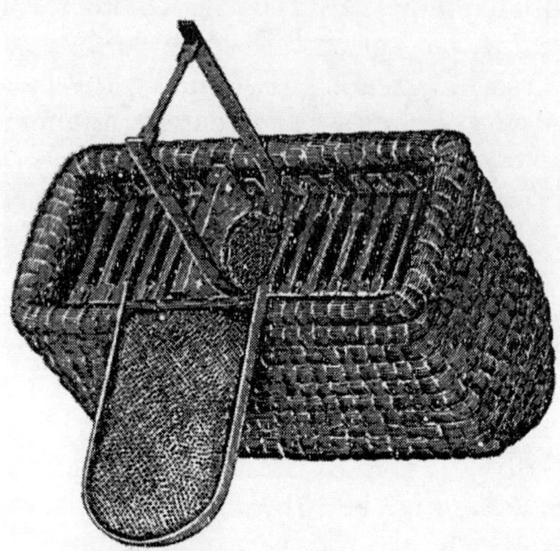

Fig. 10.—Gravenhorst hive, a combination of skep and frame-hive.

Development of frame-hives has followed two main lines, the German method of hives opening at the rear (Fig. 12) and the American method of hives opening at the top (Fig. 13), with unlimited vertical expansion. The American type of construction, which has been adopted in most parts of the world, enables the beekeeper to expand not only the hive but also the size of the colony, and for the newer methods of beekeeping any American hive is serviceable, whereas the German type definitely restricts not only the size of the hive but also the strength of the colony.

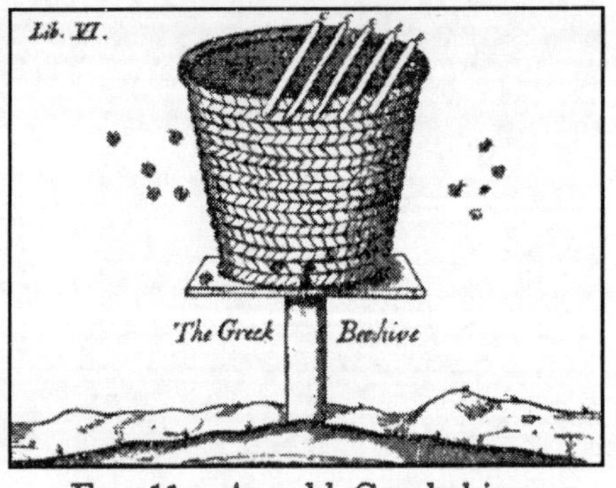

Fig. 11.—An old Greek hive.

In addition to these two types of hives, two distinct systems of management have been devised. Many German, Austrian and Swiss beekeepers provide their bees with elaborately ornamented houses (Fig. 14), each colony of course having its own hive (Fig. 15). Such a plan has been tried in America (Fig. 16) and still has some advocates, but this system has certain drawbacks and has not gained ground. The extensive commercial beekeeper would find it difficult to produce his large crops under such conditions.

FIG. 12.—German hive, opening at the rear.

The hive opening at the top has been variously modified according to what have been assumed to be differences in the needs of bees in different countries. The W. B. C. hive of England (Fig. 17), the C. D. B. hive of Ireland (Figs. 18, 19) and the Dadant-Blatt hive widely used on the continent of Europe are all modifications of the Langstroth. Many European types of hive are far less simple in construction than those used in America. The chief objections to ornate European hives opening at the top are expense, difficulty in providing for large colonies and extreme complexity, which would seriously hamper a busy American beekeeper in the midst of a heavy honey-flow. The hive which may be considered typically American is a plain box (Fig. 13) with freely movable but accurately spaced frames, capable of any amount of vertical expansion. This is an efficient tool for the beekeeper and as suitable a home for bees as any. It is easily moved, easily packed for winter or moved to a cellar, and these

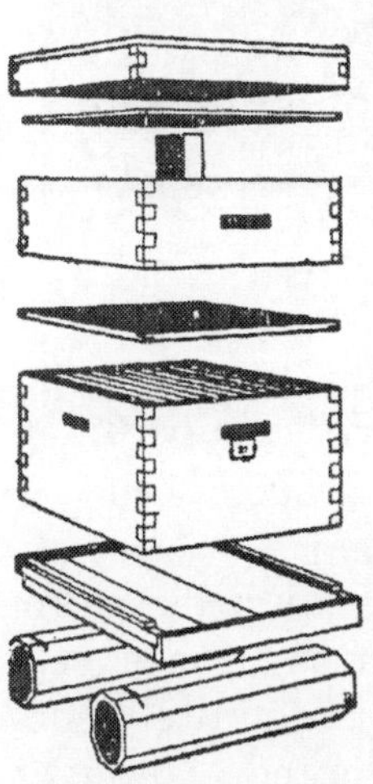

FIG. 13.—Ten-frame Langstroth hive with queen-excluder, comb-honey super and telescope cover.

and other advantages come chiefly from the extreme simplicity demanded by business beekeepers. The original

Fig. 14.—Bee-house in Carniola, Jugoslavia.

Langstroth hive was more complex than the present type, and with the advance of beekeeping every superfluous part has been removed.

Fig. 15.—Carniolan hive.

In this book the apparatus of beekeeping is definitely subordinated and put in what the author believes is its proper place. Tools do not make a beekeeper, for the prime essential is knowledge of bees; yet it is proper to give credit to American equipment as the best set of tools ever devised for

Fig. 16.—Bee-house mentioned in "The Hoosier School Boy."

beekeeping work. American manufacturers of beekeeping supplies deserve credit for their efforts to make the apparatus simple and to a large degree standard, but it is noticeable that present changes in equipment consist largely in providing larger extractors and such equipment as is accessory to the handling of the bees themselves and that little attention is today given to the hive.

Fig. 17.—W.B.C. hive of England.

American equipment is standard for Australia and New Zealand, is used almost universally in South Africa, and is gaining ground in Europe. The American standard frame of Langstroth dimensions has warm advocates among the leading beekeepers of Great Britain and the continent and promises to supplant the small hives formerly thought best suited to conditions in these countries.

RELATIVE IMPORTANCE OF EQUIPMENT AND SKILL

It is important that the relation of equipment of the apiary to the needs of the bees be understood. A hive is not only a home for the bees but a tool for the beekeeper, and being only a tool it is of far less importance in apiary mangement than knowledge of the behavior of bees and skill and experience of the beekeeper in handling them.

Fig. 18.—C.D.B. hive of Ireland.

Apparatus is often given undue importance in discussion of beekeeping among beekeepers and in the literature. Tools alone do not make the mechanic. It is, therefore, proposed here to give only a brief description of the equipment of the apiary, while for greater detail the reader is referred to catalogues of supplies which manufacturers are glad to furnish. A good mechanic adds to his skill, however, a thorough familiarity with his tools, and it has been given as a criticism of modern beekeepers that they lack such familiarity with the tools of the beekeeper.

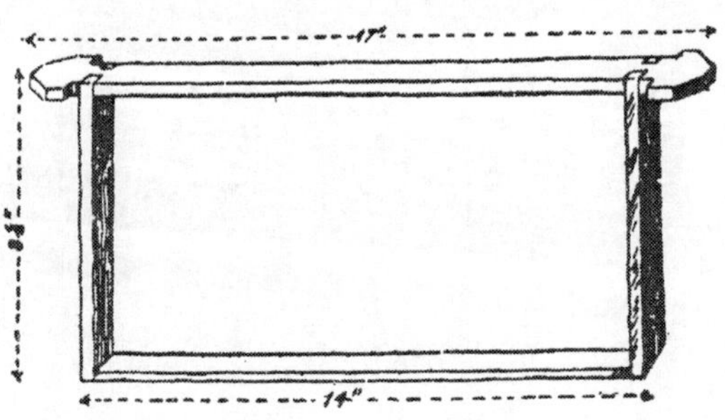

Fig. 19.—Frame of C.D.B. hive.

One does not fully understand the reasons for the dimensions and methods of manufacture of present apparatus unless he is familiar with the evolutionary processes through which they have passed, these changes having been brought about through a vast experience of practical beekeepers. The dimensions are not haphazard, but back of each one there lies a reason. In some cases, it is true, dimensions which were adopted for beekeeping methods no longer in vogue, are retained, such as those of the top-bars of frames and the depth of shallow extracting frames, but these are now chiefly interesting relics of an earlier day, a sort of rudimentary organ in hives. It would be interesting to trace the evolution of the various pieces of apparatus now in use, but this is quite beyond the limitations of this book. In a few cases later in the book, such a method of treatment has seemed desirable. There would be valid reason for a special book on the history of apparatus of the apiary, if for no other reason than to show the ardent inventor, who is usually a beginner, the steps through which the industry has already passed and to prevent the repeated re-discovery of abandoned equipment.

In an earlier day of beekeeping, the industry was well-nigh buried in bizarre hives, but of recent years there have been few modifications in the hives in general use, while many hives of former times are no longer manufactured. The industry has not ceased to advance, but beekeepers have outgrown the belief that success depends on tools. The recognized essentials of beekeeping are knowledge of the bees, skill in manipulation and simplicity of equipment, and those are important in the order named.

The supplies of the beekeeper have few prerequisites. They must be simple in construction, free of all superfluous parts, strongly built and, above all, interchangeable throughout the apiary and even throughout the country in so far as practicable. The manufacturers of beekeeping supplies in the United States and Canada have done much to simplify the equipment and deserve credit for this help. As a rule, only the best materials are employed by them.

APIARY HOUSE

In the main or home apiary, it is desirable to have a special work-shop, usually known by beekeepers as the "honey-house," where supplies are prepared and the crop is cared for and stored until sold. This house should be below the apiary if the ground slopes (p. 307). Since the needs of different beekeepers vary so widely, it is needless to attempt to give plans for a honey-house, but the experienced beekeeper will easily construct one that fits his individual requirements, while the beginner will use whatever he has at hand. One suggestion is important, however, for many honey-houses are too small to permit storage of surplus fixtures out of season as well as the honey crop in the fall. Beekeepers often fail to provide adequate space for these uses and are badly cramped in their work.

FIG. 20.—Honey-house door. The wooden door rolls clear of the opening and the screen door swings both ways.

All openings should be screened thoroughly to prevent the entrance of bees. A solid door (Fig. 20) is preferable to a screen door, as it reduces the number of bees which enter as the beekeeper passes in and out. A door which swings both ways has much to commend it, as the beekeeper can then enter with his hands full. Abundant window space should be provided for light and for ventilation during the heat of summer and these should be screened carefully.

Screens are best made by tacking wire-cloth on the outside of the casings, allowing it to extend about six inches above the opening. The upper border of wire-cloth should be held out one-quarter of an inch by narrow wooden strips to provide abundant exits for bees which accidentally get into the house. Bees rarely enter such openings and those which fly to the windows from inside tend to crawl upward and go out, promptly clearing the room of bees. Some beekeepers prefer not to permit any bees to leave the honey-house while they are at work but permit them to congregate in the upper corners of windows until the day's work is over, at which time they are released through temporary openings, thus reducing the chance of robbers being attracted to the house. If preferred, bee-escapes (Fig. 21) may be placed in upper corners of ordinary framed screens, but these are less effective. The best arrangement is to have windows which slide horizontally so arranged that the openings are entirely free of glass when open. This prevents imprisoning bees on single window-panes and also allows free circulation of air in summer.

FIG. 21.—Porter bee-escape.

Benches, cupboards and racks for small supplies and plenty of boxes for nails of various sizes can be arranged for individual needs, but all should be large and roomy. It was formerly customary to build racks for surplus combs but these are now usually stored in hive-bodies. It is desirable to provide a cook-stove for heat in cool weather and for use in wax extraction and other work. Running water will be a great convenience. A floor of concrete which can be washed down and suitably provided with a drain will save much labor. Gas and electricity are helpful adjuncts where they can be secured.

The kind of honey produced determines the other features of the honey-house. For comb-honey-production, a well-supported second story or a separate room is recommended for storage of honey. In extracting, it is desirable that the extractor, uncapping boxes and tanks be so arranged that it is unnecessary to lift heavy supers and cans and so that at no time must the crop be lifted by hand. Honey is best stored in a warm place and a second story is ideal also for extracted honey. By the use of a honey-pump, honey can be raised to a higher level and after that it can be moved by gravity in canning, bottling and packing.

For an out-apiary, a smaller house will serve and many beekeepers do not have any house in such yards. Some use a portable extracting outfit, arranged on a truck or trailer, but the usual practice at present is to carry all honey to the central plant either for extracting or for the grading and packing of comb-honey. The use of the automobile with its additional speed and carrying capacity has almost eliminated the separate honey-house for each out-apiary.

If bees are wintered in a cellar, it may be built under the honey-house.

HIVE-STANDS

The arrangement of the hives in the apiary will determine the character of the stand. Many beekeepers who winter bees outdoors, arrange them in groups of four, the hives resting on a platform which forms the bottom of the winter packing-case. Others use an arrangement which provides for placing two colonies together in a winter case, while others prefer single winter cases and consequently have their hives arranged singly. The hives should be so placed that if wintered outdoors they need not be moved for packing. For apiaries in which the bees are wintered in a cellar, any arrangement may be used which suits the beekeeper, except that it is undesirable to have hives placed too close together. On whatever type of stand the bees may be kept, it is desirable to raise the platform above the ground slightly to permit a circulation of air and thus to prevent decay of the platform. It is not desirable to raise hives above the ground more than a few inches at most, especially because they will then be too heavy for easy management in the height of the season. Some hive-stands have a flight board included to aid the bees when returning heavily laden from the field, but a projecting bottom board to the hive or an alighting board has the disadvantage that it holds snow at the entrance to the hives in winter.

HIVES AND HIVE PARTS

The hive which opens at the top and in which the combs are built in freely movable frames is generally used in America. It was invented by Rev. L. L. Langstroth, the Father of American beekeeping, in 1851, and from this invention all development of modern beekeeping has its origin. The original Langstroth hive has been simplified and changed slightly in dimensions, and as now used (Fig. 13) it is a plain wooden box holding frames hung from a rabbet at the top (Fig. 22) and which do not touch the sides, top or bottom. The "bee-space" is usually provided at the top. The box is usually dovetailed and is commonly made of white pine dressed to $7/8$ or $\frac{13}{16}$ inch. Cleats and all projecting parts are usually condemned as interfering with free use in the apiary and all outer cases and the like which appear in foreign hives are eliminated as needless and costly, as well as cumbersome.

FIG. 22.—Diagram showing spacing of frame and rabbet in Langstroth hive.

FIG. 23.—Spacing of Hoffman frames.

The greatest advance of the Langstroth hive is not so much the movable frames as in the free space (Fig. 23) all about them. The exact size of this space is of the greatest importance, it being such that the bees pass through it freely but do not fill it with either wax or propolis. This is usually built a quarter of an inch. It is possible so to build the hives as to provide the bee-space at either the top or the bottom of the frames within each hive-body, but the advocates of a space at the bottom, while having much in their favor, are few in number, and for the sake of uniformity the bee-space at the top is preferable.

The plain box or hive-body rests on a bottom board, so made that there is an entrance space (Fig. 13), and over the hive is a cover which can be entirely removed to permit the removal of frames. There are various types of bottom boards and covers in use, which are illustrated in supply catalogues. The telescope cover over a thin inner cover has much to commend it (Fig. 13).

The size of frame standard to America is that of the Langstroth hive, 9⅛ high by 17⅝ inches long. This is an increase of ¼ inch over the length designated by the inventor. Frames of other sizes, but having the same methods of hanging, have been devised, and a frame two inches deeper than the Langstroth has much to commend it, but the desirability of uniformity throughout the apiary and for general use throughout the country outweighs the slight advantages of the odd sizes. There were formerly frames in use which were supported in the middle or from below, and all sorts of hanging devices have been invented, but practically all have disappeared except the frame as Langstroth first made it. Also hives have been devised containing frames of all sizes, but especially the smaller sizes have wholly disappeared from the American market with recent changes in beekeeping practices. The only two frames now commonly seen are the Langstroth and the one two inches deeper, usually known as the Jumbo, Quinby or Dadant. Shallower frames are sometimes employed in supers for special reasons, but are not in general use.

The number of frames in the hive is likewise variable, depending in part on local requirements and on the kind of honey produced. Many comb-honey-producers of the clover and alfalfa regions prefer the eight-frame Langstroth hive, while most producers of extracted honey use the ten-frame hive. A few use hives holding twelve or thirteen frames. The ten-frame hive seems to be growing in popularity, especially among the more progressive beekeepers, although many eight-frame hives are still sold. In deciding the size of hive, the usual method formerly was to calculate the number of combs needed for brood-rearing by a strong colony, but the better beekeepers now realize that safety lies in the direction of leaving a large supply of honey with the bees for fall, winter and spring, and for this a large hive capacity is requisite. Among the best beekeepers two ten-frame hive-bodies are given to each colony throughout the year, as will be discussed in greater detail later (p. 372).

Frames of any description must be spaced so as to give room between the combs to allow brood to be reared in the cells and also to provide space enough for the bees between the combs. The spacing usually adopted is 1⅜ inches from center to center but some beekeepers prefer 1½ inches. The closed-end frames when brought together are properly spaced. While the larger number of beekeepers do not employ the closed-end type, various devices are in use for the spacing of open-end frames. The commonest frame has the end-bars wide enough for a short distance so that they touch at the top (Hoffman frames, Fig. 23). The metal-spaced frame is possibly an improvement. Some honey-producers object to spacing devices because they interfere in uncapping, and this objection is largely overcome by the use of staples in the side of the end-bar.

To obtain regular cells in the comb, comb-foundation, a thin sheet of pure beeswax embossed to correspond with the bases of cells, is placed in the frames. On this as a guide, the bees build the side walls of the cells, utilizing to some extent the extra wax in the foundation. Foundation is made in various thicknesses, the thinnest being used for comb-honey, and in both worker and drone-cell size.

To strengthen the combs, it is customary to wire the frames with fine (No. 30 gauge, tinned) wire. The wires are generally stretched horizontally, and most frames as they come from the manufacturer are pierced for wiring. After the wires are stretched tight, the foundation is fastened to the top of the frame and the wire is imbedded in the foundation, usually by pressure. The spur imbedder (Fig. 24) is generally used but is not especially good. Heat generated by a weak electric current is sometimes employed.

Whatever style of hive is adopted, the parts must be cut accurately so that the bee-spaces are of the right size and so that the apiary equipment may be interchangeable throughout. Hives or frames of different sizes or of improper dimensions are perhaps the worst inconveniences that can be found in an apiary. The materials should be the best, for the equipment is often used for many years. As a rule, it is better to buy hives and frames and, in fact, practically all the necessary supplies from the regular manufacturers of such articles. This advice is not given as an advertisement for the manufacturer but is based on the recollection of ill-spaced, inaccurately cut, home-made outfits which have been encountered in traveling among beekeepers. Obviously, an expert wood-worker can do as well as the regular manufacturer, but even then the cost of home-made supplies usually exceeds the price charged by the dealers, when one considers the time consumed.

Fig. 24.—Spur wire-imbedder.

The outsides of hives should be painted to protect them from the weather. It is most important that the joint or dovetail be painted as decay starts there in unpainted hives. White paint (white lead and raw linseed oil) is preferred as it makes a cooler hive than dark colors. For the sake of the appearance of the apiary, all hives should be of the same color. This is also important if one wishes to interchange hives in the apiary.

The hive as it has been discussed so far, is essentially the home of the bees and is occupied by them throughout the year. This portion is usually known as the brood-chamber. For surplus honey, on which the beekeeper depends for his profit, additional parts are needed and these are discussed in connection with the production of the various kinds of honey.

Fig. 25.—Smoker.

EQUIPMENT FOR HANDLING BEES

A few special tools are necessary in handling bees. A good smoker (Fig. 25), consisting of a tin or copper receptacle in which to burn rotten wood or other materials, with a bellows attached to force a draft, is indispensable. The medium-sized smokers are best for the beginner and the professional beekeeper may learn by experience what size is best suited to his needs. The German beekeeper often uses a specially constructed pipe (Fig. 26), which is naturally a dual-purpose tool.

Fig. 26.—German bee-keeper's pipe.

A veil of black material, preferably of cotton netting with a silk tulle front (Fig. 27), is needed to protect the face from stings. Even a seasoned beekeeper, who sometimes likes to brag that he never uses a veil, may find it convenient to have a veil thrown back on his hat, which can be brought down when the bees become annoying. Black wire-cloth veils are often used and, while they are a better protection than the cloth veils, are less convenient as they cannot be thrown back so easily.

A steel tool of some kind is needed to pry up covers

and to loosen and separate frames. A screw-driver will answer, but some specially devised tools (Fig. 28) may be preferable.

Gloves of cloth or leather are sometimes used to protect the hands. The handling of frames is less impeded if the finger ends are cut out. Gloves are hot, usually sticky or stiff, and are as a rule abandoned after the early stages of beekeeping are passed.

FIG. 27.—Cotton netting veil with silk tulle front.

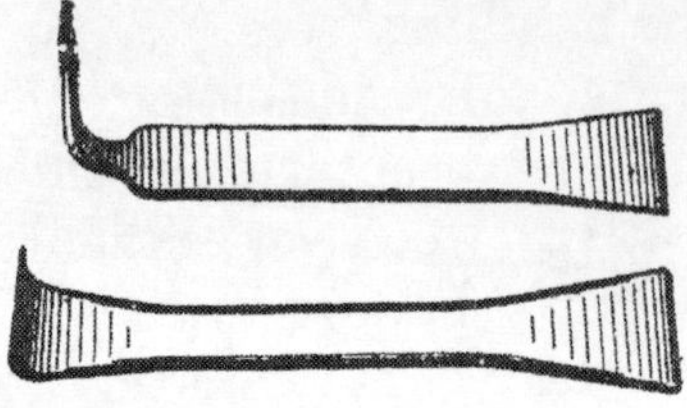

FIG. 28.—Hive tools.

A brush to sweep bees from the combs is a convenience, especially in removing bees while taking frames from the hives at extracting time. The German brush with white bristles (Fig. 29) is perhaps the best of those manufactured, but a whiskbroom or a bunch of weeds pulled as needed are as good.

FIG. 29.—German bee brush.

A tool box or portable seat (Fig. 30) and a wheelbarrow or cart for carrying supplies and honey are among the other conveniences used in handling bees. A hive-cover on edge makes a good temporary seat and has the advantage of being where it is needed, and when needed is not otherwise occupied.

OTHER EQUIPMENT

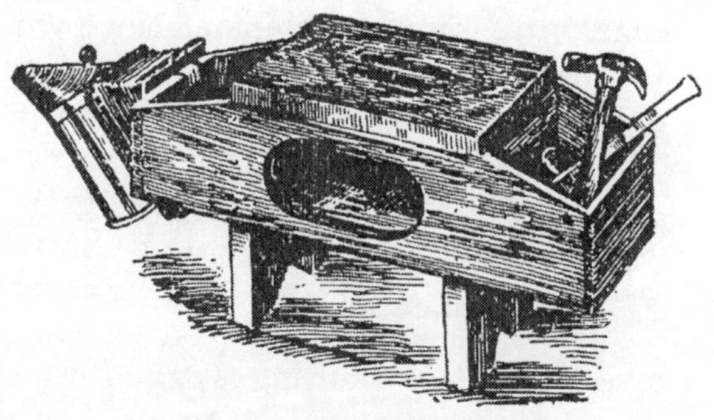

FIG. 30.—Tool-box seat.

Additional appliances may be useful in any apiary and these may be mentioned briefly. For making changes in supplies and in devising parts for special uses, the apiary equipment should include some carpenter's tolls, among which may be mentioned hammers, saws (including a key-hole saw), brace and bit, square, planes and a good supply of nails of assorted sizes. Cement-coated nails are the best for most purposes in the apiary. Queen- and drone-traps, usually known as Alley traps (Fig. 31), are useful in catching undesirable drones or in preventing the escape of a queen at swarming time (p. 287). Bee-escapes (Fig. 32) are used in removing bees from supers of honey, especially comb-honey, before it is taken from the hive. An observatory hive with glass sides will be instructive and entertaining to the beginner and even to the more experienced beekeeper, if placed where the bees may be watched frequently. A comb-foundation cutter (Fig. 33) is convenient and

FIG. 31.—Alley queen- and drone-trap.

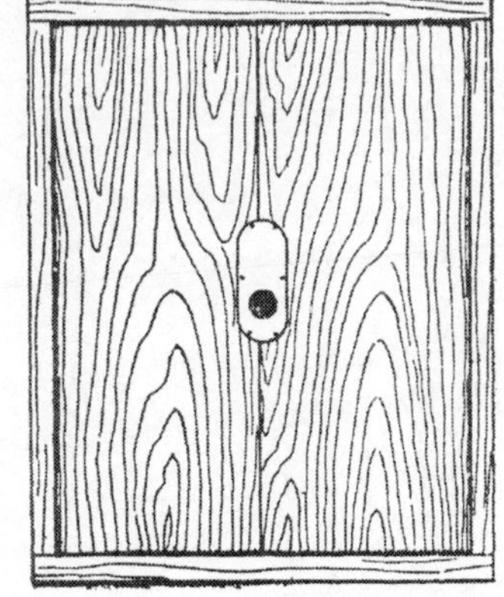

FIG. 32.—Bee-escape board

better than an ordinary knife. If the beekeeper desires to make his own comb-foundation, various machines may be obtained for that purpose. It is usually cheaper to buy foundation. In case it is necessary to feed colonies in order to stimulate brood-rearing or to provide stores for winter or during a period when no nectar is available, various types of feeders may be used. Clamps for holding the parts of the hive together (Fig. 34) are convenient in moving, but the wide (1½ inch) staples sold by dealers in beekeeping supplies are as good. Many additional pieces of equipment for the beekeeper are described in the catalogues of dealers in supplies for the beekeeper and the purposes of these are made clear in the catalogue descriptions. Some are more ornamental than useful. For special work about the apiary the beekeeper will find use for many other tools which need not be described.

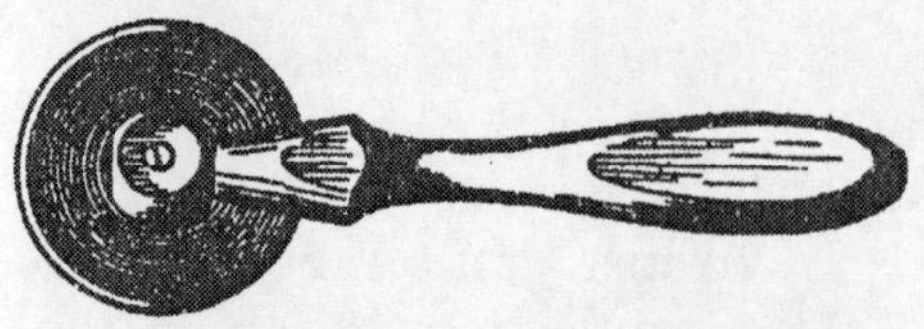

Fig. 33.—Comb-foundation cutter.

Fig. 34.—Van Deusen hive-clamp.

CHAPTER III

THE COLONY AND ITS ORGANIZATION

In the proper management of bees, all manipulations must be based on their normal activities. Bees are creatures of instinct and are limited in their ability to adapt themselves to changes in their environment. While in certain activities they show evidences of memory, learning, association and adaptive responses, in general they may be considered as responding to their environment in a "machine-like" manner. Because of the nature of most of their activities, it becomes necessary to know their normal behavior even more than would be the case were they more adaptive. In giving directions for handling bees, the systems of manipulations and apparatus are usually emphasized, but in the present book the normal activities will be made more prominent so that the reader may better understand the reasons for the usual rules and systems. Again, most of the American literature applies especially to the white clover region and the rules fail to apply elsewhere, so that there seems to be additional justification for a discussion of the more fundamental factors in beekeeping.

It frequently happens that a supposedly new plan or system is published which is old, except that it is a new adaptation of well-known principles to slightly changed conditions. The success or failure of these plans when tried by others is often attributed to peculiarities of the various localities where they are tested. The word "locality" covers a multitude of defects in knowledge of bee activities. Bees respond to stimuli in but one way and wherever a given stimulus is applied, the result is the same. If one's knowledge of the circumstances surrounding his bees is not adequate, there seems to be comfort in attributing to "locality" one's failure in the application of rules.

SOURCES OF INFORMATION

It may be worth while to extend these introductory remarks to explain the point of view held in the present discusssion of bee activities. There are several distinct angles from which one may view the actions of a colony of bees and, since they lead to unreconcilable conclusions, all cannot be correct. First to be mentioned among those who write concerning bees is the so-called student of nature who seemingly tries to find in bees a type of intelligence even higher than that possessed by man and who attributes to these insects thoughts and passions to which only the poetic may hope to attain. The complex colony life of bees offers to such a type of mind unlimited opportunity for speculation, which leads nowhere and is in fact a detriment to legitimate investigation. Allied to the just mentioned enthusiasts over nature are the amateur philosophers who hold up the bee as a brilliant example of industry. To all such speculative fancy, one may with profit turn one's back.

In studying the behavior of any lower animal, there is one source to which one should go for information. This is found in the actions of the animal in response to stimuli of its environment. If the bee makes a visible movement in response to a stimulus arising in its environment,[1] that visible movement and nothing else is of value in forming a conclusion. If there is a movement or other response inside the animal or otherwise invisible, or if the bee perceives the stimulus but does not move in response, then the observer has a negative result. It is frequent in bee literature to find the words "think," "know," "suppose" and the like applied to bees. As a figure of speech such a

[1] The environmental factor may be inside or outside the hive, or even inside or outside the individual bee. For example, pathogenic micro-organisms or irritating foods are inside but not part of the animal and are, therefore, environmental factors.

form of expression may perhaps be admissible, but if used in its absolute sense it is not warranted. It would result in a marked diminution of the literature on bees, and a great improvement therein, if such material could be wiped out of existence.

Only one source of erroneous theory is more dangerous than those mentioned and that is the observer who makes false observations and unwarranted deductions. Here, too, the bee has not escaped. Because of the wide interest in bees there has been a demand for scientific information concerning them and this has induced several untrained or poorly trained men to undertake observations on the structure or behavior of bees, for which they were not equipped. Such work, being frequently presented in a more popular and attractive form than genuine scientific work, has exerted much influence among beekeepers so that, in attempting to present the results of thorough work, it is often necessary first to show the inaccuracies of work done by unqualified writers.

It must not be supposed that present knowledge of the behavior of the bee is complete. It is, in fact, woefully meager. It is probably true, however, that a well-informed beekeeper has a wider and more accurate knowledge concerning bees than have many students of animal behavior concerning the species with which they work. The intimate acquaintance of the beekeeper with these insects results in a knowledge of their activities which, while faulty at times due to a lack of training in observation, is as a whole quite accurate. While this information is often fragmentary and is usually acquired without any special realization of the general principles of behavior, at the same time the data acquired through years of contact with the bees are perhaps as reliable as those obtained by the experimenter on other species in the course of a relatively brief investigation. A new worker in bee behavior should hesitate before denying the belief of the beekeeper until he is sure of his ground.

ZOOLOGICAL POSITION OF THE HONEYBEE

The honeybee belongs to the order of insects known as Hymenoptera, which comprises also many parasites of other insects, the solitary and social wasps, ants and the entire group of bees, from the solitary species through various stages in the development of the bee-colony to the honeybee. The honeybee is the highest of these colonial forms, highest because most specialized in its behavior and least able to exist alone. Yet, while it is highly specialized in its behavior, it is not so strikingly modified in its structure as are some of the other Hymenoptera, such as the Ichneumonidæ. Among the Hymenoptera are three groups of social insects, wasps, ants and bees, and the type of colony found in these three groups is fundamentally the same. The only other true colonial insects are the termites, "white ants," of a distinct order and with an entirely different type of colony.

The genus Apis to which the honeybee belongs also includes the species *indica, florea, dorsata* and *zonata,* all of which are natives of the Far East and none of which is as useful to man as the species *mellifica.*[1] These are briefly discusssed in Chapter IX.

[1] One of the cases of confusion originating from the application of the law of priority in scientific nomenclature is the attempted change of the name of the honeybee from *mellifica,* by which it has been known for so many years, to *mellifera.* In the 10th edition of Linnæus' "Systema Naturæ" (1758), the boundary of the prehistoric for the taxonomist, the name *mellifera* was used, while Linnæus himself used *mellifica* in later years. The name *mellifica* is found in a vast literature, it is the scientific name by which the bee is known to most zoologists and beekeepers, the name which Linnæus preferred and, last but not least, it is a correctly descriptive name. It should be recognized in taxonomy, as well as in civic legislation, that a law to be effective must be backed by public sentiment. It might, therefore, with propriety be suggested to the taxonomic purists that they cultivate public sentiment by allowing the zoologist, dealing in things not names of things, to live in peace among his old friends. Many zoologists refuse to take taxonomy seriously and there seems every reason for disregarding its laws in the present case.

COLONIAL HABITS OF BEES

Bees have been kept by men from an early stage in the development of human civilization, yet it cannot be said that they are domesticated. In all of their activities, bees under the care of man do not differ from bees in a wild state. The bee has been modified by breeding in various ways but, in so far as the natural instincts are concerned, it is doubtful whether any appreciable change has been brought about and in the greater number of phases of bee life no change has even been attempted. An escaping swarm takes up its abode in a hollow tree and the bees are often then spoken of as "wild," but this adjective is just as applicable to the bees in the apiary. Certain animal trainers become proficient in handling savage animals through their knowledge of the ways of these beasts. Similarly the beekeeper, by studying the behavior of his bees, comes to know their habits and is governed by this knowledge. This comparison of bees and wild animals must be construed not as intended to inspire fear in the uninitiated but to point out that the beekeeper actually is dealing with animals unmodified in their instincts by their long association with man. By the proper use of smoke and especially by the way the colony is handled, the beekeeper can seemingly do with his bees as he pleases. The fact is, however, that he cannot overstep the bounds set by the instincts of these animals. It is, therefore, an incorrect conception of the ability of the beekeeper to state, as did Langstroth, that bees are capable of being tamed. In view of these facts, the necessity of a thorough knowledge of bee activities is most evident.

Bees cannot live alone. Their structure and instincts fit them for life in a colony or community, where the various duties are divided among the individuals according to structural fitness and age. While an individual worker-bee may live if forcibly isolated from its mates, it cannot reproduce itself, fails to care for itself adequately and soon dies. Most insects have the ability to hibernate in winter but the honeybee seems to have lost this. Since at low temperature the bee becomes numb and finally dies, it must have the ability to make its own environment, so far as temperature is concerned. This makes a colony necessary in winter so that the bees may mutually and collectively warm each other. Efficiency, if not necessity, demands that the work of the colony be divided and such a division of labor tends to develop into a condition demanding the maintenance of the colony. The honeybee is further modified for the defense of the colony rather than of the individual. The barbed sting is used only once and is more effective because it is left behind while the former owner dies. Such a weapon of defense is of no service to the individual.

The size of the colony varies according to the season, the smallest number being usually at the close of winter, at which time the number may be reduced to 10,000 or even less. At the peak of population, which under good management should be shortly before the beginning of the heavy nectar-gathering, the number may reach 70,000, and while a larger figure is possible it is unusual. Swarms sometimes issue which contain 35,000 workers. Bees may maintain true colonial life with smaller numbers, and the small colonies used for mating queen-bees (called nuclei or baby nuclei) are normal, except for the fact that it is only with the greatest difficulty that they attain the strength of full colonies. As Nolan has pointed out, a weak colony tends to remain weak, while a strong colony usually maintains its strength, and this characteristic does not depend wholly on the ability of the queen to lay eggs.

TYPES OF INDIVIDUALS IN A COLONY

A normal colony at the height of the summer season of activity is composed of three kinds of individuals, (1) the queen (Fig. 35, *b*), of which there is normally only one, the mother of all the other bees of the colony (except just after a new queen has been reared), (2) thousands of workers (Fig. 35, *a*) or sexually undeveloped females which normally lay no eggs but do all the other work, and (3) many drones (Fig. 35, *c*) or males. The drones are often restricted in number by the beekeeper and their only func-

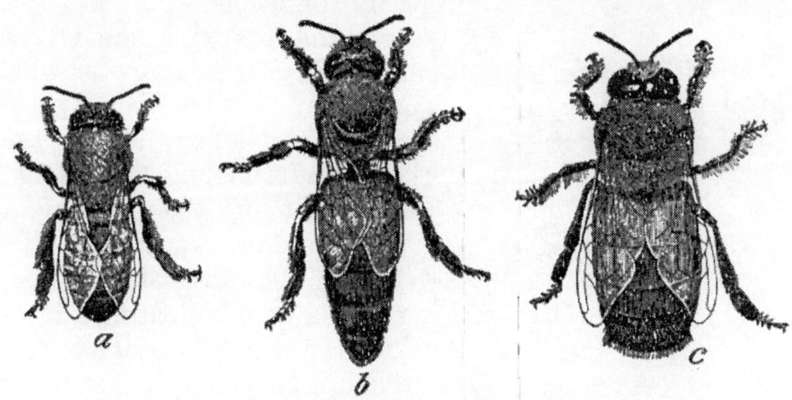

FIG. 35.—The honeybee: *a*, worker; *b*, queen; *c*, drone. Slightly enlarged.

tion is to mate with the young queens. These three types of adult individuals are easily recognizable even by a novice by differences in the size of various parts of the body. There are also during the active season all stages of developing bees (Fig. 36), known collectively as the brood.

Queen

There is normally only one queen, the largest individual in the colony. She has for her sole duty the laying of eggs and all individuals normally develop from eggs laid by her, and she is repaid for her labors by being cared for by the workers. The eggs are deposited at the bases of the cells of the comb in that portion of the nest devoted to the rearing of the brood, the brood-nest, and normally only one egg is placed in a cell. The eggs are fastened to the cell base by the posterior end (future posterior end of the larva) by means of a secretion of the queen. The number of eggs laid by a good queen[1] varies from a few daily in early spring and late fall in northern regions to about 1,500 to 2,000 at the heaviest egg-laying. Under special conditions which the beekeeper may provide she is capable of laying as many as 5,000 eggs a day, but no such figures are ever attained under the usual conditions of the colony. The weight of eggs laid by a queen in a day often exceeds the weight of the queen herself during this laying, indicating a marvelous rapidity in metabolism.

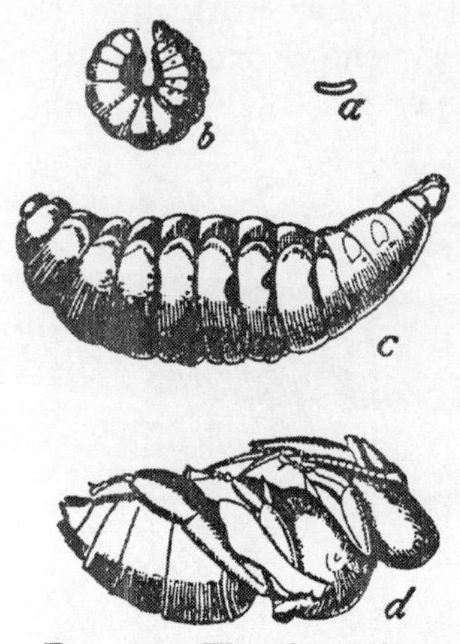

Fig. 36.—The honeybee: *a*, egg; *b*, young larva; *c*, old larva; *d*, pupa. Enlarged.

The queen is not, as her name would indicate, the ruler of the colony. It has for ages been known that there is one larger individual in the colony and the ancients gave the name

[1] In 1903, the author had occasion to study the egg-laying of normal queens. Queens were introduced to a small colony in an observatory hive on an empty comb. These queens usually deposited about four or sometimes six eggs a minute, passing quickly from one cell to another. The abdomen is inserted in the cell, the legs are braced firmly on the edges of adjacent cells and the wings are placed flat against the edges of cells to the rear. During egg-laying, the queen is often surrounded by a circle of worker-bees with their heads toward her, rubbing her with their antennæ. Frequently this rapid egg-laying is continued without interruption for twenty to twenty-five minutes and at times for a longer period. There then is usually a resting period, often of about five minutes, during which time the queen is fed by the workers. Whenever the queen comes to rest, she is surrounded by a circle of workers and, as she walks over the comb, each bee turns toward her when she gets within half an inch. This is probably a response to the stimulus of odor.

Some curious traditions have arisen about this circle around the queen, one of the most interesting being the claim that there are always twelve, the number being associated with the twelve apostles. The turning toward the queen is often ascribed to the affection of the workers for her, but this is probably as well grounded as the tradition of these being always twelve.

"king" to this supposed ruler. When it was learned that the supposed monarch laid eggs it became necessary to change the name. It is now known that the queen is mentally less highly developed than the workers and that, to some degree, the workers determine the number of eggs to be laid and otherwise determine the queen's activities.

The ovaries of the queen (Fig. 95) are highly developed, as is necessary for her specialized function, and because of this development the abdomen is greatly elongated. Her legs (Fig. 82) are not specially modified as are those of the workers and the ovipositor is curved and smooth and has attached to it a poison-sac[1] and functions as a sting. Whether it also assists in egg-laying is not determined. The eyes (Fig. 69) are much like those of the workers, the mandibles are notched and proportionately large, the head is not so elongated as that of the worker and is somewhat smaller. The antennæ have twelve segments, like those of the worker.

Mating normally takes place only once when the queen is five to eight days old, the time differing slightly in different races and being influenced also by conditions of the weather. There is reason to think that some queens mate more than once, but always before laying eggs. Mating never occurs in the hive but on the wing and the queen receives a supply of spermatozoa (male sex cells), millions in number, which are stored in her spermatheca (Fig. 95) and remain functional during the life of the queen or until they are exhausted. Egg-laying commonly begins

[1] On one occasion the author was stung by a virgin queen. While it was doubtless his own fault, this is an experience that comes to few beekeepers. This was in the early days of his beekeeping experience and that there was a poison-sac at the other end of the sting was attested by a goodly swelling. The queen was seemingly uninjured. This occurred in the apiary of the A. I. Root Co., Medina, Ohio, and, by a strange coincidence, E. R. Root received a letter the same day from a western beekeeper who had a similar experience and who considered it rare enough to be worthy of publication.

two days after mating. The queen often lives three or four years but a few exceptional cases are recorded of queens living seven years. The life of the queen seems to depend somewhat on the number of eggs which she lays. The queen, when she fails in egg-laying, is superseded by a young queen reared by the workers. While there is usually only one queen in the colony, it sometimes happens that two are found, usually mother and daughter at the time of supersedure. Records of this kind are not infrequent but usually each observer thinks that his observation is unique. von Buttel-Reepen [1] claims that there are usually two brood-nests. He records one case in which this was not true and several American beekeepers have recorded the same. The specialization which normally permits but one egg-producing female is not well understood nor is it known why a queen usually attempts to kill any rivals (except under swarming conditions).

Workers

The larger number of bees in the colony are females whose sexual organs are undeveloped and which are structurally modified in other ways. They are appropriately called worker-bees. These bees feed the growing larvæ, clean, guard and ventilate the hive, build the comb of beeswax, gather nectar, pollen, water and propolis and, in fact, do all the work of the hive, except that they lay eggs only under abnormal conditions (p. 200).

The ovaries are small and the spermatheca is greatly reduced in size. The mandibles (Fig. 70) are not notched as in the queen, the legs (Fig. 82) are variously modified, the third pair being modified for the carrying of pollen. The ventral plates of the last four visible segments of the abdomen are modified on the anterior edge to form wax-glands (Fig. 54) from which the wax used in comb-building is secreted. The sting (Fig. 84) is straight and barbed.

[1] von Buttel-Reepen, H., 1900. Sind die Bienen Reflex-maschinen? (Eng. trans., p. 10.)

The antennæ have twelve segments. The tongue is longer than in the queen or drones. The honey-stomach is well developed for the carrying of nectar to the hive. Workers never mate with drones and lay eggs only under special conditions (Chapter VIII). No such sharp differences in structure between workers and queens occur in bumblebees.

Speaking in general terms, the length of life of worker-bees is measured not so much by days or weeks as by the amount of work which they do. During the period when nectar is being gathered abundantly, they literally work themselves to death and the population of the colony is appreciably decreased unless brood is being reared heavily. During such a period, the average length of life of worker-bees is barely six weeks, while in periods when less work is necessary the life is lengthened. Those bees which emerge in the early autumn are the ones which live until the following spring. During the active season, the larger part of worker-bees die outside the hive, failing to return with the last load. It is small wonder that in addition to their other burdens they must sometimes serve as examples of industry.

Drones

The males of the bee are known as drones. The use of the word drone, meaning a lazy person, arose from the name of the male bee, and it may be reapplied to them as fitting. They are not a useful part of the colony organization in the routine, for they do none of the work of the hive nor do they assist in the gathering. The only function of a drone is that of mating with a young (virgin) queen and in this act it dies. Drones are heavy consumers of stores and are not in favor among beekeepers, so that their numbers are greatly reduced in the modern apiary. This is done either by restricting the number of cells in which they may be reared or by trapping them after they emerge as adults.

The drone is a large individual, exceeding even the queen in girth of thorax.[1] The compound eyes (Fig. 69) are so large that they meet on top of the head, forcing the ocelli (simple eyes, *O*, Fig. 69), down on the front nearer the bases of the antennæ. The legs (Fig. 82) have no pollen-baskets. The wax-glands are missing, and there is no sting (this being a strictly female organ, a modified ovipositor). There is one more segment visible in the abdomen than in the female and the abdomen is larger and blunt at the end. A row of prominent hairs is present on the dorsal side of the abdomen.

In the early spring when brood-rearing begins, the first eggs laid by the queen ordinarily develop into workers and, as the colony becomes more populous and the weather moderates, drones rapidly appear. They may be fairly abundant, if the beekeeper does not reduce their number, up to the close of the honey-flow, but at that time the workers drive them from the colony. The first indication of this exodus is to see them in numbers on the bottom board and soon workers will be seen leaving the entrance carrying the heavy drones, with the base of a wing grasped by the mandibles. They are dropped a hundred feet or more from the hive and usually fail to return. If they do return the process is repeated.[2] There is reason to believe that the drones are first starved and then carried out when they become weak. They are rarely stung to death. This slaughter of the drones is best seen in localities where the honey-flow stops abruptly. In queenless colonies, drones are not removed and cases are reported of such colonies retaining them until well into winter. Drones usually do not fly until over a week old and, while the spermatozoa

[1] This fact enables the beekeeper to trap out drones by means of the Alley traps (Fig. 31), which have openings $\frac{163}{1000}$ of an inch wide, through which workers can pass but which are not large enough for most drones and queens because of their larger thoraces.

[2] It is not usually recognized that old workers are sometimes treated in the same manner.

are developed in the pupa, they are apparently not functional until they attain an age of about two weeks.

The drones are seemingly not so fundamentally members of a single colony as are females. They may be placed in any colony without being molested and appear to enter anywhere without challenge until the time of the slaughter.

Brood

The developmental stages of bees (Fig. 36) are discussed in a later chapter (p. 103) and here it is necessary only to present a general statement concerning the numbers of individuals in these developmental stages in the colony. In the earliest stages of brood-rearing (in late winter in the North), the queen lays only a few eggs a day and the number increases to 1,500 or more a day in an average colony. In exceptional cases, however, this may be exceeded until there are in the combs at one time as many as 40,000 developing bees in all stages, and possibly of all three kinds of bees. Incidentally, this gives some basis for an estimate of the death rate of the adult bees of the colony. If bees emerge from the comb at the rate of 1,500 a day during a honey-flow, the population of the colony is not noticeably increased, indicating that 1,500 or more bees from that colony are dying daily. In the spring when the bees are working less in gathering nectar, the population increases rapidly, indicating a much lower death rate. Truly, bees are creatures of a day.

NATURAL NEST

In a wild state, the bee-colony lives in a hollow tree or cavity in the rocks, although bees thrive in the artificial hive provided by the beekeeper. An examination of a wild colony will assist in the understanding of various manipulations and hive arrangements. The combs which form their abode are composed of wax secreted by the workers (p. 118). The horizontal hexagonal cells of the two vertical layers constituting each comb have interplaced ends on a common septum (Fig. 37). In the cells of these combs are reared the developing workers and drones, honey and pollen also being stored in such cells. These combs hang

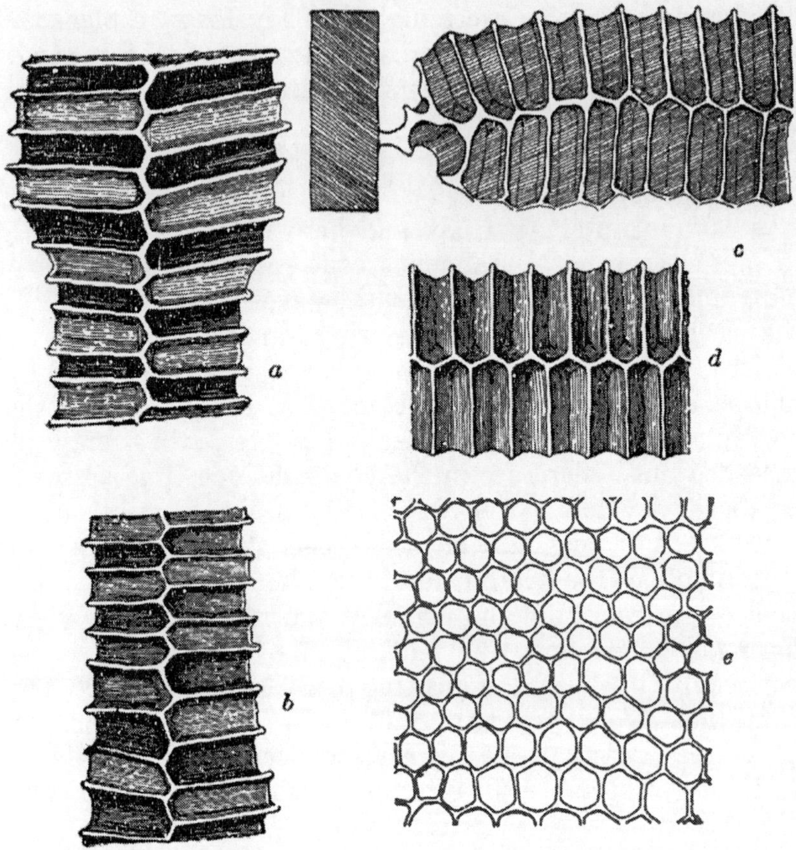

FIG. 37.—Structure of comb: *a,* vertical section at top of comb; *b,* vertical section showing transition from worker- to drone-cells; *c,* horizontal section at side of comb showing end-bar of frame; *d,* horizontal section of worker brood-cells; *e,* diagram showing transition cells. Slightly reduced.

from the top of the cavity and are frequently also attached to the sides. They are rarely built upward from a lower support.

The cells built naturally are not all of the same size.

The ones in which worker-bees are reared (worker-cells) are about one-fifth of an inch across and those used for rearing drones (drone-cells) are about one-fourth or an inch in diameter. The cells used in storing honey are usually of the larger size while pollen is ordinarily stored in worker-cells. The storage-cells are less regular and as a rule slope upward at the outer end. The side walls are not all at right angles to the midrib (the common septum) but on all the edges of the comb there may often be noticed a sloping of the outer ends of the cell-walls toward the edge of the comb (Fig. 37, *c*). Where drone- and worker-cells join, the bees overcome the lack of conformity by building transition cells (Fig. 37, *b* and *a*, and Fig. 38) of irregular shape. Such cells usually cannot be utilized for brood-rearing. Attention should perhaps be drawn to the difference between vertical and horizontal sections of comb (Fig. 37, *a*, *b* and *d*). An examination of a comb will show these illustrations to be correct, although many authors of books on bees persist in labeling drawings like Fig. 37, *d* as vertical sections. In addition to the irregular transition cells, the cells at the junction of the comb to its support are quite irregular.

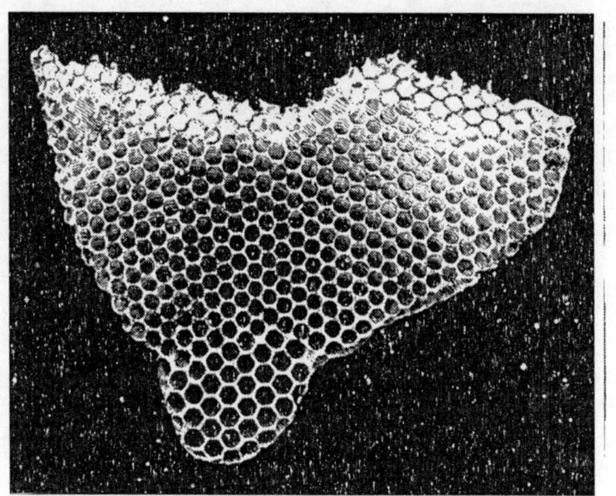

Fig. 38.—Piece of new comb showing transitional cells.

The combs of the natural nest are often not straight but are bent and curved in various ways. The several combs may be parallel or, if this is not the case, the irregular spaces may be filled with short combs. Notwithstanding the irregularity of the whole comb, individual cells are commonly quite uniform. This regularity has been greatly overestimated, however. Reaumur went so far as to advise that the width of a cell be adopted as a legal unit of measure, but even a cursory examination of naturally built comb will show how impractical this would have been. There are also in bee-lore traditions of the marvelous accuracy with which bees form the angles of the side walls and those of the side walls with the base. It has been stated that the comb is built with such accuracy that the maximum capacity and strength are obtained with the minimum expenditure of wax. Miraldi and Koenig vied with each other in the supposed accuracy of their measurements of the various angles and in their calculations of the greatest economy of wax. While it would be a marvelous accomplishment if bees were able to build so accurately, it is perhaps more marvelous that they can adapt their cells to their needs. It need scarcely be said that the formerly supposed accuracy is not actual.[1]

In addition to the horizontally placed hexagonal cells, there are on the combs at certain times cells of a different type. These hang vertically from the combs and are used for rearing queens (Fig. 39). They are circular rather than hexagonal, are larger than the other cells and the outer surface is rough and pitted, somewhat resembling a peanut.

Contents of the cells

As previously stated, the cells of the comb are used for the rearing of brood and for the storage of honey and pollen, each use being in a sense more or less restricted to cells in definite locations. As the larvæ (p. 109) reach the age when food is no longer taken, they are sealed over with

[1] Under manipulation, the size and regularity of the cells are controlled by the use of comb-foundation, sheets of pure beeswax on which the midrib is impressed (p. 35). Even when this is used, a sloping of the side walls of the cells toward the outer margin of the combs may often be observed.

a characteristic capping (Fig. 40), and when a cell is filled with ripened honey it also is sealed, but with a different capping (Fig. 41). The cells containing pollen are usually not entirely filled and, unless they are also used for the storage of honey, as is sometimes the case, the pollen is not covered.

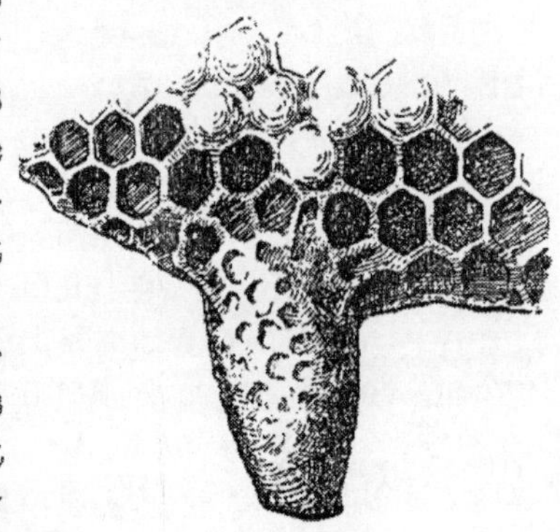

Fig. 39.—Queen-cell. Natural size.

While the common conception of the use of the combs includes only those uses just mentioned, the cells actually have an important use as places for adult bees. In winter the bees normally form their cluster over cells containing no honey and adult bees crawl into the empty cells, filling every one within the space occupied by the cluster. They are thus able to form a much more compact mass, the outside of the cluster being essentially a solid wall of bees. During the active season, bees often crawl into the empty cells, but their function during this time is not clear, except that by this means cells are prepared to receive eggs. It has been suggested that many of these bees are "sleeping," but how one may determine this has not been explained.

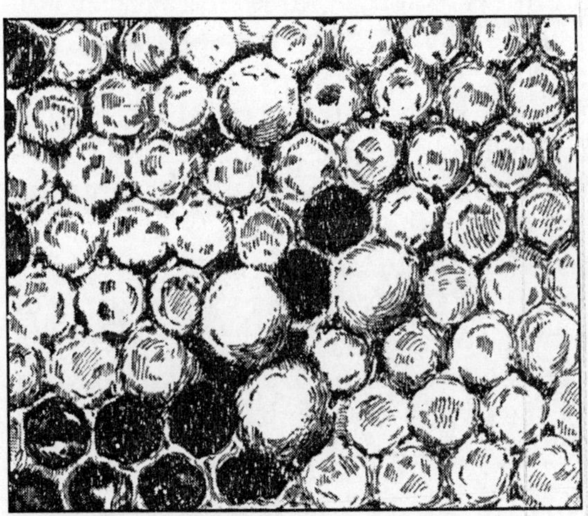

Fig. 40.—Cappings of brood; the larger cappings are over drone pupæ. Natural size.

Arrangement of the nest

There is to be observed in a natural colony a definite and virtually constant arrangement of the contents of the combs. During the active season, the brood occupies an approximately spherical space involving several combs at the lower part of the center of the comb-mass. This space may be shifted or restricted by excessive stores of honey. Around this, on the sides and above, are cells of pollen and beyond these are the honey-stores, chiefly to the back of the nest. Drone-cells are most often found in the lower corners of combs. This typical plan may be variously modified if the nest is of peculiar shape.

In natural comb-building, bees build for the immediate present, with no evidence of a plan for the needs of the future. When comb-building begins, worker-cells are built as long as the queen continues promptly to lay her eggs in the new cells. A queenless colony builds storage-cells of drone-cell size. If the colony is getting weaker and can care for only a little brood, the bees soon begin to build storage-cells and this also occurs if the queen is a poor layer. In a growing nucleus, however, only worker-cells are built. If nectar is coming in abundantly the bees are more likely to build storage-cells. It thus may happen that some combs near the center of the hive contain a superabundance of cells suitable only for the rearing of drones or for the storage of honey, and this condition remains in future years, regardless of the best interests of the colony or the beekeeper. If a comb is broken, it is usually patched with drone-cells.

Color of the combs

When first built combs are light yellow or almost white in color, varying somewhat with the sources of nectar and pollen available at the time of comb-building, and there is also some variation in physical properties from the same cause. After brood is reared in the cells the comb is darkened by the cocoons left by the brood. These cocoons consist of larval skins and excreta, with the possible addition of a portion of the delicate silken cocoon (p. 112). These deposits increase with successive rearings of brood until the bases of the cells are appreciably thickened while the outer parts of the side walls remain practically unchanged in thickness. If an old comb is soaked in water the layers of deposits may be separated readily. The combs are also darkened by deposits of propolis on the cappings of honey-cells and the tops of the combs are often strengthened by deposits of this substance, especially when the combs are attached to rough wood, as in a hollow log.

Protection of the nest

Since the nest of a colony is usually built in a cavity, it is thereby protected, at least partially, from extremes of weather and from depredations. In addition to the protection afforded by the shelter, the worker-bees cover the inside of the cavity (if it is rough) with propolis (bee-glue). This serves to protect the colony from external moisture, often strengthens the wood in a rotten tree and covers irregularities in the surface. Certain races (p. 210) are especially active in reducing the size of the entrance with the same material (Fig. 97), sometimes adding wax to it. An examination of a cavity in a tree which has been occupied by a colony for a considerable time will prove interesting in showing the ways in which bees have improved their abode.

While swarms usually seek protection in a cavity, it sometimes happens that they fail to do this but build their combs in the open. Bouvier[1] has described in detail the comb architecture of such a colony which survived the winter in Paris but died in March. Similar cases are

[1] Bouvier, E. L., 1905. Sur la nidification d'une colonie d'abeilles a l'air libre. Bull. Soc. Philomatique de Paris, Neuv. sér., VII, pp. 186-206.

reported frequently in the United States but such a colony fails to survive cold winters. On one occasion, an open-air colony was discovered near Washington and was moved to the apiary of the Department of Agriculture, then located at College Park, Maryland (Fig. 42). The colony defended itself from robbers and wasps during a period when robbing was severe and wasps were unusually abundant, and lived until nearly mid-winter, when it succumbed during a blizzard. In general, the combs of such colonies are bent so that the wind cannot blow directly through the nest, and the edges of combs are sometimes united with comb projections or propolis. This ability to live in the open suggests a similarity with the giant bees of India and the Philippines which normally build unprotected combs, the latter bees, however, usually building only a single large comb.

Comparison with stingless bees

The arrangement and protection of the natural nest of the honeybee may be compared with the arrangement found in the stingless bees, to which they are closely related. These bees do not build double rows of cells in their combs but the brood is reared in cylindrical cells fused together in single layers. The pollen and honey are stored in large spherical cells of wax. Several years ago, the author had opportunity to examine the nest of a colony of these bees minutely. In this particular species, the spherical cells for pollen and nectar are about one inch in diameter. The entrance is contracted and projects as a funnel almost two inches outward. This funnel is evidently composed of propolis and wax to which pellets of earth are added. Inside the entrance are the storage-cells for pollen surrounding the outer half of the group of brood-cells. Back of the brood-cells and partially encircling them are the cells of honey, the honey in this particular case being well ripened and of superb flavor. The contracted entrance suggests a resemblance to the work of certain races of honeybees (*e.g.* Caucasian, p. 210) in closing the entrance in the autumn, while the general arrangement of the nest follows the usual plan for the honeybee closely, except that the pollen-cells are between the entrance and the brood.

CHAPTER IV

THE CYCLE OF THE YEAR

To describe the various activities observed in the bee-colony in its response to changes in the environment, there is perhaps no better arrangement of the facts than to follow such a colony through the year, assuming that it is normal and unmolested by man. For convenience, the cycle is begun at the close of winter. As will be brought out later, the beekeeper's year starts in the previous late summer, but so long as one is confining his attention to the behavior of the bees themselves, early spring is a more appropriate season to begin the descriptions. Any arrangement of this material which one may make will be arbitrary and objections might be raised to any special time as the beginning of the story. It must also be understood that the cycle varies in different regions with differences in climate and in the sources of nectar.

In discussing the round of action, it is customary among American writers chiefly to discuss the phenomena observed in the white clover region, and they often fail to make clear that elsewhere the course of events may be materially modified. The long winter of the North is a striking feature of the year and greatly influences the activities of the bees. In this region, also, all of the seasonal influences which make up the year are intensified and the proper control of bees is more difficult. In the discussion which follows, the events typical of the North must be made rather prominent in order to follow the plan of arranging the facts to the yearly cycle, but an effort is made to include the differences which, in beekeeping literature, are often attributed to the abused term "locality." From the strong contrasts in seasons and in bee activities observed near the northern limits of the region where bees may be kept, there is a gradual fading of the boundaries of the seasons and a corresponding reduction in the extremes of bee activity until the tropics are reached, where every day to the bees is as the day before, except for the indistinctly circumscribed honey-flows and for temporary disturbances in weather conditions.

BROOD-REARING

A normal colony of bees in good condition just previous to the beginning of the season's activity may be assumed to be broodless and to consist of a mated queen and 10,000 or more worker-bees. The best spring development occurs when there are about 15,000 or three pounds of worker-bees. The combs contain an adequate supply of honey and pollen carried over from the previous year. The workers fly from the hive whenever the days are warm enough, especially after a period of confinement, and with the opening of the earliest spring flowers they replenish their stores of honey and pollen. At this time normal brood-rearing begins, due to the increased temperature within the hive and to the stimulus of incoming food. Previous to the stimulus of incoming nectar, however, the rearing of brood is begun in some colonies, but only in those which are poorly protected or which are suffering from a severe accumulation of feces arising from food of poor quality. This abnormally early brood-rearing usually commences, in colonies wintered out-of-doors, in the coldest period of winter, in February or even in January in the North, and this fact indicates strongly that in these abnormal cases the beginning of brood-rearing is not due to a rise in the outside temperature. It certainly is not due to an instinctive knowledge of the coming of spring but is due to poor protection or stores, things within the control of the beekeeper.

The first eggs (Fig. 43) are laid in the center of the space occupied by the winter-cluster, often before it is loosened. They are usually deposited in circular areas of cells on adjacent combs and, if the queen can pass around the combs without leaving the cluster, such circles of eggs will be found on opposite sides of the comb. As breeding continues, eggs are placed in concentric rings, not only on the middle comb but on contiguous combs, so that the form of the brood-nest becomes approximately spherical. The

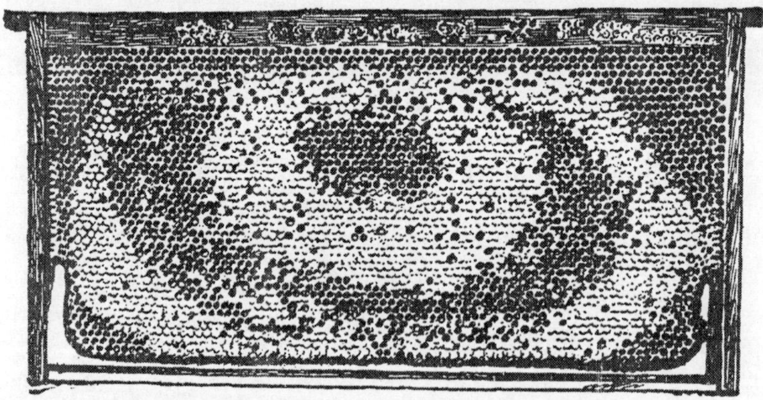

Fig. 45.—Concentric arrangement of the brood.

development of the brood (Fig. 36) will be discussed in greater detail later (p. 103) and it will suffice here to state that at the end of three days there hatches from the egg a small worm-like larva which appears pearly white in the dark comb. This is fed great quantities of food by the workers so that it grows to fill the cell (Fig. 44) in a few days. It is then capped over (Fig. 40) and undergoes metamorphosis into an adult, this transformation stage being known as the pupa. If about two weeks after brood-rearing has begun, the central comb is removed, the inner circle of the brood is seen to be sealed, surrounding these concentric circles of larvæ (Fig. 45), the smaller toward the outside, and in the outermost circle are recently laid eggs. Similarly as other combs are examined, the same succession of brood is found in circles. As the brood continues to develop, the innermost cells are first emptied by the emergence of the young adult bees and the queen then returns to the center of the sphere to deposit eggs. The emergence of the brood increases the size of the colony and consequently the amount of brood that can be fed and protected is greater, especially since the young bees normally do most of the work of caring for brood. Furthermore, as the outer temperature rises, the cluster is expanded and more brood can be included in it. Bees sometimes attempt to rear more brood than they can cover in the event of unusually cold weather, and if the weather turns cold they may contract the cluster and leave brood to die of starvation and cold. The concentric arrangement of the pollen and honey about the brood has been previously described (p. 58).

The first eggs laid develop into worker-bees, but as the season advances eggs are laid in the larger cells of the comb, from which drones emerge. The number of drones and the time when they first appear depend largely on the kind of cells in the comb. While the queen will pass over drone-cells in early spring without depositing eggs in them, if there are drone-cells near the place where the cluster is formed, they are sooner included within the limits of the brood-nest and drones appear earlier than if the larger cells were at one side of the hive.

Brood-rearing during the season

The cycle of brood-rearing has been studied by various workers in different places, with widely varying results. The literature on this subject is carefully summarized by Nolan [1] and since the work of this author is the most accurate which has been done, it is unnecessary to give details of earlier work. The records are for three years at Washington, D. C. Records were made by means of photographs

[1] Nolan, W. J., 1925. The brood-rearing cycle of the honeybee. Bull. 1349, U. S. Dept. Agr., 56 pp., 29 figs.

which show the sealed brood only, from which the total egg-laying for each period may be calculated easily. The hives used were standard Langstroth and as many hive-bodies were given as the colonies needed. To show the course of egg-laying during the season, the accompanying table is copied from Nolan's paper. The data are for the total number of sealed cells containing brood on each count. By dividing these figures by twelve, one gets the average number of eggs laid daily, and by multiplying the smaller number by twenty-one, approximately the total number of cells of brood is obtained. This record is for Colony 4 for 1921, this being the best colony studied. Fig. 46 shows the brood record of the same colony for two successive years.

Table I.—Record of Sealed Brood in Colony No. 4 During the Season of 1921, by Weeks

Date	*Sealed cells*	*Date*	*Sealed cells*
Mar. 16	5,012	July 5	13,659
Mar. 23	9,024	July 12	11,741
Mar. 29	11,186	July 19	11,084
Apr. 5	12,327	July 26	9,904
Apr. 12	14,781	Aug. 2	8,204
Apr. 19	15,402	Aug. 9	7,840
Apr. 26	14,072	Aug. 16	7,459
May 3	15,028	Aug. 23	7,871
May 10	16,982	Aug. 30	8,898
May 17	17,859	Sept. 6	9,448
May 24	17,155	Sept. 13	8,015
May 31	10,955	Sept. 20	7,862
June 7	13,079	Sept. 27	9,433
June 14	12,408	Oct. 4	7,644
June 21	13,674	Oct. 11	3,973
June 28	14,588	Oct. 18	1,143

From that locality and under the conditions prevailing, the largest average observed was 1,587 eggs a day for 1921 and 1,528 for 1920. This is in sharp contrast with loose statements which appear in the beekeeping literature about queens which lay 5,000 eggs a day, or even more. Since

Nolan's colonies were far stronger than those usually found in other apiaries, it may be stated that it is exceedingly rare for a queen to lay 2,000 eggs a day. Even at this rate the queen lays a weight of eggs in twenty-four hours about equal to her own weight at any time during the period, a remarkable performance. Variations in climatic conditions and in honey-flows influence egg-laying and work such as is recorded by Nolan is needed for other localities.

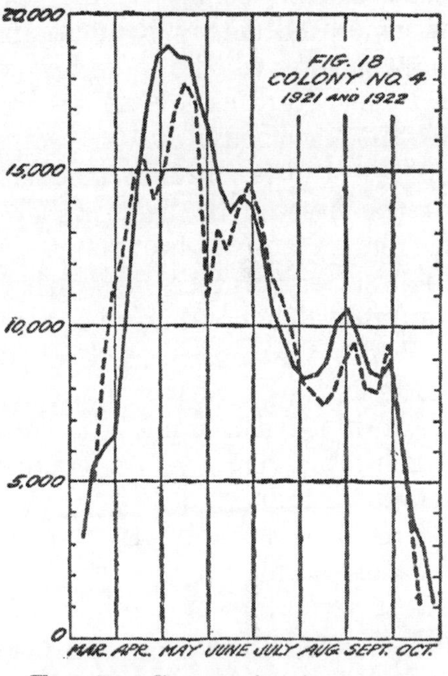

FIG. 46.—Curves showing amount of sealed brood found weekly during the seasons of 1921 and 1922 in colony No. 4. The curve for 1921 is represented by a broken line; that for 1922 by an unbroken line.

THE TEMPERATURE OF THE HIVE

In a study of the activities of a colony of bees, the question of temperature must be considered carefully. In spite of several efforts to show that the bee maintains a body temperature considerably higher than that of surrounding air, it is obvious that the bee is a cold-blooded animal (poikilothermous), that is, the temperature of the body of an individual bee is variable and it is the same or almost the same as that of the air surrounding it.[1] All cold-blooded animals usually have a temperature slightly above that of the surrounding medium, except in the case of animals having a

[1] Pirsch, Gregor B., 1923. Studies on the temperature of individual insects with special reference to the honeybee. Journ. Agr. Research, XXIV, No. 4, pp. 275-288, 1 pl.

moist skin and surrounded by air, in which evaporation on the surface may cause the temperature of the body to fall a little below that of the air. The heat which raises the temperature of the individual bees, and collectively that of the colony, above that of the surrounding air is generated chiefly by muscular activity. The individual bee can move the muscles which activate the legs at a temperature as low as 45° F., but the wing muscles fail to lift the body at air temperatures lower than about 50° F. It, therefore, becomes necessary for the temperature of the hive to be kept higher than these if the bees are to remain active throughout the winter, as they do. The highest temperature at which bees can live has not been determined but it must be over 120° F.

While the individual bee does not possess the ability to maintain a nearly uniform body temperature, as do warm-blooded animals, the colony as a whole shows some remarkable temperature changes, different from any observed in individual bees or in other cold-blooded animals. Warm-blooded animals maintain a fairly constant temperature which may be either higher or lower than that of the surrounding air. While the colony of bees may maintain a temperature either warmer or colder than the surrounding air (colder than the air outside the hive), the temperature of the colony is not constant. In warm-blooded animals, most of the heat is generated by the processes of internal combustion in the assimilation of food, augmented by heat due to muscular activity. In the bee, the chief method of heat production is by muscular activity, with possibly some additional heat from other life processes, and the bee, unlike a warm-blooded animal, promptly cools if muscular activity ceases and the surrounding air is cool. The temperature changes of other colonial insects have not been studied, but it would seem probable from present knowledge that the honeybee is the only insect which is able to generate heat sufficient to maintain active movements without hibernation throughout the winter in the North.

The most interesting and important phases of the temperature of the bee-colony are to be observed in the winter season and this will be discussed at the close of this chapter. While many observations have been made on the temperature of the bee-colony during the period of brood-rearing, the work has not been done with sufficient detail so that there is little information concerning heat generation during this season. The foregoing statement perhaps demands some explanation. If a colony of bees is disturbed, its temperature promptly changes and consequently the insertion of a mercurial thermometer into the brood-nest, or even an approach to the hive to read a thermometer already inserted, may at times produce abnormal temperature conditions. Furthermore, most of the thermometers used are of doubtful accuracy and the slow action of a mercury thermometer is an additional cause of inaccuracy. It is usually stated that during brood-rearing a temperature of approximately human blood heat is maintained within the cluster and that this temperature is practically uniform. The uniformity of the temperature has been greatly overestimated, at least in certain parts of the season, and it may vary over several degrees. It rarely exceeds 97° F. However, if the temperature of the outside air exceeds the maximum hive temperature, the bees reduce the temperature of the cluster by fanning, causing a drop inside the hive by evaporation.

In the case of other insects, the length of the developmental stages varies greatly, according to temperature. Since the bee-colony virtually creates its own temperature environment within the brood-nest during brood-rearing, the developmental stages are practically uniform in length of time. This is a great benefit to the beekeeper, especially in timing swarming and similar phenomena where queen-cells are concerned. It has been found that if brood is removed and kept at a temperature lower than is usual in the brood-chamber, development continues but, as with other insects, it is retarded.

One other point regarding the hive temperature is important. The temperature is not uniform throughout the hive but may vary over many degrees in cold weather. This will be explained in greater detail under a discussion of bees during winter. In any weather, however, the efforts of the bees in heat generation are confined to the brood-nest or, in the absence of brood, to the cluster, except when wax is being secreted, when a high temperature is also maintained at the point of building. Away from the centers of activity, however, the temperature is not raised except by chance muscular movements or by convection currents, but may be cooled if it is too hot. This perhaps explains the seemingly unreconcilable records of hive temperatures during the summer.

SWARMING

Continued and increased breeding, previously described as occurring in early summer, would result in enormous colonies if the queen were able to lay eggs with sufficient rapidity to meet the demands of such a case. It would not, however, result in any increase in the number of colonies. Obviously, it frequently happens that an entire colony of bees is destroyed, in Nature as well as in the hands of the beekeeper, and the very existence of the species depends on another method of reproduction. The colony life of the bee is so completely developed that it is permissible to think of the individuals as merely "winged organs of the colony," as Maeterlinck has expressed it. The process of reproduction known as breeding of colonies or swarming may be likened to the simple fission or division observed in the protozoa, by which they increase in number.

Preparation for swarming

As the colony increases in strength, the rearing of brood is no longer confined to the worker- and drone-cells but special queen-cells are built (Fig. 47), in which the female larvæ are fed a specially prepared food, royal jelly, and in which the course of their development is so modified that there result queens with special organs instead of worker-bees. The rearing of queens also occurs if a colony becomes queenless by the death or removal of the queen, provided eggs or young larvæ are present, or when a queen is about to be superseded by a young queen because she fails in egg-laying. Queen-cells may be built in advance of the laying of eggs in them (pre-constructed cells), as is usually the case in swarming, or the cells may be built around small female larvæ which would otherwise become workers (post-constructed cells), as is necessary in queenless colonies. The eggs from which queens and workers develop are identical, the only known cause of the difference in the course of their development being the special cells and the food provided for the developing queen.

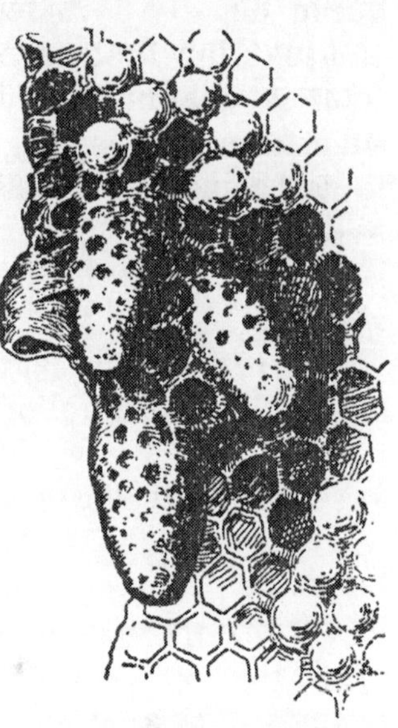

Fig. 47.—Group of queen-cells. Natural size.

Issuing of the swarm

When the larvæ in the queen-cells are fully fed, they are sealed over as are other larvæ. At about the time of this sealing, the first (prime) swarm usually issues, although it may be delayed by inclement weather.[1] Swarming consists of the departure of the old queen with most of the workers from the hive, leaving behind the brood, including the queen-cells, some adult bees and the stores, except such

[1] Races of bees differ somewhat in the time of swarming. Italians tend to swarm with the queen-cells in an earlier stage of development than other races.

honey as the workers are able to carry in their honey-stomachs. Before leaving, the bees gorge themselves until the abdomens are distended and are thus provided with food for a few days, in case the weather is inclement. The queen usually lays fewer eggs just before swarming than is usual for that season and her abdomen often becomes smaller, enabling her to fly more easily. Frequently for a time before the issuing of the swarm, the work of the colony in gathering is decreased and many of the field bees remain at home, thereby crowding the hive. The swarm usually issues on a bright day about mid-day and most of the workers in the hive at that time leave with the swarm. Those in the field at the time of swarming return to the hive and do not follow the swarm.

Stimulus to leave the hive

The stimulus to the act of swarming is not understood, but it has been observed in hives with glass sides that bees in various parts of the hive show signs of excitement, which gradually spreads throughout the hive. Sometimes the queen leaves among the first but she usually remains inside until a considerable number has left the hive. Since a swarm sometimes issues without a queen, she can scarcely be considered the leader. This is also shown by the fact that when the queen is caged, as a means of swarm prevention, the bees sometimes swarm, leaving the queen in the cage. When a queen is disabled so that she cannot fly or is detained by a queen-trap (Fig. 31), the bees may make several attempts to swarm and often finally destroy the old queen, sometimes swarming with a virgin raised at this time.

As soon as the bees leave the entrance there is a striking tendency to move upward. Some go upward within the hive and if it is opened they pour out at the top and if, as sometimes happens, the queen goes up inside instead of outside, the swarm soon returns to the hive. In an analysis of swarming this upward movement is to be reckoned with.

In seeking an explanation of the stimulus to leave the hive, some manipulations produce similar results and are of value for purposes of comparison. (1) In transferring colonies (p. 260) from a box-hive, an empty box in sometimes placed over the inverted box-hive, which is then pounded. This drumming causes the bees to fill their honey-stomachs, after which they gradually move upward until practically the entire colony is clustered in the upper box in the shape of a swarm. (2) In making artificial swarms (p. 297) or in the use of the swarm-box (p. 449) for starting artificial queen-cells, the bees gorge themselves and later cluster like a swarm. (3) If bees are smoked excessively, they gorge themselves and begin to run (especially true of black bees), usually in an upward direction. In these three examples the bees are "demoralized"; the colony is disorganized. The bees usually do not sting and most of them do not attempt to fly so long as they can proceed in the desired direction on foot. They can be moved to a new location after these operations, in which event practically none of them returns to the old location.

The same peculiar manner of leaving the hive may be induced by placing bees in a box with a small opening. If a substance with a repelling odor is now placed in the box, the bees shoot out the opening as in swarming. This manner of exit may be merely incidental to rapidity of movement and may not be specially characteristic. The fact that movements can be duplicated does not necessarily imply similar causes.

Behavior of the issuing swarm

The issuing of a swarm is one of the most exciting and interesting incidents in the apiary. The bees rush from the hive, giving the observer the impression that they are pursued or "possessed of the devil." They appear intoxicated with the "swarm dizziness" and whirl in "bacchanal delight," as if drunk with joy. Even the beekeeper becomes excited. The bees circle in the air and the whirling swarm may drift about the apiary for a time. There is an excitement in the "swarm tone" which is infectious.

It is especially to be noted that swarming bees rarely sting, and it is commonly stated that they cannot sting because their abdomens are distended with the load of honey in the honey-stomach. This latter statement is incorrect, if taken literally, but even the hardened beekeeper finds enjoyment in walking into the midst of the circling swarm, in spite of the fact that he has probably tried to prevent swarming, and he needs no veil under such circumstances.

Clustering

The swarm after a time begins to settle on the limb of a tree or some such support (Fig. 48) and the excitement is past. Like the issuing of the swarm from the hive, the incentive to cluster is not understood. The queen may be the first to alight, and this seems quite natural since she is heavy and a poor flyer compared with the workers, but she is just as likely to join the cluster after it is partly formed. However, the cluster is usually not formed if the queen has not accompanied the swarm. One feature is noticeable in the forming cluster, however, which perhaps throws some light on the subject. It is well known that when bees are thrown in front of a hive the abdomen is raised and the wings are fanned vigorously. At such a time the dorsal scent organ (p. 183), located on the intersegmental membrane betwen the sixth and seventh terga of the abdomen, is exposed by the bending ventrally of the last visible abdominal segment. During clustering, the bees on the outside of the mass expose this gland and the wings are moved rapidly so that it seems probable that the odor which is emitted and dispersed attracts the flying bees to the cluster.

If the cluster has been formed in an inaccessible place, the beekeeper often finds it desirable to have the bees move to another support. The cluster will gradually move (more readily upward) into the dark interior of a box placed nearby, this movement being more rapid if a piece of comb, or better, comb with brood, is placed inside the box. If the queen has failed to fly or has been prevented in some way, the swarm usually does not cluster but returns to the hive, and if a cluster does form it usually breaks up in a few minutes.

In a large apiary when swarms are issuing frequently, many swarms will settle on one particular support. The only plausible explanation for this peculiar action is that the support retains an odor acquired from contact with the swarm which acts as an attraction to other bees in the act of swarming. This lends considerable weight to the theory that clustering is a response to an odor stimulus. Beekeepers sometimes take advantage of this phenomenon and provide an easily accessible and readily handled support for the clusters. In Langstroth-Dadant [1] (p. 218) is the statement that swarming bees cluster on any dark object that resembles a swarm in shape, especially if that object affords adequate support. This presupposes that bees are attracted to the clustering place through sight, for which supposition there is little evidence. In this discussion an old comb is mentioned as a favorite support, but in this case it cannot be claimed that sight is the only means of perception.

Supposed aids to clustering

An old practice at the time of swarming was to beat tin pans, ring bells or otherwise to create a din, in the belief that the distracting noise would cause the bees to settle. Modern beekeepers have abandoned this relic of antiquity, since it has no effect whatsoever on the clustering. The origin of this ancient practice has been variously explained, one plausible theory being that it arose from the practice of notifying neighbors of the issuing of a swarm, so that

[1] Langstroth-Dadant, 1907. Langstroth on the hive and honey bee, revised by Dadant. Hamilton, Ill., 575 pp.

ownership could be claimed. Nowadays a bell is not a part of the apiary equipment and no evil seems to have come from neglecting this rite. Flashing lights on the swarm by means of a mirror is another theoretical impediment to long flights in which the modern beekeeper places no confidence.

Scouts

Under natural conditions, when the queen is present, the swarm will hang on the support from fifteen minutes to a day or more. The cluster is usually then broken and the swarm flies away (often for a considerable distance) to establish itself in a hollow tree or cave. That scouts locate the future abode has been claimed, probably correctly. Baron von Berlepsch, the celebrated German beekeeper, records [1] an instance of scouts working for several days in advance of swarming to prepare a place. Usually it cannot be so well demonstrated that scouts have been sent out, but the accuracy with which swarms often fly to a cavity without delay indicates that they are in some manner led to the place. How this is done is not known. Similar instances of bees being led to certain places are discussed in a later chapter (p. 128).

After the swarm has been removed (Fig. 49) a few bees will often be seen around the former location of the cluster, either at rest or on the wing. These bees are evidently attracted or held by the odor which adheres to the support. That these are scouts which return after the cluster is hived has been suggested. At any rate, the modern practice is to hive a swarm away from the clustering place for fear returning scouts may draw away the colony.

Entering the new home

When a swarm enters a new abode, the first bees to

[1] von Berlepsch, 1852. Eichstädt Bienenzeitung, VII, Nr. 7. Reprinted in von Buttel-Reepen, 1906. Are bees reflex machines? (Eng. trans.)

locate the entrance stand with their legs extended and the abdomen raised to an angle of about 45 degrees, while their dorsal scent-glands (pp. 74 and 183) are exposed. They fan vigorously and the odor given off is sufficiently strong to be perceived if the nose is placed within an inch or two of the fanning bees. Bees to the rear take up the same position until finally the whole mass is fanning and moving toward the entrance[1] (Fig. 50). This may be observed also if bees are thrown in front of the hive.

When a swarm enters a cavity, the bees promptly clean it of loose pieces and dirt, the large pieces and irregularities of the cavity being ultimately covered with propolis. Large numbers of bees, especially the younger ones, now hang on one another in curtains while the secretion of wax takes place for the building of combs. The supply of honey carried in the honey-stomachs is adequate to nourish the colony for a time if no nectar can be brought to the hive. As soon as there are cells available the queen begins egg-laying, the field bees gather the available nectar and pollen and these activities increase as the comb is supplied by the comb-builders. The swarm is equipped as a normal colony in a surprisingly short time, if the nectar supply is adequate.

Parent colony

This name is usually given to that part of the original colony which remains in the hive after the swarm issues. It is misleading in that the actual parent of the individual bees, the queen, departs with the first swarm but, as ordi-

[1] If by chance the first bees are headed in the wrong direction or if the hive is moved after the fanning has begun, the whole mass may march away in the wrong direction. In shaking bees in front of the hive it is, therefore, advisable to toss some of them in the entrance. von Buttel-Reepen attributes this action to the sound given off in fanning, but there is little to support this belief. In this marching, any slight obstacle interferes greatly with the progress of the mass of bees, which would scarcely be the case if sound were the attracting stimulus. Even the smallest amount of smoke interferes for the moment with the entrance of a swarm and smoking should be avoided at this time.

narily used, the term indicates merely the colony from which the swarm issues and is not misunderstood. The course of events in this colony will now be given, it being assumed that, in the present instance, another swarm will not be cast. In a few days (often about eight days) after the departure of the swarm, the first young queen emerges from her cell by gnawing her way out, often with the help of the workers. She may destroy the other queens by gnawing into their cells, so that she is without a rival in the colony, and she may be assisted in this destruction by the workers.

Mating flight

When a few days old, the time depending somewhat on the weather and the race of bees, the virgin queen flies from the hive for the first time. Her early flights, often several in number, resemble the first flights of worker-bees, for she circles about the entrance, gradually venturing farther away, apparently taking note of the location of the hive. At last when from five to eight days old, she flies quickly from the hive without preliminary circling and flies upward in larger and larger circles, often until she is lost to vision.[1] On such a trip she meets the drone and after

[1] In the summer of 1903, the author and an equally ardent co-worker made a series of observations on the flight of virgin queens in the vivarium of the Zoological Department of the University of Pennsylvania. Small nuclei were placed about the room, which is covered with a glass roof, and a full colony was so arranged that the workers could fly freely to the outside but the drones could leave only to the inside. The drones used had never flown outdoors, it being found that drones which had experienced flight in the open air soon wore themselves out on the glass in their efforts to escape. Virgin queens were introduced to the nuclei and their flights were observed from the rafters above. The first flights were circles of small diameter and while on these flights the queens were never seen to be followed by drones. If the virgins did not fly frequently enough to satisfy the observers they would sometimes be removed and tossed into the air, when they behaved normally. Finally the virgin would dart from the entrance and swiftly circle upward, often followed by several drones. She would soon strike the glass roof and alight and the drones would at once disperse, there apparently being no attraction in a queen at rest. It has long been the dream

mating takes place she returns to the hive. She may be followed back by a considerable number of drones which sometimes remain about the front of the hive for several hours. The mating flight may last only a few minutes or may be protracted to over a half-hour, probably depending on the number of drones in flight near by. The male genital organs which are torn off in mating may often be seen protruding from the queen's vagina and this is useful to the beekeeper as evidence of mating. These parts shrivel in a short time and are removed by the workers. In about two days after mating, the queen begins to lay eggs and from that time on the routine of egg-laying is her portion. The so-called parent colony is now normal, with a laying queen, comb, stores and brood.

After-swarms

If the colony which cast the first swarm is populous, nough bees may be left in the parent colony to cause the ssuing of other swarms. These are called second swarms, hird swarms or, collectively, after-swarms. When the irst virgin queen emerges she often does not destroy the ther queen-cells but, instead, flies from the hive with an-

f beekeepers to induce mating in an inclosure, so that mating can e controlled for purposes of selection and the observations here nentioned were instigated by this desire. No queens mated in he room. The virgin queens usually returned to the nuclei unassisted, unless the flight occurred late in the afternoon.

During the summers of 1903 and 1904, several unsuccessful ttempts were made to produce drone-laying queens (p. 200) by onfining virgin queens to prevent mating flights. During the morning the small nuclei showed no special signs of excitement but in he early afternoon the queens would attempt to leave the hive nd would be prevented by the perforated zinc over the entrances. They would sometimes continue these efforts until dark. While this vas going on, the workers would crowd around the entrance both nside and out and rush about "as if offering assistance." These fforts were not observed during the first few days after emergence f the queens from the cells and finally the queens were no longer een at the entrances. Within a month they had all died. Whether his was due to over-exertion or to the inability to mate or whether hey were killed by the workers could not be determined. Keeping virgin queens in cages was equally unsuccessful.

other swarm. This may be repeated several times as other queens emerge, the swarms usually becoming successively smaller. The queens departing with after-swarms are virgins and consequently must mate before they are able to fulfill their duties normally. Good beekeepers make every effort to prevent after-swarms as they are usually too weak to be of value and they deplete the parent colony, making the gathering of surplus honey impossible. When virgin queens fly out to mate, they may be accompanied by a little "swarm," which affords some evidence that the swarm is led out by the queen. Nuclei used for mating queens are often almost depopulated in this way.

If the old queen in a colony is prevented from flying or is unable to fly (as by having the wings clipped), the bees may make several efforts to swarm without her. They often finally kill the old queen and depart with a virgin. Such a swarm may be the first to issue from a colony in the season, but it is virtually an after-swarm in its composition and behavior. Swarms of this kind often cause the beekeeper trouble if he is unaware that the old queen has been superseded, and consequently if the old queen was clipped he thinks that the swarm is without a queen and will return.

After-swarms are the plague of the beekeeper's life, for they seem to break all of the laws of the bee-colony. They often cluster without a queen, they are fleet on the wing, they may fly directly to the woods without clustering and they cannot be foretold accurately, as can a first swarm when the queen-cells are of value as a forewarning.

Activity of swarms

It is often maintained that the bees in a swarm work with greater vigor than those which have not swarmed. While this cannot be accepted without qualification, certain activities are more in evidence at this time. Wax secretion apparently proceeds more readily than under other conditions, and if nectar is available the bees may be so manipulated that a large amount of surplus honey is obtained. To take advantage of the supposedly increased activity of the swarm, the same conditions are partially induced artificially in various manipulations. The effect of swarming on egg-laying has been mentioned. It is probable that the supposed vigor of swarms is due not so much to the accomplishment of more work as to the diverting of the labor of the colony into lines which are more conspicuous to the beekeeper. It will be shown later that colonies which swarm produce less honey than those which make no effort to swarm.

Swarming conditions induced artificially

While the so-called artificial swarms are a part of the practical manipulations to be discussed in later chapters, it may be of interest to record attempts at producing swarming conditions which throw some light on the natural phenomenon. During the summers of 1912 and 1913, the author was interested in the taking of motion pictures of bee activities. In the first season, fortune favored the project by permitting the use of a natural swarm, which was, however, artificially delayed until the camera was adjusted. In all cases the clustering was produced artificially. In the first case, a swarm issued on a Thursday morning and the queen was caught, caged and placed in the second story of the hive, thus causing the bees to return. At eight o'clock the following Saturday morning the queen was liberated and about nine o'clock the camera was focused on the entrance and front of the hive. In not more than fifteen minutes after everything was ready and as the waiting group was in attendance seated on adjoining hives, the swarm came out and the camera was put in action. When the (clipped) queen left the hive, the camera was stopped and she was put into a queen-cage which was then tied to the limb of a tree, so situated that a swarm hanging on it would show against the sky. When the bees returned to the hive they were shaken into a box and thrown unceremoniously into the branches of the tree around the caged queen. Those that returned to the hive were again brought out. In a short time the fanning observed in a natural cluster was set up and the bees gradually formed a shapely cluster. To get pictures of the settling of the swarm, the branch was now shaken, at first gently and then more and more vigorously, and the bees returned to the same branch in the exact manner of the clustering of a natural swarm. Here again the camera was busy. The further treatment of the bees was exactly as with a natural swarm.

Since the first pictures were not satisfactory, the performance was repeated twice the next year but without the aid of a natural swarm. The bees were shaken into an empty hive on the old stand with the entrance closed by a stick. The clustered bees were then loosened from the inside of the hive-cover by pounding, and as the stick was removed the camera was started. The rushing out of the bees could not be distinguished from that of a natural swarm. The bees were then shaken into a box and placed on a branch about the caged queen. These unusual procedures suggest that the clustering is brought about by the attraction of the odor from the dorsal scent-gland and that the bees may be induced to abandon their old hive by shaking incident to this manipulation. It is also suggested that the queen plays an important part in clustering.

Peculiarities of bees in swarming

A bee normally returns from the field to its own hive and, while it may make mistakes, it "knows" its own location. This is accomplished by the exercise of a memory of location (p. 191). When the swarm issues, the memory of the old location is abandoned (not destroyed), but if the queen is lost or removed this memory is again called into action and the bees return to the old hive. If the queen goes with the swarm, it may be placed in a new hive, even right beside the old one if desired, and the bees no longer return to the old hive. On the return from future trips to the field they go directly to the new home. The memory of the old location is no longer called into action and is finally lost. This is accomplished also in artificial swarming but perhaps not to so marked a degree.

When a swarm issues and the air is filled with circling bees, it sometimes happens that other colonies which are preparing to swarm will send out swarms prematurely and the various swarms will mingle in the air and in the cluster. Even if this does not happen, drones from various colonies join the swarm. These facts indicate that swarming bees have an attractive influence toward other bees. This has been attributed to the noise made by flying bees, which is so well known to beekeepers and which is sometimes called the "swarm tone." Since it is not surely determined that bees hear, it may be that this attraction is not one of sound but may be one of smell.

The issuing of premature swarms and of numerous afterswarms may become so common as to demoralize the apiary and swarms may issue several at a time, without queens, when no queen-cells have been built or when the colony has recently swarmed. Several swarms may unite in one cluster. The impulse to swarm is known among beekeepers as the "swarming fever" and the exaggerated conditions just described are often discussed as if this "fever" were infectious. Under such conditions, the usual rules for swarming laid down by the beekeeper are seemingly disregarded, which may be construed as evidence that, after all, the beekeeper knows little about swarming.

Since swarming bees influence others to swarm prematurely, it is evident that these conditions may become worse in large commercial apiaries than would be the case if colonies were scattered as wild bees are or where only a few colonies are kept together. This abnormal condition is largely the result of modern beekeeping, not only in the maintenance of large apiaries but more especially in the manipulations practiced in comb-honey-production.

It is sometimes assumed that bees from colonies about to

swarm get mixed in other colonies and serve to incite swarming in their new homes. There is no good evidence for this belief.

It should also be noted that when preparations for swarming are well under way, the various manipulations devised to prevent it are usually unsuccessful and the only way to get the colony back to normal (normal from the standpoint of the beekeeper) is either to allow it to swarm naturally, to make an artificial swarm, or to remove or cage the queen. This and numerous other facts observed in swarm control indicate that the condition of the bees which induces swarming is not one which comes into existence suddenly, but is the result of a gradual development. Whether this condition is physiological or psychological is undetermined. Whatever the condition may be, it is in a sense at odds with the gathering instinct, so that one of the most difficult problems of the northern comb-honey-producer is to keep his colonies in the optimum condition for gathering, which is equivalent to swarm prevention.

Cause of swarming

Perhaps no subject in bee behavior has been so much discussed among beekeepers as the cause of swarming. Ever since swarming came to be regarded as undesirable, beekeepers have sought means of preventing it, and it has generally been realized that adequate prevention and control of swarming should rest on a knowledge of the stimulus which sets this train of activities in motion. The simplest way is to account for this phenomenon by attributing it to instinct, but an explanation is no nearer. Instinctive activities are called into play only by definite stimuli arising in the environment, and the real search is, therefore, for the prompting stimulus or stimuli. It is also a common error to assume that bees themselves set this instinct into play when conditions are favorable, but this is a misconception similar to the giving of human motives to any of the other activities of bees.

Overcrowding of the hive, lack of ventilation, heat, abundance of drones and similar conditions which often prevail at the time that swarming is instituted have been given as causes or contributing conditions to swarming, but unfortunately for these speculations, these conditions may be wholly or partially lacking at the time of swarming and cannot, therefore, be considered as actual causes. The best analysis of the cause of swarming yet attempted is that of Demuth.[1] While this problem is not fully solved, since swarming has not been produced experimentally, an analysis of some of the facts observed helps in an understanding of the problem.

First of all it should be observed that swarming is particularly prevalent in northern regions. Near the northern boundaries of the clover region, for example, there is a definite relatively short period when swarming may be expected. This comes before and during the clover honeyflow but when nectar is coming in freely swarming may become rare. Farther south there is a less marked swarming season and the percentage of colonies which swarm usually decreases, until under tropical conditions swarming is much less abundant and the swarming season is less definite and more prolonged. Swarming seems, therefore, to be induced by some condition which prevails most frequently in northern regions.

Colonies headed by young queens are less prone to swarm than are those with older queens. This fact has long been noted and some years ago a few beekeepers tried to prevent all swarming by buying queens in the spring from the South. This practice did not prevent swarming as expected, yet when a young queen is reared by the colony itself, swarming rarely occurs the same season.

There is variation even within the clover region. In the southern parts of this section, swarming has usually ceased

[1] Demuth, Geo. S., 1921. Swarm Control. Farmers' Bull. 1198, U. S. Dept. Agr., 28 pp., 13 figs. See also by the same author, Cause of Swarming. Proc. VII. Internat. Apic. Congress [Quebec, 1924], 1925, pp. 364-369.

before nectar secretion from clover begins, whereas farther north the swarming season extends into the honey-flow. This suggests that incoming nectar is not a cause of swarming, and in fact in some parts of the southern states the beekeepers claim that when the honey-flow begins all danger of swarming ceases. If the early honey-flow fails, however, colonies are often unable to build up adequately to swarm, in which event a later honey-flow may bring about better colony conditions and swarming may then occur. Where there are two heavy honey-flows, if swarming is prevalent with or before the first, there is rarely much swarming in connection with the second. It appears then that while the honey-flow is not the cause, its absence may prevent swarming by preventing the colonies from becoming adequately strong to swarm.

Lack of adequate room for breeding is a common condition in colonies which swarm, and in comb-honey-production when the brood-nest is contracted excessive swarming may occur. However, if the brood-nest is greatly contracted, swarming is much reduced. Furthermore, colonies swarm from enormous cavities, so that crowding of the colony as a whole is not the cause of swarming.

In the production of extracted honey, in which the bees are usually provided with an abundance of empty combs, swarming is much less common than in the crowded hives usually considered necessary for the successful production of comb-honey. Some years ago, Aspinwall devised a hive in which an abundance of room was provided for bees in the brood-chamber by the insertion of slatted wooden separators between the brood-combs, and under his personal management this hive was a great success, yet others failed to get such good results. So far as contraction is concerned, when swarming is less common there is usually more room available for the young bees which have recently emerged and which have not yet begun their field duties.

In the analysis of swarming by Demuth mentioned earlier, he sums up the case as follows: "Although the cause of swarming has not been definitely determined, the one factor which is universally present in normal swarming is that of a congestion of bees within the brood nest (not elsewhere in the hive). Other factors often mentioned as causing swarming are not universally present. Such a congestion of bees within the brood nest is usually brought about by a preponderance of recently emerged and emerging young bees, but the effect of such crowding may be greatly intensified by numerous factors in the environment, not universally present, which may be considered as contributing factors, but not causal. Whether a preponderance of bees too young for outside work or some other factor is responsible for swarming, this theory forms a good working hypothesis, since the successful preventive measures are those which reduce the congestion or alleviate its effects, and the successful corrective measures are those by which the balance in the proportion of hive bees and field bees is restored." While the various methods of swarm prevention and control are reserved for a later chapter, the fundamental principle that there must be a temporary disturbance in the continuity of brood emergence, which Demuth was the first to point out, is of primary importance in considering the cause of swarming. His theory fits the observed facts as does no other.

Some years ago Gerstung advanced the theory that swarming is caused by too many young bees in the hive. These bees, as will be shown later, are those which feed the larvæ and the supposition made by Gerstung was that too much larval food is prepared and that the presence of this extra supply induces the worker-bees to construct queen-cells. It is unfortunate for Gerstung's theory that he did not rest his case on the congestion which he observed, instead of attempting a physiological explanation which fails to explain. Swarming is often controlled by the removal of all brood, and if Gerstung's theory were correct, all colonies so treated should immediately prepare to swarm, which is exactly contrary to what is observed.

Swarming sometimes occurs in a colony which seems to lack the conditions which have been mentioned. When a queen is being superseded during that period of the year when swarming usually occurs, the colony may swarm when the queen-cells are sealed, even though a congestion in the brood-nest is lacking. In such cases the presence of queen-cells, built for quite a different cause, apparently sets in motion the chain of events which leads to the issuing of a swarm. Such swarming differs somewhat from that observed under the usual conditions, yet it indicates a lack of infallibility on the part of the bees which is interesting.

When because of some accident the queen is lost, or when she is removed by the beekeeper, several queen-cells are usually built if there are larvæ of the proper age in the hive. When the young queens thus reared begin to emerge swarming may be expected, even though the usual congestion is lacking. Such colonies behave much as do those which cast second swarms and their activities are unlike those of normal colonies casting a first swarm.

Swarming-out

Bees sometimes abandon their nest and to this action beekeepers give the name "swarming-out." The name is misleading since it indicates some relation between this and swarming, and it is not definitely known that any such relation exists. Swarming-out may occur under a variety of conditions, the most common of which is in the early spring (or at other times) if the stores are exhausted. These are known as "hunger swarms." Some of the published records of extraordinarily early swarms are doubtless instances of swarming-out rather than of swarming. Nuclei used in queen-rearing are frequently depopulated, but this may be a case of bees accompanying the virgin queen on her mating flight. When American foulbrood is present in a colony, swarming-out is common, the bees abandoning the hive when this disease is well advanced and when the odor of the decaying material is offensive. They sometimes abandon a newly painted hive, possibly because of the odor, and may also desert a hive in which wax-moth larvæ are plentiful. The bees which are deserting their hive seldom cluster but may fly for a considerable time or may enter another colony.

Somewhat similar is the abandonment of the hive so frequent after hiving artificial or natural swarms or after treatment for American foulbrood by shaking. After the artificial swarm is made, the bees may leave immediately or they may begin work and then desert the hive within twenty-four hours or even later. This is prevented if a comb containing unsealed larvæ is given the colony or, if a queen-trap is placed over the entrance, the deserting bees will return to the abandoned queen. After artificial swarming, a colony may repeatedly attempt to swarm-out, suggesting an intensified swarming sometimes observed in northern comb-honey apiaries. After sufficient comb is built and when larvæ have hatched, this trouble disappears. The swarming-out of colonies under adverse conditions suggests the action of giant bees (p. 206) which are said to abandon their combs if attacked by the wax-moth, or to migrate with the changes in seasons to districts where nectar is available, sometimes many miles distant.

GATHERING OF NECTAR AND STORING OF HONEY

At any time that nectar is available and the weather is suitable for flight, bees gather nectar to be converted into honey for use as food. Usually, as early in the spring as bees are able to fly freely, there is some nectar available, but under the adverse conditions of spring, when the colonies are weak in bees and the weather makes flying difficult, no more honey is obtained than bees need for immediate use, and usually they must draw on their old stores during this season. In almost every locality, there are later periods when no nectar is available or when there is less than enough to maintain the colony. That honey-production may be possible, there must be other periods when the amount of honey produced is in excess of the requirements of the bees until the next such period. This surplus may become the beekeeper's and these periods of abundance are called "honey-flows."

Periods of surplus depend solely on the plants of the region and consequently they vary with different localities, as do the plants. The problem confronting the beekeeper, therefore, is to manipulate his bees so that, when nectar is available near at hand, the bees may be in condition to secure the maximum quantity. Varying conditions call for different systems of management. This fact is well known to practical beekeepers but, nevertheless, these differences lead to confusion. For example, a beekeeper in the clover region works out a method whereby he is able to control swarming and thereby secure maximum returns. The method is published, whereupon it is perhaps tried by beekeepers in buckwheat, alfalfa or sage regions. The bee-journals are then filled with articles from these beekeepers who perhaps report failure. There would be great good in this interchange of results did it not tend too often to create a belief that bees in the various regions behave differently. In other words, the differences observed are too often considered as a matter merely of geography or as a variation in bee behavior, whereas they are differences in timing the apiary operations. The fault usually lies in a failure to record adequately the peculiar conditions of the locality, to appreciate the underlying causes of the behavior of the bees and to learn why a given manipulation is a success or a failure. Obviously a beekeeper should not only know what to do but when to do it and why. Frequently a beekeeper moves to a new locality and tries to use methods which he has learned from some other beekeeper or which he has worked out for himself in his former location, and this usually leads to at least temporary failure, unless he is quickly adaptable.

The nectar which is of value for surplus honey must come

after the colonies are strong, but earlier honey-flows are of great value in providing stores and in furnishing a stimulus to breeding. For each situation it is, therefore, most desirable that the plants which furnish nectar be known and that the usual time of blooming be learned. With such information, the beekeeper can so manipulate his colonies as to obtain maximum results. The study of the periods of blossoming is especially necessary in the northern regions where the honey-flows are sharply circumscribed, whereas in the South the honey-flows are less definite and often run together, and there is less difficulty in having strong colonies for the surplus honey-flows. In each locality the number of species of plants which furnish nectar in surplus quantities is usually small, so that the beekeeper need not be a botanist to determine these points, yet he will find that there is usually a large number of species which contribute to the welfare of his colonies, and it is a good plan to know these plants.

Bees do not cease to store honey in the tropics. Just where the erroneous contrary statement originated is difficult to learn, but the supposed fact is sometimes used as a demonstration of the wonderful adaptibility of bees in learning that surplus is unnecessary because nectar is always available. The great crops of honey from some tropical countries are sufficient denial. As a matter of fact, nectar secretion is usually less abundant in tropical countries than in northern regions and beekeeping is poorly developed in the tropics. It may be that the fallacy mentioned above arose from this fact, which deals with the physiology of plants and not with the behavior of bees.

The gathering of nectar and the storage of honey constitutes an interesting chain of instinctive activities, in that every step is made without previous experience, for a definite purpose and without knowledge of the end to be gained. As will be made clear in the discussion of swarm control (p. 279), preparation for swarming interferes with gathering of nectar. The gathering of nectar is normally the work of the older bees. The nectar is carried to the hive in the honey-stomach (Fig. 61) where is it regurgitated and where the ripening process is finished by younger bees (p. 132). The ripening process consists in the removal of surplus moisture by ventilation of the hive, the water-content of honey usually not exceeding 20 per cent, whereas nectar may contain as high as 60 per cent water. The chemical composition of nectars is also changed, for the percentage of cane-sugar is greatly reduced, it being changed into invert-sugar (levulose and dextrose). Removal of surplus moisture and the chemical changing of the cane-sugar continue at all times when nectar is being gathered and not merely at night, as is sometimes believed.

In the laboratory, inversion of cane-sugar is accomplished by the addition of an acid and the application of heat to a sugar solution. There is acid in honey, most of which is probably malic acid, but in chemical analyses the acid-content is usually calculated "as formic acid," which must not be misinterpreted as indicating that the acid is actually formic. It was formerly believed that the poison of the bee-sting is formic acid and various fanciful theories have been advanced to explain the origin of the supposed formic acid of honey. The most fantastic explanation is that just before sealing the honey, the worker-bee puts a drop of poison from the sting into the honey to preserve it. No such action has been observed, but this speculation is perhaps the reason why the chemist calculated the acidity of honey in terms of formic acid. No acid is necessary to preserve honey, for it is so concentrated a solution of sugars that fermentation cannot occur if the honey is fully ripened.

The conversion of cane-sugar to invert-sugar may also be accomplished by the action of an enzyme (invertase or sucrase) and the bee produces this in quantity, it being present in all parts of the body of the worker-bee. This enzyme acts at temperatures far below that of boiling, so that no heating is required other than such as is provided within the hive. Honey, as stored in cells, contains some suspended pollen-grains which are an additional source of invertase. Most of the chemical change in the sugars occurs before the honey is sealed but goes on afterward, since this enzyme occurs in honey itself. The behavior of the bees in the ripening and storing of honey will be discussed in a later chapter (p. 131).

Every beekeeper knows that weather conditions play an exceedingly important part in the gathering of the bees. Some definite data on this subject have been obtained by Lundie[1] in a study of flight activity. For full details the reader is advised to read all of this important paper, but it may be pointed out that a threatened storm of about one hour duration reduced the flights from the hive about 8 per cent for the day. A wind velocity of sixteen to twenty-one miles an hour on one occasion reduced flights by 28 per cent. Temperature of the outer air plays an important part, the bees rarely leaving the hive for free flights until the temperature reached about 50° F. During a heavy honey-flow the average time for each trip from the hive may be as short as eight minutes, while during periods of dearth the average length of trip may extend to almost two hours. The average number of trips made by each bee is found to be about thirty-two. Hambleton[2] has attacked this problem from a different point of view by correlating the changes in weight of a strong colony with records of external conditions. Here again the full paper should be consulted. He found that external temperature, hours of sunshine, variation in daily temperature, solar radiation and variation in relative humidity are all positively correlated with gain in weight, while variation in relative humidity is inversely correlated. Variations in external conditions seem to play a small part in evaporation during the night. He

[1] Lundie, A. E., 1925. The flight activities of the honeybee. Dept. Bull. 1328, U. S. Dept. Agr., 37 pp. 13 figs.

[2] Hambledon, J. I., 1925. The effect of weather upon the changes in weight of a colony of bees during the honey flow. Dept. Bull. 1339, U. S. Dept. Agr., 52 pp. 12 figs.

found that the factors which influence nectar secretion do not effect changes in weight of the hive in just the same manner, so that the peculiarities of bee behavior play a considerable part. In the preparation of these results a technical use of mathematics was essential, so that the average reader will have difficulty in interpreting the data, but this is one of the outstanding contributions to bee activities.

Much energy is required to change liquid water to vapor (535.9 small calories to a gram), so that the energy expended in evaporating nectar is considerable. This process is aided by warmth from sunshine and from heat-producing activities within the hive, but assuming that all the energy comes from the consumption of honey, to produce 100 pounds of honey from nectar containing 50 per cent water, there would be required the consumption of 10 pounds of honey. If the water-content of the nectar is 60 per cent, this mounts to 16.4 pounds. It is sometimes stated that nectar may contain 80 per cent water, in which event 49 pounds of honey would be consumed to ripen 100 pounds of such nectar to honey. It is thus seen that such activities in the colony require considerable consumption of food, which is part of colony maintenance.

The gathering of nectar and the ripening of this into honey is, therefore, an elaborate process, requiring much energy and considerable time. Incoming nectar is thin and the excess water must be eliminated in order that the honey may not ferment. The larger amount of cane-sugar in nectar must be changed to invert-sugar, which is accomplished by enzyme action. The resulting product is primarily a super-saturated solution of three sugars which remains liquid for a considerable time, varying in this regard according to the nectar source, a condition which is possible only because of the peculiar mixture of the sugars. The beekeeper who tries to make an 80 per cent solution of sugar will have difficulty in obtaining one which does not crystallize promptly, whereas the bees with their chemical magic are able to make such a solution which sometimes remains liquid for years. Honey contains a useful mixture of salts derived from nectar, possibly one of the vitamins, five coloring materials, aromatic substances, at least four enzymes, a few pollen-grains, some protein, a little acid and sometimes rare sugars and other carbohydrates, which perhaps account in part for the considerable percentage of "undetermined material" in ordinary chemical analyses. The physical and chemical wonders of the hive are far from being fully understood.

Collection of other materials

The gathering of pollen and propolis and the collection of water are likewise activities of the colony. It is sometimes stated that pollen is gathered only when needed but this is not true, for queenless colonies gather large quantities. The advice is occasionally given to watch the entrances of colonies in the spring to determine whether pollen is coming in, it being stated that queenless colonies may be detected by a lack of pollen-gathering. This is not a safe criterion. Propolis is collected most abundantly in the late summer and autumn and usually only when there is no heavy nectar-flow. Water is needed at practically all times during the breeding season, perhaps more especially in hot weather. The bringing of water to the hive is most noticeable in the early spring.

KILLING OF THE DRONES

At the close of the honey-flow and after the swarming season, the drones are driven from the hive. They are not stung to death as is commonly reported. The first indication of the exodus of the drones is that numbers of them are seen on the bottom board or around the entrance. There is some evidence that before removal the drones are starved, they normally being fed by the workers and not taking food directly from the stores. Then the worker-bees drag them out one by one and fly away, dropping them some distance from the hive. This driving out of the drones is more marked in the northern regions where the main honey-flow usually ceases abruptly. If a colony is queenless the drones may be retained, some of them often living into the winter and, even in normal colonies, a few drones are sometimes retained for a time. The cause of the driving out of the drones in most cases and their retention under some conditions is so far not explained satisfactorily.

THE END OF BROOD-REARING

In northern localities brood-rearing ceases in autumn and for several months normal colonies are broodless. As one goes southward, the length of the broodless period becomes shorter, but apparently there is a broodless period of some duration in normal colonies everywhere that bees are kept, and a cessation of brood-rearing is a regular occurrence in the annual cycle. It is shown earlier that a reduction in egg-laying occurs when the honey-flow ceases and during the latter part of the summer the amount of brood in colonies is usually considerably below that at the peak of brood production. When the days become cold, brood-rearing is still further curtailed and finally egg-laying ceases and the last brood emerges, leaving the colony broodless. The last eggs laid may be removed by the workers before they hatch, or larvæ and pupæ may be carried out.

In seeking an explanation of the stoppage of brood-rearing, one becomes involved in some difficulties. In the first place, various races of bees differ in regard to the amount and continuance of brood-rearing in autumn. Italian bees decrease the amount of brood when the honey-flow stops while Carniolan and Caucasian bees rear more brood "out of season," or after the honey-flow. But all races rear some brood at this time, so that the final discontinuance of brood-rearing cannot be considered as due to lack of incoming stores. Even among colonies of the same race there is considerable variation in a single apiary.

Of course no colony can rear brood without food, and

pollen is absolutely essential. Colonies of any race vary in the amount of brood reared late in the summer according to the age of the queen, young queens being inclined to rear more brood than older ones. The stoppage of brood-rearing is sometimes attributed to low outer temperatures, but brood is sometimes reared in the coldest months of winter. As will be seen later, the cold outside during January is the cause of a high temperature within the winter-cluster, and this raising of temperature as a protection against cold, together with the effects of an accumulation of feces, is the cause of higher cluster temperatures than occur with the same intensity of cold in earlier parts of the winter. When a colony has once begun brood-rearing in winter, the presence of brood seems to induce the production of more heat to protect it, and brood-rearing once begun is usually continued throughout the winter, unless the colony dies before spring comes. Since a moderately low outer temperature induces more active heat production in a small colony than in a strong one, this explains why weak colonies continue brood-rearing longer and why they sometimes fail to discontinue brood-rearing and die of overwork.

If an explanation of the cessation of brood-rearing is sought from these facts, the paradoxical conclusion is reached that in the fall (1) the outer temperature is not high enough for brooding-rearing without artificial heat production, and (2) it is not low enough to cause the bees to produce sufficient cluster heat for brood-rearing. Egg-laying and brood-rearing may seemingly be stimulated by either a high or low outer temperature.

THE WINTER-CLUSTER

There are three possible ways by which an animal can survive a protracted period of adversity like a northern winter, when food is not available in the field or when it could not get food even if it were present, because of the cold. The first method is hibernation, in which the only storage of food is within the animal, and at low temperatures the vital functions are greatly reduced. This is the universal mode of wintering among solitary insects which pass the winter as adults and, even among social species, in bumblebees and wasps, the larger part of the colony dies off while the queens hibernate like solitary adult insects. Ants hibernate in a mass during extreme cold weather. Another method is migration, but this is not open to most insects because of their size and inability to fly long distances, as do birds. The giant bees, the nearest relatives of honeybees, migrate long distances to avoid adverse conditions. If a cold-blooded animal cannot hibernate, as the honeybee apparently cannot at least in part because of its small storage of food in the body, nor migrate, there is but one course open to it. This is to lay up a store of heat-producing food outside its body and, when the surrounding temperature falls below that at which the animal can live and move, to generate heat, virtually to create a thermal environment of its own. This remarkable procedure, in which the honeybee is unique among insects, is the one encountered in a study of bees in winter. Beekeepers have long known that the winter-cluster is warm but they have perhaps failed to comprehend the marvel of an insect which can use this method of overcoming adverse conditions.

The hoarding instinct, the instinct to store food in great excess of immediate needs, now becomes of vital importance to the continuance of the species, but it would serve no useful purpose in the winter season if the bees in a colony did not also have the ability to generate and to conserve heat. As will be seen, the generation of heat is by a method common to all animals, while the conservation of heat depends on the structure of the winter-cluster.

When the last brood has emerged, the high uniform temperature of the brood-rearing period ceases and the colony and its nest are then in condition to pass the winter. In cold weather the bees form a single compact cluster and leave the hive only on occasional warm days for cleansing flights. Bees do not normally discharge their feces in the hive, but even after a short confinement will venture out as soon as the outer temperature permits. They may try to fly for this purpose at 50° F. if such a flight is needed, but will remain quietly in the hive at 70° F. if no cleansing flight is needed.

Movements in winter

The cluster is first normally formed where the last brood emerged; here the bees find empty cells into which to crawl, so that they form themselves into a compact mass, separated only by thin walls of wax. They do not form the winter-cluster where the combs are filled with honey and it would probably be impossible for them to conserve the heat of the cluster if sheets of honey separated the bees in adjacent spaces. As the contiguous stores are consumed and additional cells are emptied, the cluster is shifted so that the bees are always near stores. This shifting is, however, apparently impossible in extreme cold weather, when colonies sometimes die in a way that can be explained only as due to starvation through inability to reach stores just a few inches distant. The early fall-cluster is usually low on the combs, near the entrance, if there is considerable honey stored, and the movement of the cluster is usually upward and toward the rear of the hive as winter progresses, and as stores are consumed. If a colony is in a two-story hive, the cluster is often in the upper story in the spring.

Responses to outside temperature

The cluster varies in size with the outside temperature. After the emergence of the last brood in the fall, if the temperature is about 60° F., the bees do not cluster and do not fly from the hive, even on bright days, but remain inactive on the combs, at which time there is less activity in the hive than at any other season. A cluster is unnecessary since this formation is for the conservation of heat. When the temperature of the air immediately surrounding the bees falls to 57° F. (the lowest temperature which normal bees ever experience in the hive), they form a definite cluster. As the outer temperature continues to fall, the cluster becomes more compact and the temperature of the cluster soon reaches a point higher than that attained before heat generation was necessary. Within certain limits, the temperature of the cluster rises and falls inversely with the changes in outer temperature. Heat generation is renewed whenever the outer temperature falls, and the temperature drifts downward as the outer temperature rises (Fig. 145). Efforts have been made to show a periodicity in heat generation within the cluster, but in all the records made by Demuth and the author no such periods were seen. It is of the utmost practical importance that if temperature conditions within the hive are suitable, heat generation on the part of the bees virtually ceases.

Conservation of heat

The cluster consists of a hollow sphere of bees several layers thick, those between the combs with their thoraces in contact and abdomens extending outward. The cells within the cluster are also filled with bees. The hair on the thorax assists in making this living shell an excellent non-conductor of heat, so effective in fact that a point inside the cluster may sometimes be 75° F. warmer than a point a few inches away but outside the cluster. The number of inactive bees varies with the outer temperature, being larger at warmer temperatures when less heat production is required and smaller when more bees are engaged in activities involved in heat production.

Source of heat

Within the hollow sphere are bees which move about freely, these being the ones most concerned in heat generation. They produce heat by muscular activity, such as movements of the legs and abdomen, but perhaps most effectually by vigorous fanning. The bees which form the shell constantly shift their positions and exchange places with insects from within. A bee from the center forces its way head first through the shell, then turns around and remains for a time on the outside layer. The shifting seems to be more rapid in cold weather than in mild.

Effect of accumulation of feces

In the winter, the bees consume the honey stored during the summer. The undigested portion, which forms excreta, is retained in the rectal ampulla (hind-intestine) until the bees have opportunity for flight, for normally no feces are deposited by the workers within the hive. In the cold winters of the North there are times when bees cannot fly for several weeks and the generation of heat during such a period of cold weather requires increased consumption of food and causes an increase in the amount of feces. The presence of feces, on the other hand, causes the bees to become restless, to generate still more heat (see Fig. 151) and to accumulate still more feces. Apparently a colony in winter confinement is in the confines of a vicious circle and the successful wintering depends preëminently on good food. If, however, the colony is so placed that little or no heat must be produced, the situation is relieved and this the beekeeper accomplishes by placing colonies in the cellar, provided conditions within the cellar are correct.

Bees wintering in the open fly out whenever the outside temperature will permit, and after a considerable period of confinement many will fly out when it is so cold that they are unable to return. On these winter flights the feces are voided, consequently they are of the highest value to a colony wintered out-of-doors.

While numerous other points concerning the activities of bees in winter are left to be discussed in the chapter on wintering, it is evident from what has been said that bees are highly sensitive to changes in temperature, and that they have a remarkable ability to overcome the adverse conditions of winter by the generation of heat. It is to be noticed especially that they usually do not warm the whole hive or cavity but confine heat production to the cluster. It might, therefore, be concluded that a hive is actually little protection for them in winter but it should be remembered that this protects them from wind, rain and snow. They further seal the hive with propolis to make the top water- and even air-tight and some races contract the entrance with propolis. The practical bearing of these facts forms one of the most vital problems of the northern beekeeper and the discussion of this subject from the standpoint of practice forms a later chapter.

CHAPTER V

THE LIFE OF THE INDIVIDUAL IN RELATION TO THE COLONY

In the preceding chapter the activities of the colony are discussed, much as if the colony were an individual or unit. While this is a true picture of one side of the life of the species, it is not complete, for the individuals not only fulfill their own life processes but pass through individual cycles. A knowledge of the interrelationships of the individuals within the colony is important for an understanding of the colony organization, for this complex society is based on a division of the labors of the hive, which is of the highest interest and of the greatest practical value to the beekeeper. While in this book there is no attempt at a complete discussion of the anatomy or development of the bee, it is necessary that these subjects receive some attention to outline correctly the little that is known concerning the physiology of the species. The discussion of physiology is reserved for another chapter.

DEVELOPMENTAL STAGES

This subject is one of mystery to the beekeeper. While the development of the bee in the egg has been investigated by several observers,[1] the papers are not readily

[1] Bütschli, O., 1870. Zur Entwicklungsgeschichte der Biene. Zeit. f. Wiss. Zool., XX.

Kowalevski, A., 1871. Embryologische Studien an Würmern und Arthropoden. Mèm. Acad. Impér. Sci., St. Pétersbourg, (7) XVI, 12, pp. 1-70.

Grassi, Battista, 1882-84. Studi sugli artropodi. Intorno allo sviluppo dell Api nell' uovo. Atti dell' Acad. Gioenia di Sci. Nat. in Catania, Sere. 3, XVIII, pp. 145-222.

accessible, and writers of books on beekeeping have not given to this subject as careful consideration as to the anatomy of the adult bee. The changes taking place during metamorphosis (pupa stage) are so wonderfully complex that an account of the transformation of the larva into an adult bee is almost unbelievable.[3] Because of the lack of attention given to the development of the bee in literature, relatively more space is here devoted to it than to the anatomy of the adult bee.

Cellular structure of tissues

To form a correct understanding of the development of the bee or of the structure of the adult, one must know something of the units of which the tissues are formed, called cells. This word, as used by the biologist, has a special significance, being applied to a type of structure which makes up the tissues of all plants and animals. This unit of structure is usually microscopic and a single organ of the bee may contain many thousands of them. The cell consists of a minute mass of protoplasm (living substance) containing a nucleus (Fig. 51). Protoplasm is a complex organic substance characterized by life; the nucleus is a differentiated portion of the protoplasm which is especially active during the division of cells and carries the special organs (chromosomes), instrumental as the bearers

Dickel, O., 1904. Entwicklungsgeschichtliche Studien am Bienenei. Leipzig: Engelmann.

The work of Carriere u. Bürger (1898, Entwicklungsgeschichte der Mauerbiene. Abhdl. der kaiserl. Leop. Carol. Deutsch. Akad. der Naturf., LXIX, 2) on the mason bee, Calicodoma, is of value in a study of this subject. The work of Dr. Jas. A. Nelson of the Bur. Ent. (1915, the embryology of the honey bee, 282 pp., 95 figs., 6 pl., Princeton Univ. Press) is the most complete on this subject and is the most thorough work on the development of any insect. It is the only discussion of the embryology of the bee in English and should be consulted by any one interested in this phase of the life of the bee. The author is indebted to Doctor Nelson for help in the preparation of this section.

[3] The metamorphosis of the bee is described in detail by Anglas, J., 1900. Observations sur les métamorphoses internes de la guêpe et de l'abeille. 111 pp. Lille: Danel.

of hereditary characters. The nucleus and surrounding protoplasm are closely united in their functions and are incapable of separate existence. The nucleus is, in its resting condition, usually rounded in form, while the remaining protoplasm is of various shapes according to the special functions of the cell. Protoplasm is characterized by ability to take in nourishment, to grow, to give off waste, to divide and to move in response to stimuli, but in each organ the cells become specialized to do some one thing especially well and they often lose some of the functions of primitive protoplasm. For example, a nerve-cell loses its power of contractility but becomes specialized for transmitting nervous impulses, while a muscle-cell has a marked power of contractility. A detailed discussion of the structure and function of the various portions of the cell in different tissues is, of course, impossible here, but these few suggestions are sufficient to indicate the extreme complexity of the organizations of each tissue that goes to make up any organism, such as the bee.

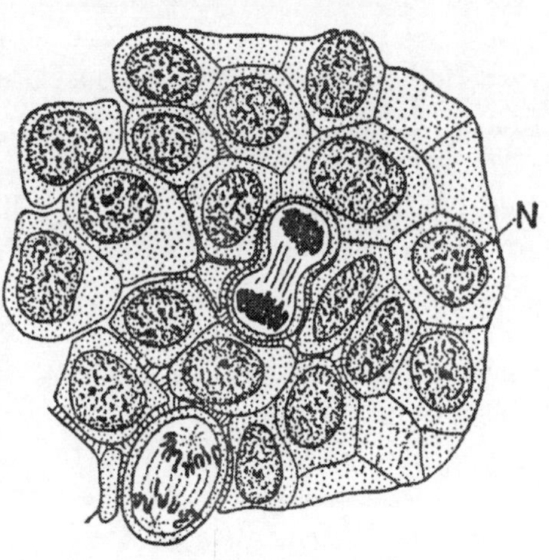

FIG. 51.—Group of tissue cells from skin of young salamander.

The egg

The egg, as it leaves the ovaries of the queen where it is formed, is essentially a single cell. The eggs of most animals known to the layman require fertilization (a union with one of the reproductive cells of the male) before they can develop, but there are many cases in which this is not necessary and the development of the drone-bee is of this character. The eggs which develop into females are, however, fertilized. This difference has so important a bearing on practical beekeeping that a discussion of it is reserved for a future chapter.

The egg of the bee is a small white cylindrical object about $\frac{1}{16}$ of an inch long, somewhat larger at one end (future head end) and slightly curved. It is deposited on the base of the cell of the comb by the queen and is fastened in place by a secretion. The head end of the future larva is always formed away from the point of attachment. The egg is covered by chorion, a thin tough membrane, the surface of which is ridged. These ridges are, however, minute and are not so conspicuous as most illustrations of bee eggs would indicate. In addition to the nucleus and surrounding protoplasm, the bee egg contains a relatively large amount of non-living stored food, yolk. The embryo is formed on the convex side of the curve of the egg, which becomes the ventral side of the larva. The fate of the various parts of the egg is, therefore, in a sense determined. Because of the presence of so much yolk, the early cells are not clearly marked off from one another.

Early embryonic development

Development consists of the repeated division of the egg-cell into numbers of united cells and of the rearrangement and differentiation of the resulting cells to form definite organs. As development proceeds, the cells become more and more specialized until the final adult condition is reached, and even in the adult, certain changes in some cells continue through the life of the individual. As cell division (or rather, in this case, nuclear division, for the protoplasm is continuous in the early stages) progresses, the nuclei move from the interior to the surface. During the second half of the second day, a thickening appears on the convex side, and, on the anterior end (larger end) of the egg, the first indications of the future appendages are soon visible (Fig. 52, *a* and *b*). These consist of the rudiments of the antennæ (*Ant*) and mouth-parts (mandible, *Md* and maxillæ, *1Mx, 2Mx*) on the head and of the three pairs of legs (*1L, 2L, 3L*) on the thorax. These rudiments are simply slightly rounded swellings which are at first smaller toward the posterior end of the egg, since development progresses from the anterior end. The embryo shows at first no division into head, thorax and abdomen, but the fate of the various swellings must be determined by following them through. The rudiments of the stigmata (*Sp*, openings of the tracheal system) appear early and

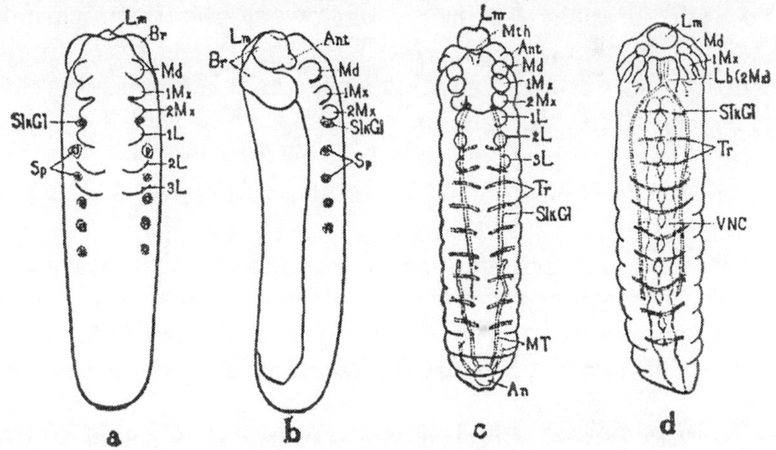

Fig. 52.—Three stages in the development of the embryo.

the first evidence of the silk-glands (*SlkGl*) becomes visible about the same time just behind the second maxillæ. The first external indication of the nervous system is in two pairs of swellings (*Br*) on the upper side of the head. Even in this early stage, a number of important organs are already outlined.

Later embryonic development

In a later stage (Fig. 52, *c*), the embryonic band on the ventral side of the egg has widened and in the next stage here illustrated (Fig. 52, *d*) the band completely envelops the egg. In the stage shown in Fig. 52, *c* the mouth (*Mth*) and anus (*An*) have appeared as pits. These continue to grow into the egg and ultimately join with certain cells on the interior to complete the alimentary canal. The portions formed by the two invaginations from the outside are the fore- and hind-intestine, while the part arising from the interior is the mid-intestine. The Malpighian tubes (*MT*), the excretory organs, arise as outgrowths from the anterior end of the hind-intestine. The pits (*Sp*) which are the rudiments of the spiracles, deepen and send branches forward, backward and downward to meet corresponding outgrowths from other pits, finally forming the tracheal trunks with their commissures and branches. The silk-glands (*SlkGl*), which function only in the larva, project backward as long tubes.

Segmentation

The most striking feature of the late embryo is the fact that it is constricted into a series of segments (metameres or somites) which are plainly recognized in the larva. These segments are characteristic of all insects and part of the metameres of the abdomen are still plainly marked off in the adult. From the fact that segmentation is recognizable in various parts of adult insects and is present in insect embryos; it is assumed that this form is characteristic of the primitive organism from which all insects have arisen. The typical appendages are arranged in pairs on the segments but in their later development are modified according to their fate. The stigmata and the ganglia of the nervous system are also arranged segmentally at first, but this primitive arrangement is later partially lost. The segmentation of various species studied does not wholly agree, but it is usually assumed that the first six or seven segments coalesce to form the adult head, the next three the typical insect thorax, and the remaining ones, usually twelve in number, form the abdomen. The thorax of the adult bee is not typical, as well be explained later.

Fate of parts of the embryo

Some of the head appendages of the embryo disappear early, being rudimentary organs. For example, the appendages of the second segment become the antennæ while those of the third disappear in insects, but in Crustacea (*e.g.*, shrimps and lobsters) form the second antennæ. Several of the segments of the primitive insect head are not recognizable in the bee. In the adult insect, these segments fuse completely and by growth of various parts are so distorted that an examination of the adult head does not suggest segmentation and, without a study of the developmental stages, this segmental origin would be unsuspected.

The three thoracic segments are fused in the adult bee but, since the three pairs of legs arise from them, the segmental origin is suggested. The wings arise as secondary outgrowths or appendages, dorsal to the legs, from the two posterior thoracic segments and do not correspond with other appendages. In the adult bee, the first abdominal segment is also fused with the true thoracic segments to form the part known as the thorax, which therefore does not correspond exactly with the thorax of lower orders of insects. This fusion also occurs in most of the other Hymenoptera. The remaining posterior segments form the abdomen of the adult but not all of the segments remain visible to the outside. In the adult worker and queen-bee, the five posterior segments are turned in to form a pocket around the sting and anus. In the drone, only four segments are so turned in.

The embryo, just before leaving the egg, shows no rudiments of antennæ or legs, these temporarily disappearing. The nervous system is now well organized, consisting of the brain and a chain of ganglia arranged segmentally. The second maxillæ fuse to form the lower lip (*Lb*).

Larval development

At the end of about three days of embryonic development, the embryo breaks the chorion and becomes a young larva. During the larval period the most striking feature is the enormous growth of the animal. Fig. 36 shows an egg, a relatively young larva, a fully grown larva and a pupa drawn to the same scale and, when it is realized that the growth from the youngest to the fully grown larva takes place in a few days, the rapidity of growth is astonishing.

It should be pointed out that the development of all insects is not similar. In the grasshopper, for example, a young insect hatches from the egg which resembles the adult in most respects. Such a development is known as incomplete metamorphosis. In the higher orders of insects, there hatches from the egg a larva unlike the adult and usually more or less worm-like, which when fully fed undergoes a complete and relatively sudden change into the adult. This type of development is known as complete metamorphosis.

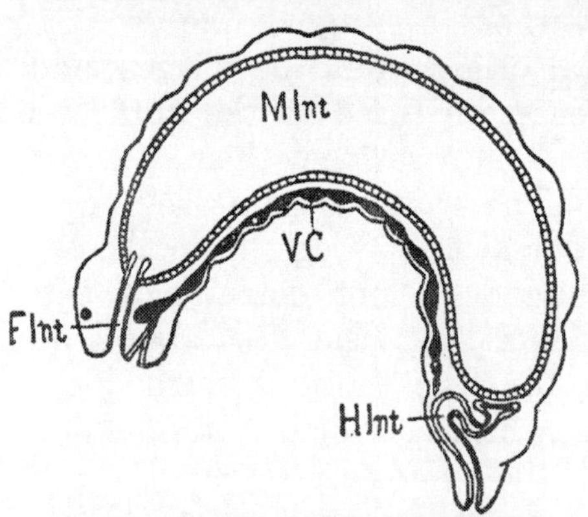

Fig. 53.—Diagram of a longitudinal median section of a bee-larva.

The bee-larva is an extremely simple organism, lacking legs, wings, antennæ and eyes, and is unprotected by hairs or thick chitin. A longitudinal section through the larva (Fig. 53) shows that the largest organ is the stomach, as is necessary for excessive growth. Being protected from enemies and from adverse environmental conditions in the cells of the comb, the bee-larva needs no protective covering and, being fed by the worker-bees, it does not require organs which will enable it to see or even to detect food or to masticate solid food. It is ideally adapted to the protected condition in which it is placed in the colony scheme and quickly perishes if removed and exposed to adverse conditions.

Rate of larval growth

The excessive rate of growth of the bee-larva is shown by data obtained by Nelson and Sturtevant,[1] from which the following table is drawn:

TABLE II.—THE AVERAGE WEIGHTS OF BEE-LARVÆ AT INTERVALS OF 24 HOURS

Age in days	*Average weight in mg.*	*Percent of daily increase*
0 hatching	0.100	...
1 day	0.650	550
2 days	4.687	621
3 days	24.640	426
4 days	94.692	284
4½-5 days	157.642	66 maturity

This great growth is made possible by extensive feeding, which is done by the nurse-bees. Lineburg[2] finds that the number of visits made to each developing bee from the time the egg is laid until the larva is fully grown averages about 1,300 a day. For the first two days of larval feeding, food is given in quantity (mass feeding), whereas after that time it is given frequently (progressive feeding). The total number of visits made to a developing larva is about 10,000, a total expenditure of time amounting to 4.75 hours. At the close of the second day of larval feeding, the character of the food changes to include undigested pollen and honey, a change which was supposed by earlier writers not to occur until the fourth day. During the last day of feeding, there is on the average a nurse-bee feeding each bee-larva almost 20 per cent of the time. During this period of rapid growth the bee-larva molts its skin

[1] Nelson, J. A., and Sturtevant, A. D., 1924. The rate of growth of the honeybee larva. Part 1 of Dept. Bull. 1222, U. S. Dept. Agr., pp. 1-24, figs. 1-11.

[2] Lineburg, Bruce, 1924. The feeding of honeybee larvæ. Part II, Dept. Bull. 1222, U. S. Dept. Agr., pp. 25-37, figs. 12-13.

at intervals of about twenty-four hours,[1] each molt being indicated by changes in size of various structures.

Metamorphosis

After the excessive growth, the larva is sealed in the cell with a capping of wax (Fig. 40) and it then spins a delicate silken cocoon with the secretion of the silk-glands (*SlkGl*) within the cell. Soon after this, all external motion ceases and the animal begins to undergo that wonderful series of changes known as metamorphosis. During the larval growth the mid-intestine and hind-intestine are not connected (Fig. 53) but this connection is made after sealing and the feces of the larva are then cast out.

The organs which served the larva are of course not suitable for the adult insect and the changes necessary to obtain suitable adult organs take place in the pupal stage. Anglas has described many of these changes but the metamorphosis of insects is so complex and so much disputed by various workers that it is hoped the changes in the bee may be again investigated. The simple alimentary canal of the larva is discarded and a new one formed in its place. The segmentally arranged muscles of the larva either disappear or are changed into those of the adult. The nervous system apparently loses some of the segmental ganglia by the fusion of various ganglion pairs. The antennæ, eyes, legs and wings develop from rudiments which have remained undeveloped in the larva. Not only do the internal organs change and new structures appear but the animal alters its outward appearance. The small head of the larva grows to adult size, the thoracic segments and the first abdominal segment unite and undergo marked external changes to form the thorax of the adult. The abdomen changes least in external form but marked internal alterations occur. This brief category of the vital modifications can give only a suggestion of the changes

[1] Bertholf, Lloyd M., 1925. The moults of the honeybee. Journ. Ent., XVIII, No. 2, pp. 380-384.

which the pupa undergoes. All of this occurs in an animal which externally seems lifeless, but the internal changes require such large expenditures of energy that the animal loses half its weight by the consumption of the food which the greedy larva stores up in the fat body.

The external changes of the pupa are interesting, even though of minor importance. The compound eyes first change from white to pink by the deposition of a pigment around the rhabdomes of the eye (p. 178) and later this pink pigment is gradually covered by a darker external pigment so that the eyes appear brown and then black. The thorax shows coloration earlier than the abdomen. Toward the close of the pupal period, the outside of the animal becomes covered over with a layer of hard chitin for the protection of the adult and to serve as a skeleton for the insertion of the muscles. The legs and wings originate as hollow bud-like outgrowths on the thorax and after the last molt of the larva these invaginations are suddenly extended by blood-pressure. The wings are at first small thin sacs which grow and finally take on the adult form, after which the two sides of the sac fuse and the blood in the sac returns to the body cavity, leaving the wings as dry non-living membranes.

Length of developmental stages

The length of the various stages of development varies among the different types in the hive. The preceding account applies especially to worker-bees, which have been most frequently investigated, probably because of the ease of obtaining material. The stages are essentially similar in queens and drones. While the rapidity of development is slightly modified by changes in temperature of the hive, it is, in the main, quite uniform and it is therefore possible to give the time from egg-laying to emergence of the adult. It must be understood that these vary somewhat and it is rather remarkable that the variation is not more pronounced. On account of the variation the tables given for the length of stages are not uniform. The following is a fair average:

TABLE III.—DEVELOPMENT STAGES IN DAYS

Stage	*Queen*	*Worker*	*Drone*
Egg	3	3	3
Larva	5½	6	6½
Pupa	7½	12	14½
Total	16	21	24

The figures given in this table for the pupal stage include all the time that the developing bee is sealed up in the cell. During part of this time, the larval stage is continued but no additional food is taken. This is followed by a semi-pupa stage, when the insect resembles a larva but has undergone a molt and the hind- and mid-intestine are connected. The true pupa stage follows this and the transition to the adult is gradual, the separation between the two stages being marked by the emergence of the insect from the cell.

The structure of the adult bee will be discussed briefly in conjunction with the functions of the various organs. When the young bee emerges from the cell it is structurally in the adult condition. It does not grow in size nor do any marked changes in most of the organs occur during adult life. This is true of all insects. While certain internal organs undergo change, these are not of a character to alter the outside appearance. The food taken by the adult is not stored up within the body, as in the larva, but is for immediate use.

THE CYCLE OF DUTIES OF THE ADULT WORKER-BEE

When the worker emerges from the cell, it is covered with a soft skin, the last pupal molt, which is quickly removed. For a day or two the young bee remains on the combs, frequently on the one from which it emerged, and moves about little. Numbers of young bees are often seen in the upper part of the hive and especially in the supers. In a few days they begin the inside work of the hive which consists of feeding and caring for the larvæ, feeding the queen and the drones, cleaning, ventilating, comb-building when necessary, guarding the hive from intruders and other work inside.

When about a week old, on bright days, the young bees take "play flights" in front of the hive. Suddenly, as if in response to a signal, the young bees fly out, circle about the hive, usually with their heads toward the entrance, and as a rule they do not at first venture more than a few feet away. In a short time this flight is over and the young bees return to the hive. This flight of young bees is often mistaken by beginners in beekeeping for the attack of robber bees but the action in the two cases is so different that close observation soon makes the dissimilarity clear. When robbers are numerous, they dart toward the hive and alight about every crack, while young bees circle about, rarely alighting on the hive. The flight of the young bees is also sometimes mistaken for the beginning of swarming.

Later flights are more extended, and when workers are from fourteen to twenty-one days old (if during a honey-flow), they begin their field duties of gathering nectar, pollen, propolis and water. Normally, they now abandon the work inside the hive. It sometimes happens that a colony will contain relatively too many young bees or too many old ones, these conditions often arising in practical manipulations. If there is a lack of young bees, the old ones act in their stead, but they secrete wax slowly (p. 119) and do not produce larval food adequately. If a colony is made up artificially of young bees, some of them begin field work earlier than normally.

DIVISION OF LABOR

From the preceding chapter, it is evident that there is a definite division among the different members of a colony. In a colony composed of perhaps 60,000 individuals, the very existence of the bees depends on an orderly performance of the various duties, and the development of colonial life, therefore, rests on the evolution of some system for the division of labor. The organization of the colony, already described, shows one of the most marked cases of apportionment of work, for the egg-laying is normally performed by one individual, the queen, while all the other females (workers) are so constituted that egg-laying is not normal and mating is impossible. The drones or males are so specialized in function that they are probably useful to the colony only in the mating of young queens. While the duty of egg-laying devolves on the queen, the care of the brood falls entirely to the workers. Since they must do work both inside and outside the hive, there arises the further necessity of a division [1] of these functions and this, as has been stated, is based on the age of the individuals.

Since it may not at first glance be clear how the age at which bees perform certain functions is determined, it may be well to explain the simple method by which this is accomplished. If the queen is removed from a colony of black (German) bees and a yellow (Italian) queen is at once introduced, for a period of twenty-one days after the removal of the old queen the young worker-bees which emerge from the cells are black, since they are the progeny of the old queen. At the end of that time, however, the worker brood from the black queen has all emerged and yellow bees begin to appear. The time at which the yellow bees first perform certain functions may now be determined. This experiment may be variously modified, as by the removal of all the brood of the black queen at once or by the placing of a frame of brood from an Italian colony in

[1] The division of labor is as highly developed among bees as in any insect community. Among certain species of ants, a greater diversity of structure accompanies the performance of certain duties. For example, there may be soldiers which serve only as protectors of the community and there may be two types of workers, differing structurally and in their duties. While structural differences do not occur in so marked a way, the members of the bee-colony are fully as greatly specialized in their labor but the performance of specific duties is determined in some manner other than by structure.

a colony of black bees. The introduction of Italian bees into Germany and later into America has been an important factor in enabling investigators to learn many of the phenomena of the hive, for the use of bees of two colors[1] is often of the highest importance.

The labor within the hive

When the workers first emerge from the cells they take no part in the work of the hive for a day or two, nor do they leave the hive. The first flight in front of the hive is usually when they are about a week old, if the weather is favorable, and these flights are continued on warm bright days until they are nearly three weeks old. Although they do not go far at first they may remain on the wing for a considerable period. That these early flights are necessary in enabling the young bees to void their feces is indicated by the fact that if confined they become restless.[2] The abdomens of young bees are frequently distended with feces.

Dönhoff[3] states that he offered a stick dipped in honey to young bees daily. Until they were fifteen days old they did not lick the honey eagerly. The younger bees never attempted to lick it, but as they grew older they paid more attention to it. He concludes that the "impulse for gathering honey" is not developed in young bees. Not until his experimental bees were seventeen days old did he find any on his outdoor feeders and not until they were nineteen days old did any fly to the field.

[1] Another method of marking bees for observation is mentioned by Casteel, Circ. No. 161, Bur. Ent., p. 5. The method employed was to paint bees with different colors and also to number them.

[2] This was observed when colonies containing young bees were placed in a cellar for winter, in connection with work of Demuth and the author on winter activities. The entire colony became active and a high temperature was maintained. The condition was removed by taking the colonies from the cellar for a flight. Bees that emerged from brood-combs were also kept in a warm room, away from older workers. These had distended abdomens and if one escaped from the hive it usually flew at once to the window, leaving a spot of feces on the pane.

[3] Dönhoff, 1855. Eichstädt Bienenzeitung, p. 163.

Comb-building

Beeswax is a yellow or yellowish material consisting chiefly of a mixture of crude cerotic acid and myricin. It also contains in small quantities free melissic acid, uncombined ceryl alcohol and other organic substances, a mixture rather than a chemical compound. It is rendered from combs by melting, and the waxes obtained in various regions vary according to the honey used by the bees while the combs were constructed. Beeswax melts at about 144-9° F., bleaches on exposure to sunlight and has a specific gravity of about 0.96.

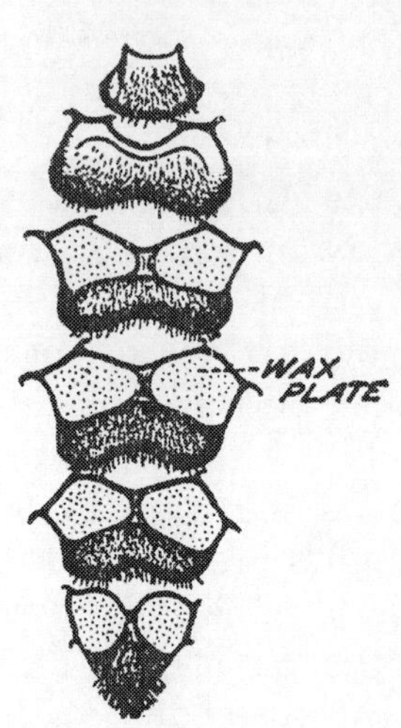

Fig. 54.—Ventral plates of the abdomen of a worker-bee.

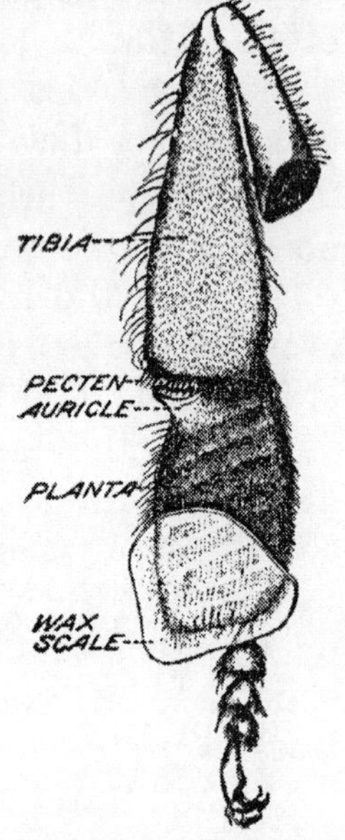

Fig. 55.—Inner surface of the left hind leg of a worker-bee, showing a wax-scale.

If there is need for more combs, the workers form curtains by hanging on one another from the top of the hive or cavity. The temperature within the curtains is raised to about 97° F., and in a few hours wax-scales may be seen on the ventral sides of the abdomens of the hanging bees. Finally some of these scales are removed and manipulated and the bees begin building new comb. The new comb has a thickness at the base of about 0.003-4 inch and the side walls about 0.002-3 inch [1] for worker-cells and about 0.002 inch greater for drone-comb. In the process of building,

[1] Dadant, H. C., 1926. The behavior of bees in comb building. Amer. Bee Journ., LXVI, No. 5, pp. 224-226; No. 6, pp. 278-280.

the small pieces of wax are put approximately in the right place and are later sculptured into their proper shape. Years ago Huber showed that bees can build wax on a diet of sugar alone, and it is usually held that a consumption of about 20 pounds of honey is required in building a pound of comb.

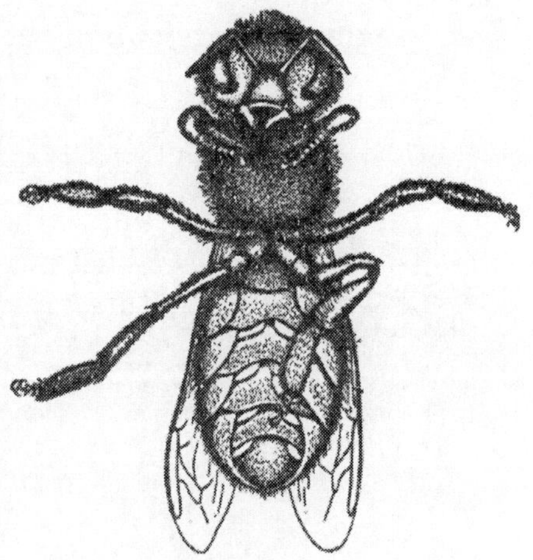

Fig. 56.—Ventral view of worker removing wax-scale. Enlarged.

Dreyling[1] has shown that in just emerged worker-bees the cells of the wax-glands are not fully developed and that as the worker grows older the cells elongate. As the bee ages, however, these cells decrease and degenerate. These results fully support the observations of beekeepers that bees secrete wax best before they become field bees. If, however, a colony of old bees is required to build comb, they can still secrete some wax, but for some reason not understood they usually build irregularly.

Fig. 57.—Side view of worker removing wax-scale. Enlarged.

Beeswax is secreted in pockets on the ventral side of the abdomen on the wax-plates (Fig. 54) situated on the sternal

[1] Dreyling, L., 1903. Ueber die wachsbereitenden Organe der Honigbiene. Zool. Anz., XXVI.

———, 1905. Die wachsbereitenden Organe bei den gesellig lebenden Bienen. Zool. Jahrbücher, Abth. Anat. u. Ont. d. Thiere, XXII.

plates of the last four visible segments of the abdomen. Each segment bears two of these plates, making eight in all. As the secreted wax comes in contact with the air, it hardens, forming the scales of wax.

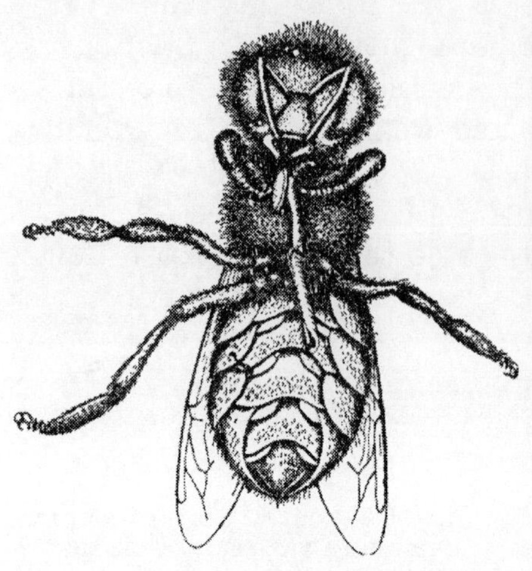

Fig. 58.—Ventral view of worker passing wax-scale forward. Enlarged.

The manipulation by the bees of the wax-scales has been carefully described by Casteel.[1] The scales are removed from the pockets by spines of the pollen-comb (Fig. 55) on the first tarsal segment (planta) of the third pair of legs. The surface of the planta is passed over the ventral side of the abdomen (Figs. 56, 57) and after the scale is loosened the third leg is bent forward (Figs. 58, 59), thus passing the scale to the front pair of legs. It is then masticated by the mandibles, after which it is ready to put in place in the new comb. The various movements in manipulation are so well shown in Casteel's figures that further description is unnecessary. It is clearly shown that the so-called wax-shears, which are described by so many authors as being used to remove wax-scales, have in fact nothing to do with the wax manipula-

Fig. 59.—Side view of worker passing wax-scale forward. Enlarged.

[1] Casteel, D. B., 1912. The manipulation of the wax scales of the honey bee. Circ. No. 161, Bur. Ent., 13 pp.

tion. It is shown later that these are concerned in pollen-gathering.

Feeding of larvæ

It has already been shown (p. 111) that an enormous amount of time is spent by worker-bees in feeding developing larvæ. The origin of the brood food has been one of the most debated questions in bee behavior, the controversy arising whether it is regurgitated from the ventriculus (Fig. 61) or secreted by the pharyngeal glands (Fig. 60). There are in the head of the worker-bee two systems of glands, the lateral pharyngeal (*1 Gl*) and the salivary glands of the head (*2 Gl*) and in the thorax the salivary glands (Fig. 61, *3 Gl*), homologous with the salivary glands of other insects. Presumably the secretions of some of these assist in digestion. The lateral pharyngeal glands (*1 Gl*) are absent in the drone and never more than rudimentary in the queen, leading to the conclusion that they function in some way which is especially useful to the worker. Although many efforts have been made to show that larval food is regurgitated from the ventriculus, it is now clear that this material has its origin in the lateral pharyngeal glands. Evidence for this view has also been obtained from a study of other bees. Snodgrass[1] has summarized the evidence for the two views, but since the publication of his bulletin the evidence in favor of regurgitation has faded

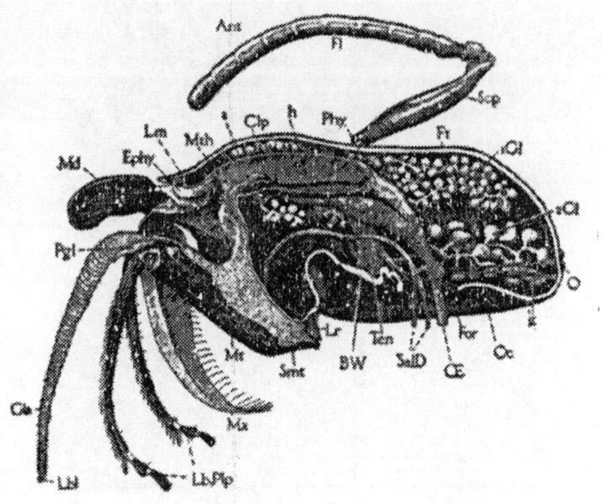

FIG. 60.—Median longitudinal section of head of worker, showing the glands (*1Gl* and *2Gl*).

[1] Snodgrass, R. E., 1910. The anatomy of the honey bee. Tech. Bull. 18, Bur. Ent., 162 pp.

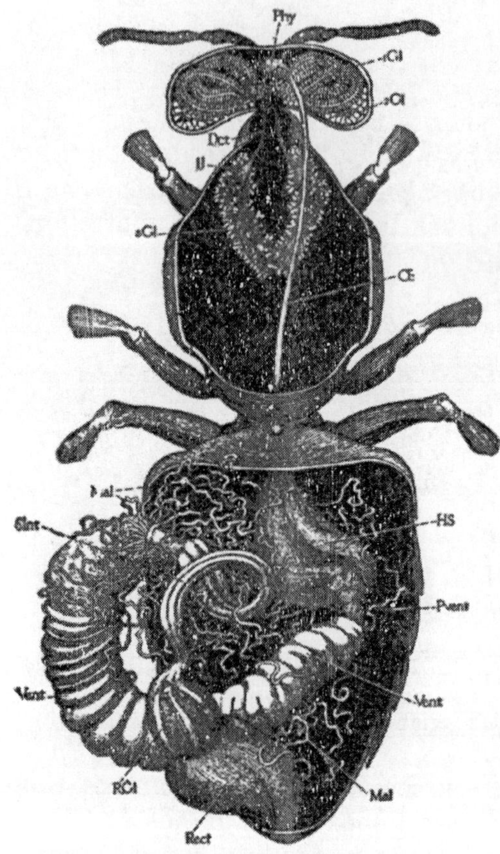

FIG. 61.—Alimentary canal of worker, showing glands, pharynx (*Phy*), œsophagus (*Œ*), honey-stomach (*HS*), proventriculus (*Pvent*), ventriculus (*Vent*), intestine (*SInt*), rectal ampulla (*Rect*) and Malpighian tubules (*Mal*).

into insignificance and in his later work [1] he does not consider it worth while to repeat it. Some work by Soudek [2] gives conclusive evidence on this undisputed point.

The enormous gain in weight of the larvæ in a short time indicates that the food provided by the workers is high in food values. This entails, therefore, a high consumption of food by the workers so long as they are secreting this larval food. As will be shown later, there is a change in food for the older larvæ of workers and drones, but apparently not for queen larvæ. At present it is impossible to give an accurate figure for the expense to the colony for feeding the great number of larvæ present at the peak of brood-rearing, but years ago Taylor estimated that each adult bee

[1] Snodgrass, R. E., 1925. Anatomy and physiology of the honeybee. New York: McGraw-Hill Book Co., 327 pp. 108 figs.

[2] Soudek, St., 1927. The pharyngeal glands of the honeybee. Bull. de l'école Supèr. d'agronomie, Brno. [In Czecho-Slovak. with summary in English], 63 pp., 3 pl.

has cost the colony the amount of honey contained in one cell. There are various confirmatory facts which can be used in support of such a high estimate, but as they are at present rather speculative, they need not be given.

Composition of larval food

The chemical composition of larval food was investigated by von Planta[1] and later investigations have been conducted by Koehler.[2] Table IV gives the various food constituents as determined by von Planta.

TABLE IV.—COMPOSITION OF LARVAL FOODS

	Queen	*Drones*		*Workers*	
		Under 4 Days	Over 4 Days	Under 4 Days	Over 4 Days
Proteid	45.15	55.91	31.67	53.38	27.87
Fat	13.55	11.90	4.74	8.38	3.69
Sugar	20.39	9.57	38.49	18.09	44.93

The larval food is not a mere mixture of honey and pollen, nor is the food given the various kind of bees at different ages the same. von Planta shows differences between the early and late food for drones and workers, but Koehler thinks that the observed differences may be due merely to variations in analyses. von Planta's views are as follows: The three kinds of bees require different food, and, for the drone- and worker-larvæ, the food changes after the third day, being then mixed with half-digested pollen-grains and honey in the case of the drone and honey only in the case of the workers. On the other hand the queen-larvæ received the rich food supplied the young larvæ of other castes throughout her entire larval period (called royal jelly) which is free from undigested

[1] von Planta, Adolf, 1888. Ueber den Futtersaft der Bienen. Zeit. f. Phys. Chemie von Hoppe-Seyler, XII, pp. 327-354; 1889, *idem*, XIII, pp. 552-561.

[2] Koehler, A., 1922. Neue Untersuchungen über den Futtersaft der Bienen. Verh. Zool. Ges., XXVII, pp. 105-107.

pollen and completely predigested. Several changes must now be made in these conclusions. In the first place, worker-larvæ also receive pollen at older stages and undigested pollen-grains occur in royal jelly. Furthermore, according to the work of Lineburg previously mentioned, the change in food occurs at the end of the second and not at the end of the third day of larval life, being accompanied by a modification in the method of feeding.

The food of the young larvæ is a gummy paste of milky-white color when fresh but takes on a yellow color when dried somewhat. It mixes very little with water, is strongly acid and has a sharp taste. In early stages a considerable amount of larval food may be seen on the bottoms of the cells containing the larvæ, but later the food is given about as needed and less of it appears in the cells. The later food is more transparent and contains pollen-grains. Royal jelly taken from queen-cells seems to have good keeping qualities, for some queen-breeders keep it for months and find it necessary only to moisten it slightly before using. Aeppler[1] claims that larval food contains vitamin B and some vitamin A, and if these substances are necessary for the growth of bee-larvæ, the larval food should be expected to contain them.

Feeding of queens and drones

Although queens and drones are capable of taking honey themselves, it seems to fall to the lot of the workers to keep these two castes supplied with food under usual circumstances. The excessive egg-laying of the queen (p. 65) calls for food in large quantities and during the season of egg-laying the queen usually stops for a few minutes every half-hour and during this resting period she is almost constantly fed. Since she can produce eggs equal to her own weight in a day, she requires much nourishment. The

[1] Aeppler, C. W., 1922. Tremendous growth force. Gleanings in Bee Culture, L, pp. 151-153, ill.

feeding of drones is less commonly observed, but when the honey-flow comes to an end, the workers cease to feed the drones and they rapidly become weak. They are then driven to the lower parts of the hive and finally they are unable to resist the workers who carry them from the hive to starve. Apparently drones and queens do not take pollen themselves. For both queens and drones, frequent feeding is apparently needed, for bees of all castes will starve to death in a few hours if deprived of nourishment, the food reserve of adult bees apparently being exceedingly small.

Other inside work

Little remains to be said in detail of the inside work of the hive which is performed by the workers. They clean

Fig. 62.—Lizard incased in propolis.

the hive, and in case they are unable to remove the débris, they may cover it with propolis. Lizards (Fig. 62), small snakes and other intruders to the hive, which are too large for the workers to remove, are sometimes found as "mummies" on the hive bottom, sealed in propolis. The ventilation of the hive for the renewal of the air and for the evaporation of the nectar requires a large expenditure of energy and is accomplished by fanning of the wings. The colony exhibits an astonishing degree of efficiency in its ability to protect itself and the brood from excessively high inside temperatures by rapid ventilation through a relatively small opening at the entrance. The ripening of nectar into honey is a complex duty of the younger bees of the colony and will be described later (p. 131).

The guards

The guarding of the colony from intruders is interesting and of great importance to the colony. This is done by bees which stand about the entrance and on the lower edges of the combs of the brood-chamber. These bees usually do not remain long at this work for the guards are constantly changing. The hand may be placed right among them if the movement is slow, while a swift movement will cause them to dart out and will bring others to the entrance. The honeybee is capable of preventing the entrance of insects larger and more powerful than itself, such as wasps and bumblebees. During the summer of 1909, small yellow-jackets were especially abundant in the apiary of the Department of Agriculture, then at College Park, Maryland, and many dead ones were found daily in front of the hives. Numerous large wasps with hard chitinous covering are also killed by the bees. The bee-moth in some way often succeeds in entering the hive but usually the eggs or larvæ are removed before any harm is done. Their success probably depends upon their habit of flying by night.

Of all these labors which the workers perform within the hive, none monopolizes the time of certain individuals as completely as does comb-building, in which the bees hang in curtains from the comb support. Casteel has shown that even in this the bees change their duties frequently. Bees are constantly changing from guards to feeders of the brood or from ventilators to cleaners, and yet the work of the hive is done well and, one is almost tempted to say, systematically.

The labor outside the hive

As has been seen, there is a division of labor inside the hive and this can be explained partially on the basis of age of the workers. The division of the outside work presents problems of far greater perplexity, partly because of the difficulties of observation. That there is an order to this work is an inevitable conclusion, but how this order is brought about among the thousands of field workers is not easily determined. Worker-bees go to the field to collect nectar, pollen, water and propolis. If there were no "system," one should expect to find colonies lacking one or more of these substances in sufficient quantity, or, perchance, a colony with the brood-nest choked with pollen or a hive over-propolized. There are variations in these items but there are no cases that can be considered abnormal. Furthermore, on the grounds of an apiary of a hundred colonies may be found nectar-secreting flowers right at hand. The bees are not falling over each other in such a case to reach a certain flower, leaving other flowers untouched, as would sometimes be the case if bees were guided merely by the chance sight of a flower. Or, assuming only that there is a system whereby each colony divides the surrounding territory, there would be cases of conflict between bees from other colonies in their attempts to reach the same flower. If then one dares assume a prearranged plan, it must include the entire apiary and even all the colonies within range of flight. While bees get nectar from flowers near at hand, they are no more numerous on such flowers than on those farther away but within easy flight range.

During the rush of the day's work when a bee flies from the hive, the flight is usually not uncertain but is directed toward a source of supply. It is usually stated that bees carry either nectar or pollen back to the hive but not both, but this is not always correct. As a rule, they gather from only one species on a given trip.[1] Some additional facts

[1] This characteristic of gathering is of the highest importance in a consideration of the value of honeybees in cross-pollination. Since their trips are usually confined to flowers of one species, the beneficial results of these visits are increased many fold, for if they wandered promiscuously from one species to another they would thereby scatter pollen where it would be ineffectual in pollination. Bees fail to discriminate among the various varieties of a given species which is a distinct advantage since certain varieties are pollinated

concerning the gathering of bees are of interest. If honey is exposed where it is accessible to bees, they go to it by hundreds if there is no nectar in the fields, and under such circumstances they are on the lookout for openings in other hives so that they can rob. On the other hand, during a honey-flow honey may be exposed in the apiary without a bee coming near it. This leads sometimes to the conclusion that bees prefer nectar to honey. Even if honey is placed in a feeder within the hive, it is often not touched during a heavy honey-flow.

Division of labor in gathering

There has been little done on the division of labor outside the hive, but Bonnier [1] has written a paper of great interest on this subject. Whether his conclusions may be accepted must depend upon future experiments, but a resumé of his paper is of interest. The field bees are divided by him into two classes, searchers and collectors. Searchers fly to

better and sometimes only with pollen from another variety of the same species.

When the theory of evolution was first announced, great stress was placed on the importance of constancy of insect visits in bringing about the evolution of various species visited by these insects. This induced numerous investigators to study this problem in detail, and while constancy is found to be usual, there are many recorded cases of mistakes on the part of bees and other insects of similar behavior. Observers who worked in gardens where there were many species of flowers found many cases of "error" on the part of bees, while those who worked in fields where a given species of plant is abundant found few such cases. All that can be claimed is that if there are enough flowers of one species easily accessible, the bees seem to prefer those of one kind. They usually do not fly from dandelion to apple blossom, although one such case is recorded. No more than this degree of constancy is needed to make bees far more beneficial to the fruit-grower than they would be if their visits were entirely promiscuous. The case for the honeybee has been stated by Oertel, Everett, 1926, Honeybees as pollinators, Gleanings in Bee Culture, LIV, No. 5, pp. 294-296. Various other Hymenoptera and most Diptera also exhibit constancy, while Lepidoptera do not. Some bees confine their visits to a single species of flower.

[1] Bonnier, Gaston, 1906. Sur la division du travail chez les abeilles. Comptes Rendus de l'Acad. des Sci., CXLIII, pp. 941-946.

various plants, gathering some nectar and some pollen and lighting on many neighboring objects, and behave much as do wasps, which are generally searchers. A bee is transformed from a searcher to a collector when a suitable source of nectar or pollen is discovered, and other bees come to the same source. During a good honey-flow, searchers are sent out only in the early morning and soon all become collectors (which may account for the lack of robbing and the indifference to honey about the apiary at such times) but during a dearth of nectar, searchers are out all day. Bonnier further claims that bees "commanded" to collect either nectar, water, pollen or propolis do not leave their work and will not stop even to collect honey placed in front of them. This claim is supported by experiments. The following translation of a portion of the paper cannot well be summarized:

". . . I shall cite the following which shows . . . how the division of labor among bees of the same hive is organized and so a sort of tacit understanding, which is manifested among bees of different hives. I detached six branches of flowers of Lycium, each having about the same number of open flowers. I put each branch in a bottle filled with water. On placing these bottles in the same place from which I had taken the branches, I saw that the workers continued to visit the flowers of the branches put in water just the same as those on branches not detached from the plant. This verified, I carried the six bottles containing the branches to the fruit garden, September first, away from all nectar-bearing plants, consequently to a new place for the bees. I remained constantly watching the six bottles containing Lycium branches. No bees came to visit the flowers on these branches. The next day I saw the first bee as a searcher, which discovered them. She inspected all the branches and took some nectar and pollen; I marked her on the back with talc colored red. In about three minutes she returned to the hive.

"Five minutes afterward the same first bee (which I call 'A'), as shown by the red mark, came back with another and the two bees as collectors undertook a methodic visit to the branches, one to collect nectar and the other pollen. I call the second bee 'B' and marked her white.

"Ten minutes after, there were three visiting bees. A new one 'C,' which I marked green, came to join the other two from the same hive, as I verified.

"Later the same three workers, A, B, C, A and C always collecting nectar, and B only pollen, came back regularly to the flowering branches and visited them in the same order. All the next day these same three bees, A, B, and C, visited the six branches.

"I then asked myself why other bees of the same hive or of other hives did not come to collect from these branches, as well as the three bees. Remaining under the branches, I observed attentively what took place on the second day. Early in the morning and several times in the forenoon, once in the afternoon, other searchers came to the branches of the flowers and each of these searching bees did the same thing as A. She observed the collectors with great care, their number, their manner of work, and, after two to four minutes of inspection, she flew away and did not come back. It seems that these bees, finding the place occupied, and the number of collectors sufficient for the small amount to be collected went elsewhere to search.

"The fact is that the day after, I saw more and the same bees, A, B, and C continued to visit the six branches in the same manner, A and C always for nectar, and B for pollen.

"Then I replaced the six flowering branches of Lycium with twelve branches which appeared to me about the same; I saw two new recruits arrive, 'D' and 'E,' which I marked differently with colored powder; ten minutes after, two others, 'F' and 'G,' and A, C, D, E, [F in the text, evidently a typographical error] and G came for nectar, B and F for pollen. There were seven bees visiting in place of three.

The number of flowering branches was double, the number of collectors was about double.[1]

"The next day other searchers came. The seven marked bees continued their visits. I took some pollen from the stamens of Lycium and put it in a mass below the nectar of one flower. When bee 'C' arrived at that flower, she stretched out her proboscis as usual to suck up the sweet liquid but saw that it was not there and that something different was in the flower; she examined it carefully for more than a minute, did not collect the pollen but renounced it and went to pump nectar in the neighboring flowers. I made the inverse experiment and bathed the pollen of one flower in nectar; 'F,' after pollen, came to this flower, found the sweet liquid on the anthers, examined it, did not touch the anthers of that flower, but renounced it and went to continue her collecting on the neighboring flowers."

Bonnier further found that certain bees confined their visits to a certain limited portion of a row of plants which were all in bloom. He concludes as follows: "They thus accomplish on the whole, the collection of the most in the least possible time of the substances necessary to all colonies of bees in the same region."

If division of labor as described by Bonnier is even partially true, it may help one to understand why it happens that the flowers visited on a single trip are usually of one species. It is hoped that these interesting observations may be repeated by other investigators.

Nectar ripening

The change of nectar to honey is a cooperative effort between the field bees and those which have not yet begun field work. After the field bee has found a supply of nectar, it fills the honey-stomach if enough nectar is available and

[1] "Similar experiments have shown me that the number of bees visiting a definite number of flowers of the same species under similar environmental conditions is quite proportional to the number of flowers, except when the visit is disturbed by the arrival of wild Hymenoptera as numerous."—Bonnier.

then returns to the hive. Various beekeepers have observed that returning laden bees give forth a fine spray, from which it has been concluded that the removal of the excess water in nectar is accomplished in part by the field bee while on the way back to the hive. By what sort of physiological process this might occur is wholly unexplained. Since bees often ingest more of either honey or nectar than they can handle comfortably, it seems more probable that the observed mist consists merely of regurgitated nectar, given out to relieve the pressure on the honey-stomach, but there seems little doubt that something is sometimes dropped. There is no evidence that nectar deposited by the field bee at the hive contains less moisture than does that of the flower, but such evidence would be extremely difficult to obtain.

The process of handling nectar within the hive has been described by numerous observers and has recently been given by Park[1] with some good illustrations. When the field bee returns to the hive the nectar is given to a young bee and not placed in an empty cell as sometimes stated. When the ripening process is going on, the nectar is forced in and out by the partial extension of the tongue, during which process it is assumed that changes are taking place in the nectar. This process is repeated several times, after which the partially ripened nectar is placed in a cell, usually near the brood-nest. After various handlings, the material finally reaches the consistency of honey, when it is carried to a storage-cell and is finally sealed over with wax as fully ripened honey. The changes in moisture-content and composition have been described (p. 92).

Pollen-gathering

Pollen is carried to the hive in the pollen-baskets or corbiculæ (Fig. 63) situated on the outer surface of the tibiæ of the third pair of legs. The activities of the bees

[1] Park, O. W., 1926. How bees "make" honey. 25th annual report, Ill. State Beekeepers' Assoc. [for 1925], pp. 32-39, 2 figs.

in collecting pollen have been admirably described by Casteel.[1] In collecting from a flower, the worker not only secures pollen on its mandibles and tongue but also on the hairs of the legs and body, and this pollen must be transferred to the baskets and securely packed before returning

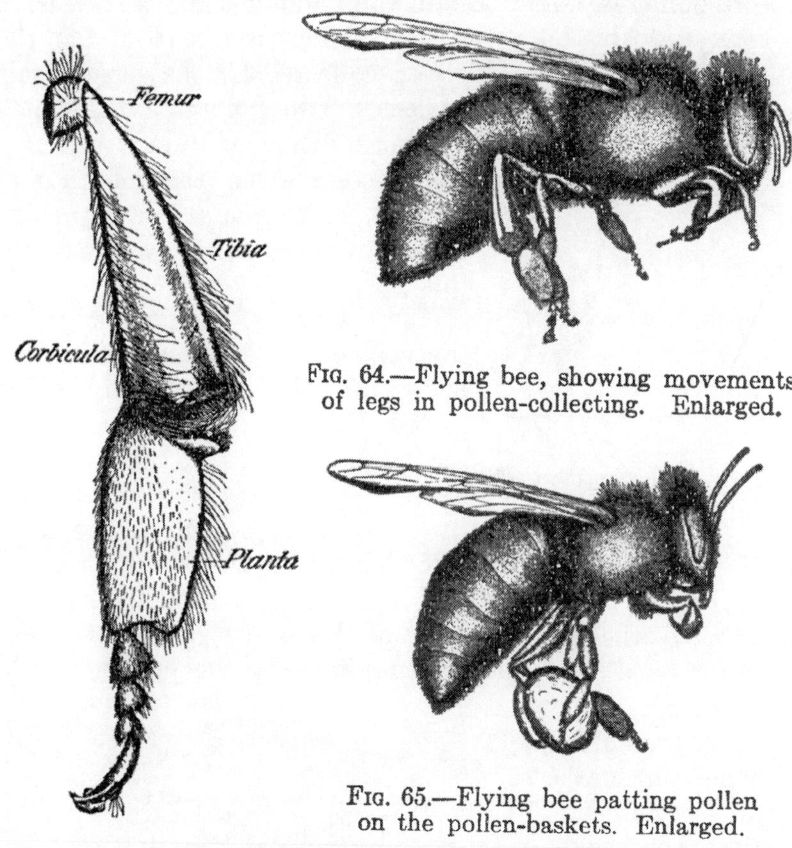

Fig. 64.—Flying bee, showing movements of legs in pollen-collecting. Enlarged.

Fig. 65.—Flying bee patting pollen on the pollen-baskets. Enlarged.

to the hive. This is done either while resting on the flower or on the wing. The action of the pollen-brushes on the legs is as follows: (1) those of the first pair of legs remove pollen-grains from the head and the region of the neck, and also take the moistened pollen from the mouth-

[1] Casteel, D. B., 1912. The behavior of the honey bee in pollen collecting. Bull. No. 121, Bur. Ent., 36 pp.

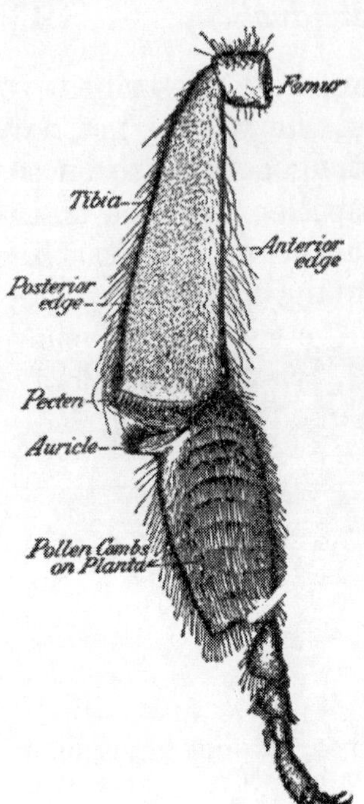

Fig. 66.—Inner surface of left hind leg of worker.

parts (Fig. 64); (2) those of the second pair remove pollen from the thorax, especially from the ventral portion, and also receive the pollen collected by the front legs; (3) the third pair of legs collect pollen from the abdomen and also receive on the pollen-combs (Fig. 64) the pollen collected by the second pair of legs. The pollen is moistened by the addition of fluid substances which come from the mouth and Casteel presents analyses (by Dunbar) showing that honey is used for this purpose.

The method of loading pollen on the pollen-baskets has been variously described, it usually being stated that it is put in place by the second pair of legs. This is not the usual method, however, although a little pollen is added to the mass while the bee pats down its load with the second pair of legs (Fig. 65). The loading is accomplished by the rubbing together of the inner surfaces of the hind legs (Fig. 66, 67). It is removed from the pollen-combs by the pecten-combs, is pushed upward by pressure of the auricles and is forced against the distal ends of the tibiæ and on into the pollen-baskets from below, being pushed upward

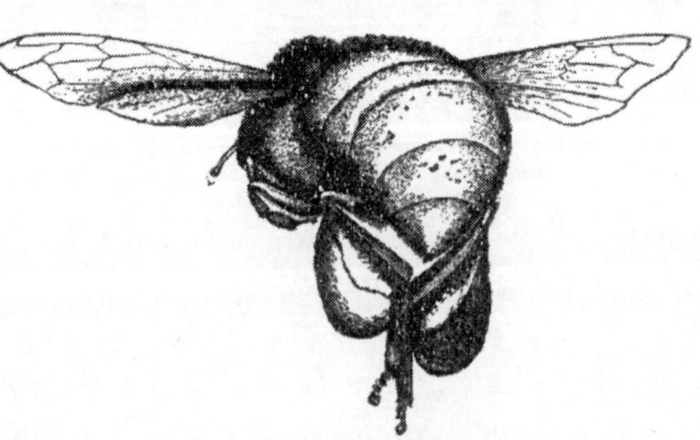

Fig. 67.—Flying bee loading the pollen-baskets.

against any pollen that may have been loaded previously. The long lateral hairs of the pollen-baskets help to retain the pollen-masses. It is thus clear that the so-called wax-shears, formed by the pecten and auricle, are part of the apparatus for pollen-packing and, as shown earlier (p. 120), they have nothing to do with wax manipulation. Casteel shows also that in packing pollen in the cells of the combs additional moisture is probably used, for analyses show a higher percentage of sugar than in pollen from the legs.

Propolis collection

Propolis is a resinous material which bees collect from exudations of trees and which they use for sealing the hive and for covering roughness within the hive. The method of collection has not been described adequately, but it is known not to be packed on the corbiculæ as is pollen but that it is placed on these organs from above. It is usually gathered most abundantly in late summer and autumn, and races of bees differ in the amount of propolis which they collect. Caucasian bees gather more propolis than any other known race (p. 210). Propolis is deposited on any rough surface within the hive and also is used to fill any opening through which light enters. It is sometimes placed on the upper portions of combs and constitutes the "travel stain" seen on comb-honey which has remained too long on the hive. Propolis is not deposited in openings wide enough to constitute a bee-space, but they may build wax in such spaces if they are large enough.

Water-gathering

The collection of water by field bees is most commonly observed in early spring and during the hottest parts of the summer, there probably being less need for water when the humidity within the hive is high because of the evaporation of nectar. It is carried in the honey-stomach as is nectar. Bees have been known to collect water in quantity in extremely hot weather and to place it on the bars within the hive, from which places it disappears by evaporation, thus reducing the temperature within the hive.

DURATION OF LIFE

The length of life of the various members of the colony under different conditions presents a problem of great interest. The queen normally lives several years, and Jay Smith has recently reported a queen which lived nine years, probably the oldest on record. The worker-bees, which develop from eggs identical with those from which queens issue, live six to ten weeks in summer and possibly six months or longer in winter. Drones usually live not to exceed four months, unless they are in queenless colonies, and their death is usually hastened. They die immediately on mating and are driven from the hive at the close of the honey-flow.

The most interesting facts are those concerning worker-bees. Those which emerge in time to take part in the gathering of a heavy honey crop usually live about six weeks, but if no nectar is available the length of life is extended. Those workers which emerge at the close of summer are the ones which must live until the following spring if the colony is to survive, for there is no rearing of brood in normal colonies in winter. It is obvious that the length of life is influenced to a marked degree by the amount of work which they are called upon to do. Similarly queens live longer if they are not compelled to lay such large numbers of eggs. Various observations of the beekeeper support these views. If bees winter badly, so that they are compelled to produce much heat, they often die in spring faster than they are replaced by oncoming bees, a condition known as "spring dwindling." Queens are superseded more frequently after a year in which there has been a heavy honey crop, which has induced a large population. Not all bees die in summer within six weeks of their emergence, for if all brood-rearing is prevented, it may happen that the last bee will not die for four months.

All these facts and many others observed in the apiary indicate a peculiar condition found in bees which may be expressed figuratively as follows: a bee is born with a definite amount of ability to do work and when its energy is expended the bee dies. It is sometimes likened to a small electric cell that continues to give out energy until it is exhausted, for it seems that bees cannot be "recharged." It must not be concluded that bees have no recuperative power, but it is obvious that their term of life is limited by the amount of work they do.

This situation has certain extremely practical applications in beekeeping. In order that bees may live over winter and still have energy or ability to do the work required of them under the trying conditions of spring, the colony should be kept in such condition that during the winter only the minimum work will be required. This the northern beekeeper does by insulating his bees so that excessive heat production (muscular activity) will not be necessary. In summer when nectar is available the beekeeper has no compunctions about his bees working themselves to death, for it has been for that purpose that he has conserved their energy through winter and spring. It is commonly observed that very few bees die in the hive, except in winter, for during the active season their lives end in a futile attempt to return to the hive with the last load.

Possible determining factors

The cause of the wearing out of bees is not well understood, because so many phases of bee physiology are still unknown. An old bee loses the hair on the outside of the body and the wings become frayed, but these are non-living parts, and only the wings might be important in preserving life. If bees are confined in a cage and constantly stimulated[1] their life is considerably shortened, under which conditions wings are of no service to them. Koschevnikov[2] has described the fat body of the bee and records that in

[1] Phillips, E. F., 1922. The effect of activity on the length of life of honeybees. Journ. Econ. Ent., XV, No. 5, pp. 368-371.

[2] Koschevnikov, G. A., 1900. Ueber den Fettkörper und die Œnocyten der Honigbiene (*Apis mellifeca*). Zool., Anz., XXIII, pp. 337-353.

old age the fat-cells become vacuolated and the cells are filled with granular plasma, while the cell boundaries are lost and the nuclei remain distinct. The œnocytes are cells found in the fat body, and in old bees these are filled with yellow granules which appear to be excretory products. Death may be due, therefore, to a loss of excretory function in these cells.

Changes have also been observed in the nervous system of aging bees. This was first described by Hodge [1] and more recently his work has received confirmation from the work of Smallwood and Phillips [2] and especially by that of Mrs. Goodrich-Pixell.[3] It appears that certain nerve-cells are destroyed during the life of the bee, apparently an adequate explanation for its inability to rejuvenate its energy, if the nerve-cells are unable to rebuild as worn out.

Some comparisons with other insects help to make clear the difficulties of the problem. Worker-ants have been known to live for several years and one ant-queen is recorded as living fifteen years. There is no aid from the lives of bumblebees and wasps, since the colony is not maintained over winter and the queens live only one year. It is perhaps not legitimate to compare the larval and pupal stages of insects which require several years for their development (*e.g.* Cicada, Lachnosterna). Some insects take no food as adults and it is, therefore, not surprising that they do not live long. If ants and bees are compared, it is seen that (1) ants walk and do not fly, and (2) ants live on a mixed diet and not chiefly on sugars as do bees. Carbohydrate food is not suitable for the rebuilding of worn tissues

[1] Hodge, C. F., 1894. Changes in ganglion cells from birth to senile death. Observations on man and honey-bee. Journ. Physiol., XVII, pp. 129-134, Pl. iv.

[2] Smallwood, W. M., and Phillips, Ruth L., 1916. Nuclear size in the nerve cells of the bee during the life cycle. Journ. Comp. Neurology, XXVII, No. 1, pp. 69-75.

[3] Pixell, Helen L. M. Goodrich, 1920. Determination of age in honey-bees. Quart. Journ. Micros. Sci., n.s. 254 (Vol. LXIV, Pt. 2), pp. 191-206, 1 pl.

and the partial explanation of the short life of worker-bees may be the kind of food which they take. The queen is fed on predigested food which doubtless contains considerable protein, so that she is able to form eggs and to rebuild her own tissues as they are worn out.

Flying insects live rapidly and their metabolism is excessive. If to this is added the fact that bees consume chiefly sugars in honey, there is apparently adequate explanation of the short term of life. They are creatures not of a day but of a few weeks and they well serve as examples of industry in that they die in a vain attempt to supply the colony with one more load of nectar.

CHAPTER VI

THE LIFE PROCESSES OF THE INDIVIDUAL

THE practical management of bees depends chiefly on a knowledge of their behavior but in many ways beekeeping practice demands an understanding of the physiology of bees, and without such knowledge beekeepers frequently make serious mistakes in practice. The discussions in previous chapters have dealt with the colony and the relation of the individual bees to the colony as a whole. Other phases of behavior will be discussed in the special chapters devoted to the nervous system and reproductive organs. In the present chapter a brief account is given of the life processes of the individual. The entire form and structure of the body is so fundamentally different from that of man that it is difficult to form an adequate idea of these processes.

To gain a knowledge of the physiology of bees it is obviously necessary to know the structure of the parts which function in the various activities. Fortunately the anatomy of the honeybee has been carefully studied and described by Snodgrass.[1] Previous to the appearance of his first bulletin various books and papers on bee anatomy were published but unfortunately in many cases the descriptions were erroneous and the conclusions unjustified. The more recent studies in this field have been better.

In presenting the present subject, it is better to treat the

[1] Snodgrass, R. E., 1910. The anatomy of the honey bee. Tech. Bull. 18, Bur. Ent., U. S. Dept. Agr., 162 pp., 57 figs.

Snodgrass, R. E., 1925. Anatomy and physiology of the honey bee. New York: McGraw-Hill Book Co., 327 pp., 108 figs.

bee as a living animal and to describe the functions of the various systems of organs, giving only such anatomical details as are necessary to understand the point discussed. This point of view is emphasized by Snodgrass and those who desire to know more of this subject are urged to study his writings. In the illustrations of various structures, used in the present book, all of which are from Snodgrass, parts are labeled which are not discussed and to remedy this necessary shortcoming the symbols used by Snodgrass are given in the Appendix (pp. 467-476). The errors in practical beekeeping which are made because of a lack of knowledge of physiology come chiefly in the winter period, when the bees are least able to manage their own affairs, and it will pay the beekeeper to give special attention to the discussions of digestion and respiration.

GENERAL PLAN OF THE BODY OF THE BEE

The entire plan of the body is quite unlike that of the human body, so that it is imperative that conclusions as to the functions of the various organs are not formed from supposed analogies. There is no internal skeleton for the attachment of muscles and to serve as a support for the organs, but the chitinous external covering serves as a skeleton. The body of the bee is divided into three portions, head, thorax and abdomen, the legs and wings being attached to the thorax. These parts of the body vary in their chief functions. The head is the seat of the brain and carries the two kinds of eyes and the antennæ which are covered with sense organs. It also carries the complex mouth-parts. The thorax is chiefly concerned in locomotion, being almost entirely filled with the large muscles for the movement of the wings. The abdomen contains the more important parts of the alimentary canal, the reproductive organs and large air-sacs. These systems of organs are by no means confined to the parts mentioned but the nervous system extends through the thorax and abdomen and the respiratory system is found everywhere in the body.

Head

On the head are located numerous sense organs, the discussion of which is reserved for a later chapter. Aside from these, the most interesting features are the complex mouth-parts. The general appearance of the head of a worker-bee (with all the hairs removed) is shown in Fig. 68. It is roughly triangular with the apex below, where the mouth-parts are situated. The sides are rounded out by the compound eyes (*E*). From front to back, the head is flattened and is concave on the posterior surface to fit the

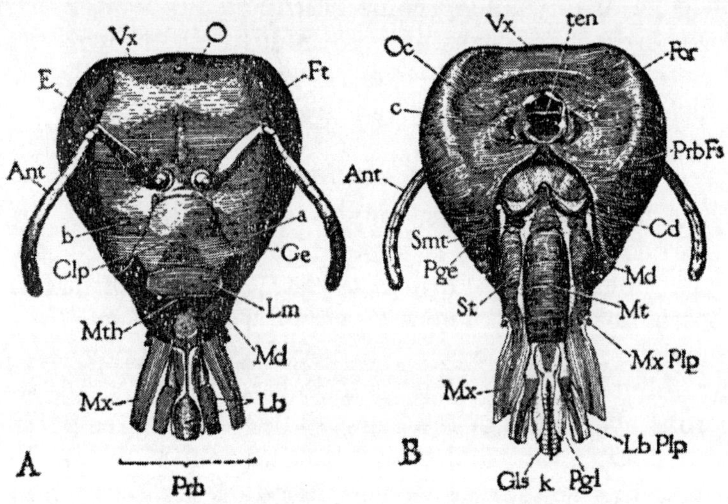

FIG. 68.—Front (*A*) and back (*B*) views of head of worker-bee with the mouth-parts cut off near their bases.

rounded thorax. The three ocelli (*O*) in the worker are arranged in a triangle at the top of the head, the antennæ (*Ant*) arise from the center of the face. On the posterior surface is the foramen magnum (*For*) through which pass nerves, œsophagus, dorsal blood-vessel and tracheal tubes connecting the head and thorax. Below the foramen magnum is the fossa (*PrbFs*) where the proboscis is attached.

The heads of the queen and the drone differ from that of the worker in size and shape (Fig. 69). The face of the queen (*B*) is more nearly round and is relatively wider. That of the drone (*C*) is larger and nearly circular, this being due to the unusual development of the compound eyes (*E*) which meet at the vertex of the head, crowding the ocelli (*O*) to the front near the bases of the antennæ. The head of the queen is smaller than that of the worker.

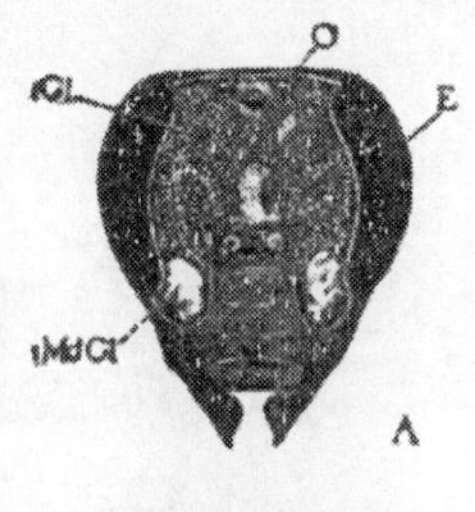

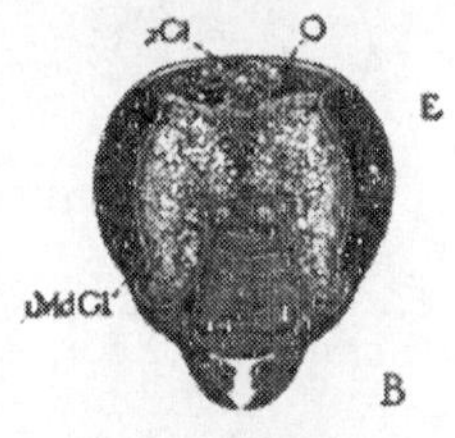

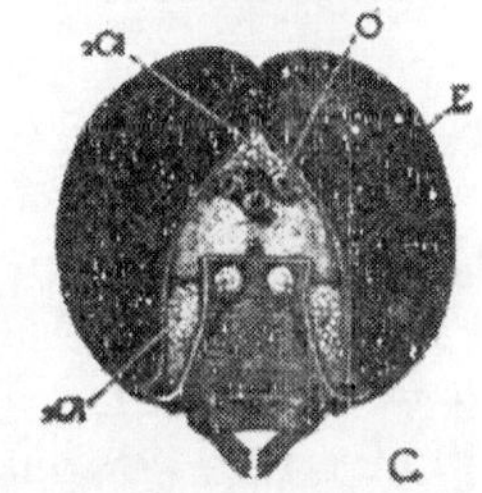

FIG. 69.—Anterior view of heads of worker (*A*), queen (*B*) and drone (*C*), with front, antennæ and proboscis removed from each.

The mandibles (Fig. 68, *A, Md*) or jaws, which are of special interest to the beekeeper, are situated on the sides of the mouth anterior to the base of the proboscis, being attached to the clypeus (*Clp*) and the postgena (*Pge*) by two articulations, so constructed that they serve to crush, bite and grind food. The mandibles of insects, when present, work sidewise and not up and down in a median plane, as do human jaws. The mandibles of the three types of bees differ in shape and size. Those of the worker (Fig. 70, *A*) are hollowed out and have smooth and rounded edges, while those of the drone (Fig. 70, *B*) and of the queen (Fig. 69, *B*) are pointed and notched. The typical mandible of the Hymenoptera is like those of the queen and drone while the worker mandible is a specialized type. The fact that the latter is smooth and rounded is often noted in connection with the fact that worker-bees cannot puncture fruit. It need scarcely be said that queens and drones never injure fruit. The mandibles are moved by two sets of muscles (Fig. 70, *A, EMcl* and *RMcl*) with their origin in the head. On each mandible is the opening of a gland (*lMdGl*), located in the head (Fig. 69, *A, B;* Fig. 70, *A, B*), which is a large sac in the worker (Fig. 70, *A*) but is

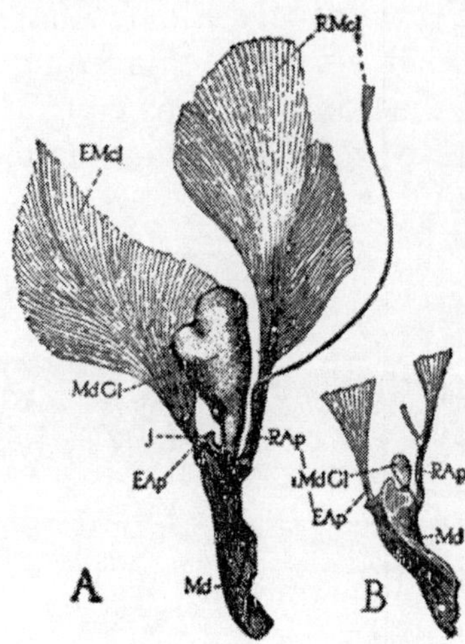

FIG. 70.—*A*, right mandible of worker with muscles and mandibular gland (*1MdGl*) attached; *B*, corresponding view of mandible of drone with muscles cut off.

reduced in the drone (Fig. 70, *B*). In the queen (Fig. 69, *B*) it reaches its greatest size. It was originally described by Wolff [1] as a mucous gland which serves to keep the surface of the roof of the mouth moist, where he thought the olfactory organs are located. The function of this gland is not clear, but it is supposed by Arnhart [2] to function in softening wax. This theory rests on the assumption made by Cheshire and others that the wax is changed chemically when it is manipulated by the mandibles. A second gland (Fig. 71, *2MdGl*) is found in workers only on the inner wall of the postgena (*Pge*) with an opening at the base of the mandibles.

The proboscis consists of the external mouth-parts other than the mandibles (Fig. 68, *Prb*, Fig. 72). This group of organs serves in taking up liquid food. The name "tongue" is usually given to the slender median portion (*Gls*) but is loosely applied to the three median parts, the labrum. Snodgrass explains the relation of these parts to the mouth-parts of other insects and points out the true homologies,

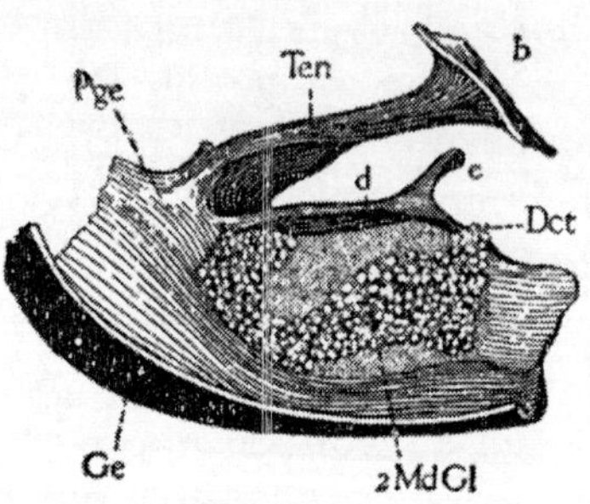

FIG. 71.—Internal mandibular gland (*2MdGl*) of worker.

[1] Wolff, O. J. B., 1875. Das Riechorgan der Biene. Nova Acta der Ksl. Leop.-Carol. Deutsch. Akad. der Naturf., XXXVIII, pp. 1-251.

[2] Arnhart, Ludwig, 1906. Anatomie und Physiologie der Honigbiene. In Alfonsus' "Allgemeines Lehrbuch der Bienenzucht," Wien (99 pp., 4 pls., 53 figs.).

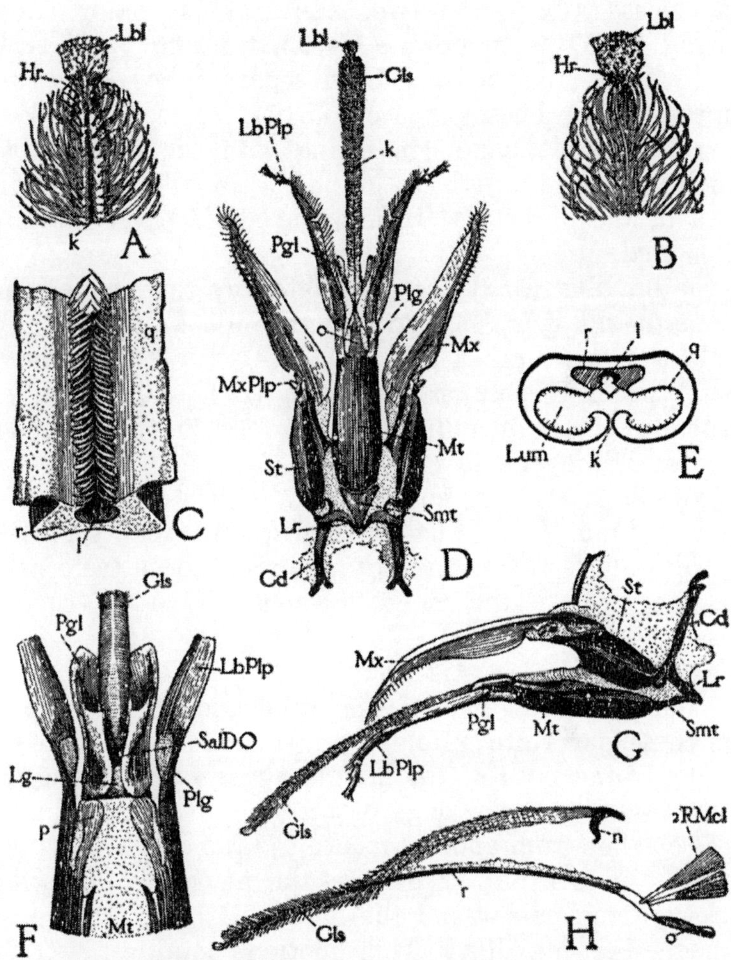

Fig. 72.—Mouth-parts of the worker: *A*, tip of glossa; *B*, same from above; *C*, small piece of glossal rod; *D*, parts forming the proboscis, flattened out, ventral view; *E*, cross-section of glossa; *F*, end of mentum (*Mt*) and bases of ligula (*Lg*) and labial palpi (*LbPlp*); *G*, lateral view of proboscis, showing parts on left side; *H*, lateral view of glossa with its rod detached.

at the same time showing the errors into which various writers on bee anatomy have fallen. Fig. 72 shows the structure of the organs of the probscis. It will be seen

(Fig. 72, *D*) that there are three terminal pieces, the central glossa (*Gls*) and two lateral labial palpi (*LbPlp*) arising from the mentum (*Mt*), a medium basal sclerite, and two maxillæ, arising from separate basal pieces, the stipes (*St*). These in turn articulate with the lorum (*Lr*), a flexible band connecting with the cardines (*Cd*) which attach the whole proboscis to the head at the fossa of the proboscis (*PrbFs*, Fig. 68, *B*), on which it is suspended.

The maxillæ (*Mx*) are articulated by the cardines (*Cd*) to the maxillary suspensoria on the side walls of the fossa while the mentum (*Mt*) articulates with the submentum (*Smt*) which is held in the lorum (*Lr*). These parts are suspended in the membrane in the fossa floor, giving great freedom of movement.

The glossa (*Gls*) is covered with circles of hairs and the tip (labellum, *Lbl*) is spoon-shaped. The tip is protected by spiny hairs (*Hr*), formerly supposed to be taste organs, between which is the end of the ventral groove (*k*) of the glossa.

When the proboscis is not in use the labium and maxillæ are folded back against the mentum and stipes. When in use, these parts are unfolded and held together. In sucking liquid the base of the labium slides between the bases of the maxillæ. To acquire this motion, the submentum turns on the lorum and the mentum turns on its articulation with the submentum. This gives the mentum a forward and backward movement and the labium is pulled and pushed through the maxillæ. This motion doubtless effects a pumping action, bringing the liquid through the temporary tube formed by the curling of the glossa. It is probably sucked farther by the pharynx. The glossa is also retracted into the mentum and this with its own contractility gives it great flexibility of movement.

Thorax

As explained earlier (p. 109), the functional thorax of the

bee (Figs. 73, 74) consists of the three segments which form the thorax in other orders of insects and the segment which is the first abdominal of other orders. This modification is found in most other Hymenoptera but the fact has seemingly escaped most writers on bees. The prothorax (1st thoracic segment) is reduced and the first pair of legs, arising from this segment, are loosely attached. The mesothorax (second thoracic segment) is specially well developed to accommodate the large muscles which propel the fore-wings, while the metathorax (third thoracic segment) is reduced, consisting only of a narrow plate (*T3*), the metatergum, and two lateral plates on each side (pleural plates, *Pl3* and *pl3*). The tergum (dorsal plate) of the first abdominal segment (*IT*) is fixed to the metathorax. The posterior portion of this segment (propodium or median segment) forms the peduncle (*Pd*) to which the functional abdomen is attached. The legs and wings are discussed under organs of locomotion (p. 166).

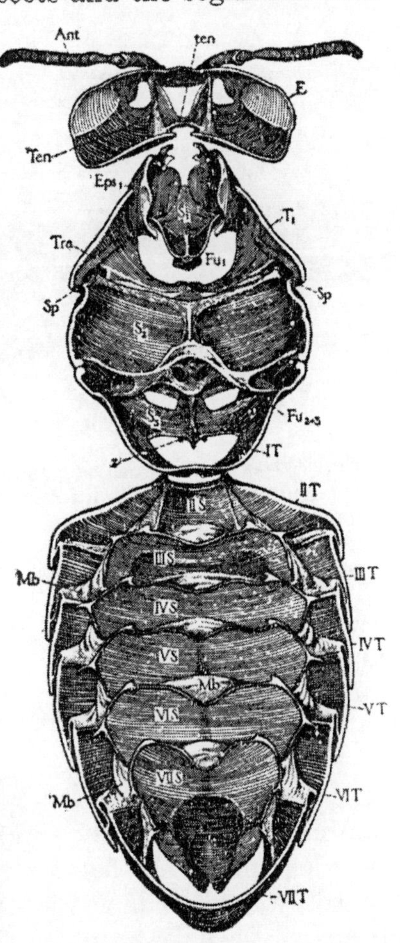

Fig. 73.—Dorsal view of ventral walls and internal skeleton of worker. Much enlarged.

Abdomen

The abdomen of the female bees (queens and workers) appears to consist of six segments (Fig. 75) but to this number must be added the modified abdominal segment on the thorax (*IT*). In the drones, there are additional segments partially visible externally. Snodgrass has figured (Fig. 76) the tip of the abdomen of the worker, showing that the eighth abdominal segment is invaginated and the eighth abdominal spiracle opens within the invagination. Zander[1] further claims that the quadrate plate (*Qd*) is a part of the ninth tergum. The anal opening (*An*) is in a tube (without chitin) which represents the tenth abdominal segments (*X*) so that the bee, like most other insects, has ten abdominal segments. In the drone, nine of these segments are partially visible. The plates of the abdomen are easily movable, being connected by membranes so that the abdomen may be distended by food, or in the queen by the growth of the ovaries. In the typical segments (*II-VII*), there is a tergum (*T*) covering the dorsal and lateral surfaces, overlapping a sternum (*S*) or ventral piece. The spiracles (see p. 163) (*Sp*) are on the terga (see Fig. 73 and 75).

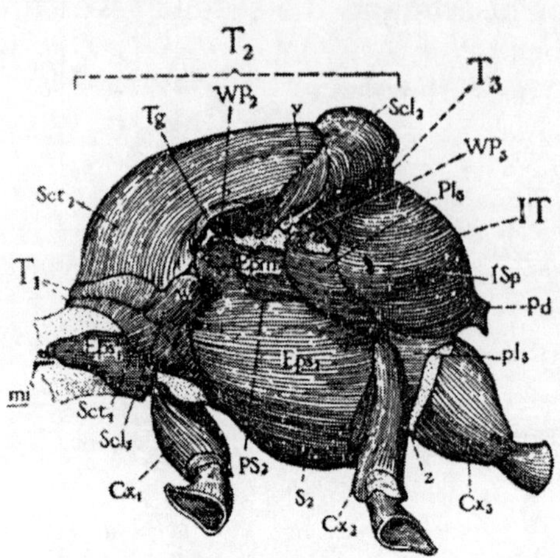

Fig. 74.—Thorax of worker, showing propodium or first abdominal segment (*IT*).

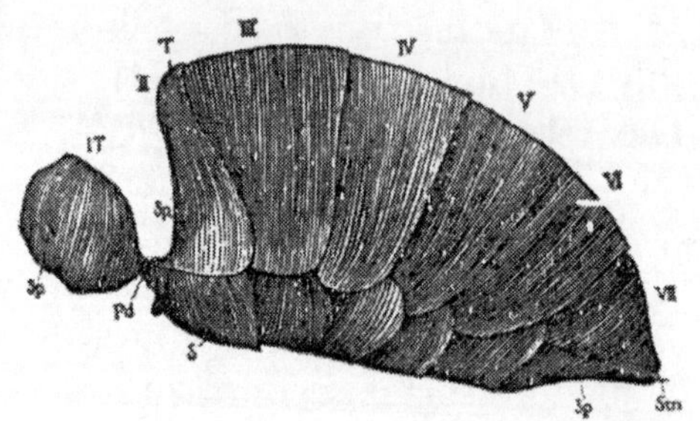

Fig. 75.—Lateral view of abdomen of worker.

[1] Zander, Enoch, 1899. Beiträge zur Morphologie des Stachelapparates der Hymenopteren. Zeit. f. Wiss. Zool., LXVII, pp. 288-333.

The eighth, ninth and tenth segments of the drone are not typical. The tergum of the eighth segment (Fig. 96, *D, VIIIT*) is partly covered by that of the seventh and carries the most posterior of the spiracles (*Sp*). The sternum of this segment (*VIIIS*) is likewise concealed on the ventral side. The dorsal portion of the ninth segment is chitinized to only a small extent but the ventral portion (*IXS*) is chitinized and carries two pairs of clasping organs, used during copulation (*1Clsp* and *2Clsp*). The penis is extruded during mating between the clasping organs.

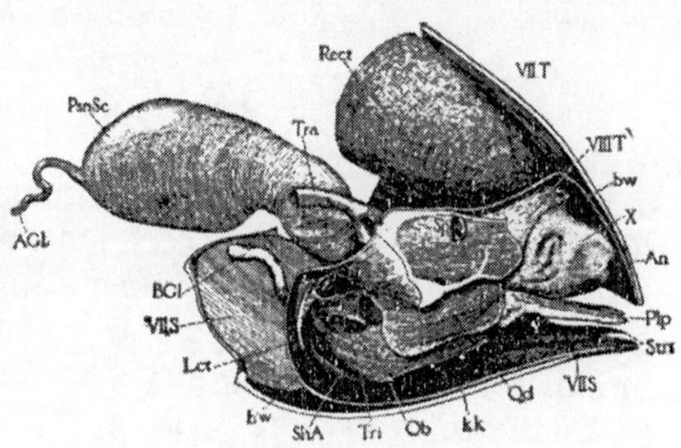

Fig. 76.—Tip of abdomen of worker with left side removed, showing normal position of sting and anus.

DIGESTION

The workers take in food not only for their own nourishment but also that they may be able to provide food for the larvæ. The queen eats frequently during the period of active egg-laying, and a rapid metabolism must take place to permit her to produce the enormous number of eggs which she lays. The larvæ take enormous quantities of food, given them by the worker-bees, permitting the rapid growth which has been described (p. 111). The workers also normally feed the queen and the drones, but the composition of the material furnished is not determined. Bees are exceedingly active and in order that they may do the work required, great quantities of food are needed. The surplus honey which may be taken by the beekeeper, therefore, forms a small part of their gathering. Unfortunately no accurate data can be given on these proportions.

All the food of the various members of the colony comes

from nectar and pollen. The workers take these foods for their own use but modify the raw materials before feeding the young larvæ. That these raw materials may serve their purposes as food, they must be modified so that they may pass through the walls of the alimentary canal and then remain liquid in the blood until taken up by the several tissues. To accomplish this, various enzymes are needed and those found in the bee are not always the same as those present in other animals.

Considerable work has been done on the digestive processes of bees, but much remains still to be learned. The whole structure of the alimentary canal is so unlike that of man that analogies are dangerous on that account alone, and there are even more striking differences in the utilization of various foods. For such reasons it is entirely unwarranted to apply such names as "chyle stomach" to the ventriculus or "large intestine" to the rectal ampulla. These apparently analogous structures have quite different functions in man and bees. It seems annoying perhaps to learn a new set of names, but this is preferable to errors which arise from the use of terms that are better known.

The structure of the alimentary canal has been studied thoroughly by Snodgrass and other workers. The digestive processes in insects and the nutritive requirements have attracted considerable attention of recent years, especially since a knowledge has been gained of the vitamin requirements in food. Petersen [1] was the first to study the digestive processes, and he is to be commended for his stand against analogies with human digestion. Other papers [2]

[1] Petersen, Hans, 1912. Beiträge zur vergleichenden Physiologie der Verdauung: V. Die Verdauung der Honigbiene. Pflüger's Arch. f. d. Gesammte Phys. d. Menschen u. d. Tiere, XLV, pp. 121-151.

[2] Pavlovsky, E. N., and Zarin, E. J., 1922. On the structure of the alimentary canal and its ferments in the bee (*Apis mellifera* L..) Quart. Journ. Micros. Sci., n.s. 263, LXVI, pt. iii, pp. 509-556, 3 pls.

Zander, Enoch, 1921. Handbuch der Bienenkunde in Einzeldarstellung, IV. Das Leben der Bienne, 2 Auf., 195 pp. Stuttgart: Ulmer.

Consult also other papers by Zarin (Sarin).

have appeared which record results of a study of enzymes in the alimentary canal. There is also a large literature on the enzymes in honeys which has some bearing on the problem of bee digestion, but it is somewhat dangerous to assume that an enzyme is present in the alimentary canal because it occurs in honeys. The problem of digestion has been attacked from still a different point of view [1] by determining on which foods bees are able to maintain life, a method which seems to give somewhat safer results than attempts to separate the enzymes of the alimentary canal. The vitamin requirements of bees have not been studied but considerable work has been done on vitamins in honey,[2] and as this is a question in which beekeepers have shown great interest, a partial bibliography is included. Briefly this work indicates that honey contains no vitamin C, very little if any vitamin A and there is a difference of opinion regarding vitamin B. Honey enthusiasts, like Caillas, find it; others do not, so at present it seems best not to make a definite statement on this subject. Aeppler, whose work was mentioned earlier, found vitamin B in royal jelly. Pollen is probably a prolific source of vitamins, while one would scarcely expect nectar to be.

[1] Phillips, E. F., 1927. The utilization of carbohydrates by honeybees. Journ. Agr. Research, XXXV, no. 5, pp. 385-428. [Summarized, Gleanings in Bee Culture, LII (1924), pp. 76-79.]

Bertholf, L. M., 1927. The utilization of carbohydrates as food by honeybee larvæ. *Ibid.*, pp. 429-452.

[2] Hawk, P. B., Smith, C. A., and Bergheim, O., 1921. The vitamine content of honey and honey comb. Amer. Journ. Physiol., LV, no. 3, pp. 339-348.

Faber, H. K., 1920. A study of the antiscorbutic value of honey. Journ. Biol. Chem., XLIII, pp. 113-116.

Dutcher, R. A., 1918. Vitamine studies, III. Observations on the curative properties of honey, nectar and corn pollen in avian polyneuritis. Journ. Biol. Chem., XXXVI, pp. 551-555.

Bachman, Freda M., 1919. Vitamine requirements of certain yeasts. Journ. Biol. Chem., XXXIX, pp. 235-258. (Contains data of tests of honey.)

Scheunert, A., Schieblich, M., and Schwanebeck, E., 1923. [Vitamin content of honey]. Biochem. Zeitschr., CXXXIX, p. 47.

Caillas, Alin, 1926. Le miel contient des vitamines. France Apicole, XXXII, pp. 3-5; 54-55.

The mouth-parts have already been described (p. 143), and those glands (*1Gl, Fig.* 60) which are supposed to be concerned in the production of larval food have also been discussed (p. 121). Behind the mouth is an enlargement of the alimentary canal called the pharynx (*Phy*, Fig. 61), leading to a long narrow tube extending through the thorax, the œsophagus (*Œ*). Behind the constriction between the thorax and abdomen, the alimentary canal widens to form the honey-stomach (*HS*), homologous to the crop of other insects. This is a thin-walled muscular organ used by the worker in carrying nectar to the hive. Behind the honey-stomach is a valvular structure, the proventriculus (*Pvent*, the anterior part being often called the stomach-mouth) which separates the honey-stomach from the ventriculus (often called the chyle-stomach). The proventriculus is of special interest in the bee, since when closed it prevents the nectar from mixing with the contents of the ventriculus and makes it possible for the honey-stomach to function as a carrying vessel. It is claimed by Schöfeld that the anterior end of the proventricular valve may be moved forward to touch the posterior end of the œsophagus, so that the contents of the ventriculus may be forced out as larval food. Snodgrass has shown that this cannot happen without tearing the muscles of the honey-stomach, and furthermore, as is shown later, the contents of the ventriculus could not escape were this contortion possible. Cheshire claims that the hooks of the proventriculus serve to separate the honey and pollen in the honey-stomach, but no proof is presented. The only known function of the proventriculus is that of opening to allow food to pass to the ventriculus. There is no evidence that it assists in the mastication of pollen.

Behind the proventriculus is the ventriculus (*Vent*), a thick-walled organ ringed by numerous constrictions. It consists (Fig. 77) of longitudinal and transverse muscles surrounding a much folded epithelium, the cells of which

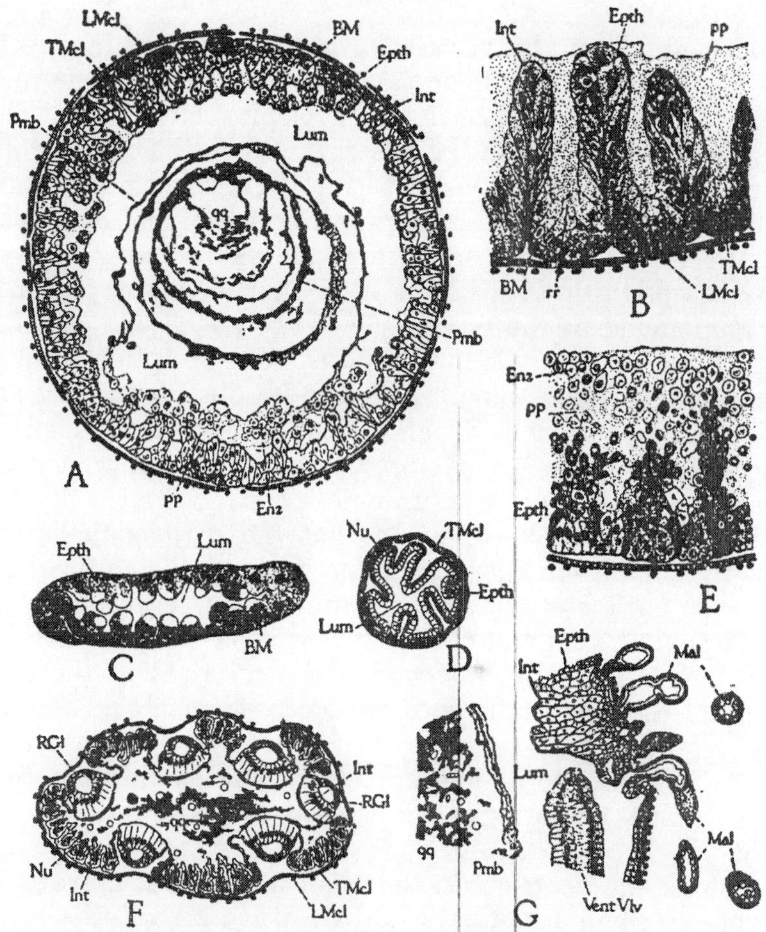

FIG. 77.—Histological details of alimentary canal of worker: *A*, cross-section of ventriculus; *B*, section of ventriculus wall; *C*, section of Malpighian tubule; *D*, cross-section of small intestine; *E*, section of ventriculus wall, showing formation of enzyme cells; *F*, section of anterior end of rectum, showing rectal glands (*RGl*); *G*, slightly oblique section of posterior end of ventriculus, showing openings of Malpighian tubules.

are supposed to produce some of the digestive enzymes. The inner depressions of this epithelium are filled with a gelatinous mass (*pp*) which extends into the lumen. The food contents of the ventriculus are surrounded by layers of membrane (peritrophic layers, Fig. 77, *Pmb*), formed from the gelatinous mass in the enveloping epithelium. The peritropic layers are often described as chitinous but this, according to Petersen, is an error. These membranes do not seem capable of allowing the passage of the food contained in them to the ventriculus wall and probably little or no absorption of food occurs here. Furthermore, pollen is usually found at the posterior end undigested and, according to Snodgrass, it is not prepared for absorption until it reaches the rectal ampulla. Snodgrass observed in certain parts of the ventriculus wall a sloughing off of the ends of the epithelial cells (*Enz*), presumably enzymes, which are seen in the gelatinous peritrophic mass. Petersen, in confirmation of this view, found that the peritrophic layers (which come from the peritrophic mass on the epithelium) are not chitinous but contain proteolytic ferments. The peritrophic layers and their attachment to the proventricular valve effectually prevent the regurgitation of the contents of the ventriculus into the honey-stomach. The contents of the ventriculus does not at all resemble larval food. It, therefore, appears clear that the theory that larval food is regurgitated can no longer be considered tenable.

Behind the ventriculus, the alimentary canal narrows to form the small intestine (Fig. 61, *SInt*) and at the point where the ventriculus and small intestine join, the Malpighian tubes (*Mal*) empty into the alimentary canal. The small intestine is coiled and finally empties into the rectal ampulla (*Rect*, rectum or large intestine). The inner epithelium of the rectum is thrown into six longitudinal folds, the so-called rectal glands (Fig. 77, *RGl*) of unknown function. It is usually believed that they increase the absorbing surface but, since they are covered on the inner surface with chitin, this explanation seems improbable. The rectal ampulla is capable of considerable expansion and normally retains the feces when bees are confined to the hive, as in winter. It is supposed that most of the absorption of food takes place in the hind-intestine. Petersen advances the fantastic theory that the rectal glands are the source of the hive odor.

Sources of food

All the food of bees comes from nectar and pollen. Nectar contains cane-sugar and a varying amount of levulose and dextrose, and in the ripening process the cane-sugar is largely changed into the other two sugars named (p. 92). This indicates the presence of the enzyme invertase, which has already been found in various parts of the bee's body. It appears, therefore, that bees are able to modify cane-sugar into the two sugars, which are both capable of being absorbed without further change in the higher animals and doubtless also in bees, so that the digestive process of cane-sugar begins with the ripening of honey.

Various other carbohydrate materials occur occasionally in the natural or the artificial food of bees and it, therefore, is interesting to learn which of these carbohydrates they can utilize. The author has shown that worker-bees can utilize maltose and trehalose, two disaccharides of a composition comparable to that of cane-sugar, and melezitose, a trisaccharide more complex than the others. They cannot maintain life on galactose, a constituent of lactose or milk-sugar, or on milk-sugar itself, indicating the absence of the enzyme lactase. They are unable to live on dextrins, starch, inulin or glycogen taken as food, indicating the absence of the enzymes dextrases, amylase (diastase), inulase and glycogenase. Diastase has been claimed for the alimentary canal by various workers but the presence of this material is most questionable in the lumen of the alimentary canal, although it may be present elsewhere in the body. Bees are also unable to make use of raffinose, indicating the absence of the enzyme which simplifies this sugar. The inability of bees to utilize starch becomes important, since many pollens contain starch-grains, and the inability to use dextrins is of the greatest importance in providing bees with food for winter, for this material is found in most honeys, more abundantly in the darker honeys, and especially in honey-dews. The application of these facts will be considered under a discussion of wintering (p. 378).

The next important constituent of the food of bees is protein, derived chiefly from pollen. There is a small amount of protein in honey, but this is perhaps derived mainly from included pollen-grains. Protein is absolutely essential for the growth of the body, consequently it becomes especially important in the food of larvæ. Petersen shows the presence of proteolytic (proteoclastic) enzymes which act on proteins in the peritrophic membranes of the ventriculus and in the salivary glands. He makes the interesting observation that bees are unable to digest the proteins in pollen-grains unless the grains are broken before they are digested, since bees cannot digest away the pollen-coats. This opinion is fully supported by observations of the digestive tract. Apparently absorption of protein materials occurs only after the food has passed to the small intestine or to the rectal ampulla and not in the ventriculus. The amount of pollen used by a colony during the brood-rearing season is enormous, yet there are few accurate estimates of the amount. Every beekeeper knows that brood cannot be reared in an absence of this material. Protein is not only utilized as food by the larva but great quantities are stored in the so-called fat body of the larva to be utilized during the changes to the adult condition. Strauss[1] shows that the larva contains about 11.25 per cent of protein at the time of sealing. Workers doubtless modify protein materials before preparation of larval food by secre-

[1] Strauss, J., 1911. Die chemische Zusammenzetsung der Arbeitsbienen und Drohnen wahrend ihrer verschiedenen Entwicklungsstadien. Zeit. f. Biol., LVI, pp. 347-397, 9 figs.

tion, but it is quite unknown how much they use for repair of their own bodies during adult life.

Fat is a third common constituent of food and there is considerable of this material in pollen. If pollen is used for the secretion of larval food and if this food contains fat, this suggests that the adult worker-bees are able to break down fat into its simpler constituents before absorption, yet the fat of the pollen-grains appears to pass through the alimentary canal of the adults without change, indicating an absence of lipase at that point. Furthermore, starved bees still retain fat in the adult fat body after death, indicating also the absence of this enzyme there. However, von Planta and others have found fat in the larval food, but this might be elaborated from carbohydrates absorbed by the adults. The larvæ get not only the secreted fat in the larval food but also fat from pollen-grains direct, and it is assumed that they utilize it. Further work is needed here.

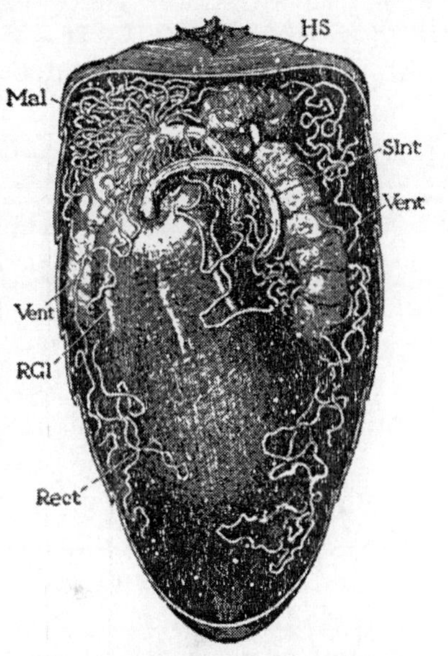

Fig. 78.—Interior of abdomen of an over-wintered worker before first flight in spring, showing rectum (*Rect*) enormously distended with undischarged feces.

The retention of feces by bees so long as they remain within the hive, except when dysentery develops, is highly important in their management. The great distention of the rectal ampulla is shown in Fig. 78. The relation of this distention to the wintering problem is discussed elsewhere (p. 378) and it appears that this becomes much worse when there is a high dextrin-content in the food. During the active season when the bees fly frequently, there are numerous opportunities for the ejection of feces and a serious condition rarely develops in the period of brood-rearing, but in early spring a protracted spell of bad weather may cause dysentery to appear. So far no evidence of auto-intoxication due to the retention of feces has been presented, but it causes a disturbance of the winter-cluster and consequent high temperatures which are serious. Because of the high temperatures under this condition, brood-rearing usually occurs in such colonies.

An interesting circumstance arising from a good apiary practice is that adult bees can live for long periods on a solution of cane-sugar which is solely carbohydrate. Such food contains no vitamins. A vast experience has shown that bees winter well on such food, yet it still remains to be shown whether they are fully nourished by it. Under such a regime digestive processes are reduced to the minimum, especially since beekeepers usually invert part of the sugar before feeding by boiling the sirup with tartaric acid, which brings about the same action as the enzyme.

From the evidence presented, which is obviously too scant, it appears that bees have a highly specialized digestive system, incapable of much flexibility. The mixed diet of many other insects is wholly unsuited to utilization by bees. The larvæ are known to utilize certain foods which adult bees cannot. All of these facts point to the danger of assuming any similarities between bees and man.

Not all the materials necessary for the body of the bee are included in what has been said about carbohydrates, fats and protein. Aronssohn[1] has analyzed the ash obtained from old drones and on the basis of 100 grains of desiccated insects, he gets the following results: Total ash, 4.23 g., sulfur, 1.413 g., chlorine, 0.294 g., iodine, 0.00009 g., phosphorus, 0.953 g., arsenic, 0.0000015 g., silica, 0.034 g., copper, 0.006 g., iron, 0.015 g., manganese, 0.002 g.,

[1] Aronssohn, F., 1911. Sur la composition minérale de l'abeille. L'Apiculteur, LV, pp. 293-294. (Extracted from Comptes Rendus de l'Acad. des Sci., Paris.)

zinc, 0.012 g., aluminum, 0.01 g., calcium, 0.056 g., magnesium, 0.099 g., potassium, 0.025 g., sodium, 0.049 g., fluorine, ?. These bees were taken in a region with a clay-limestone soil, where there were no manufacturing industries and where no insecticides were used. Presumably these mineral constituents were obtained from nectar or pollen, or both.

During pupal life a large proportion of the body weight is made up of chitin, which forms the skeletal covering of the adult body. No analysis of the chitin of bees is available, but analyses of other chitins indicate that this is largely a sugar derivative (81 per cent), with which is mixed certain nitrogenous compounds, all of which materials must be formed of constituents derived from honey and pollen.

CIRCULATION

When the products of digestion are absorbed and traverse the alimentary canal wall, they must be carried to the various tissues for assimilation. This is done by means of the blood. In the higher animals blood is normally confined in blood-vessels which carry it throughout the body, but in the bee, as in other insects, the blood bathes the various organs, filling up the interstices between them. These spaces may, however, be so arranged that the blood flows in definite channels or sinuses. The blood is further confined to definite paths by membranes stretched across the dorsal and ventral walls of the abdomen (*DDph* and *VDph*, Fig. 79) which bound the chief sinuses. These diaphragms have a rhythmical motion and assist in the circulation of the blood. The heart (*Ht*) is located dorsal to the dorsal diaphragm, this sinus being therefore known as the pericardial chamber. The heart is a long muscular tube consisting of four chambers lying in the third, fourth, fifth, and sixth segments of the abdomen. In each of these segments is a valvular opening (ostium, *Ost*) on each side for the admission of blood from the pericardial chamber,

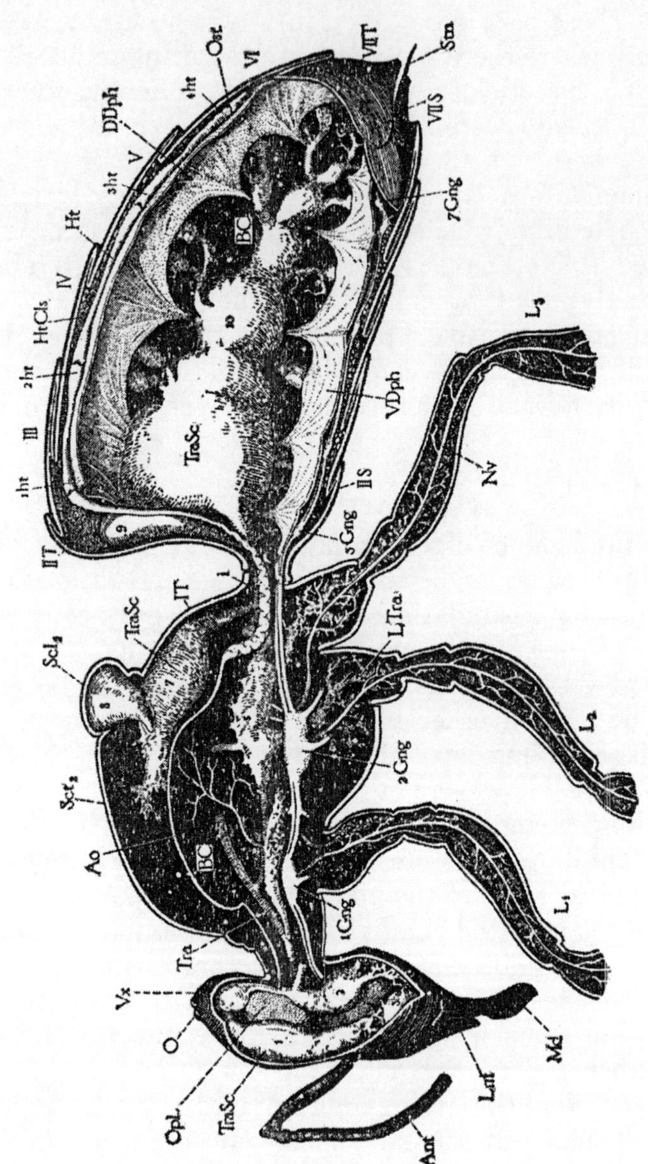

FIG. 79.—Longitudinal median vertical section of body of worker, showing nervous system, tracheal system, dorsal and ventral diaphragms and dorsal blood-vessel.

and there are also segmental valves to prevent a backward flow of blood. The posterior end of the heart is closed but on the anterior end it is continued in a long tube (aorta, *Ao*) extending in various convolutions and arches through the thorax and opening by simple branches into the head cavity.

The blood of the bee is a colorless liquid containing certain corpuscles, but no red ones such as are found in mammals. The blood is forced through the heart and aorta to the head cavity. It then flows backward through the sinuses of the thorax into the ventral sinus of the abdomen. Pumped backward by the pulsation of the ventral diaphragm, it flows through various definite cavities between visceral organs in the abdomen and into the pericardial cavity, from which it again enters the heart through the ostia. In its passage through the sinuses about the viscera, the blood takes up the food which has passed through the walls of the alimentary canal. This nourishment is promptly carried to all parts of the body by circulation.

No analysis of the blood has been made, so that it is not known in what form the food constituents pass to the various organs. In the case of insects, circulation is not important in carrying oxygen to the organs and carbon dioxide back to the lungs, since respiration is effected by a different method, but the blood may assist locally in the transmission of these gases.

METABOLISM

It is not proposed at this time to enter into a long discussion of the ways by which each organ is built or how they are repaired as needed. Each cell is capable of taking such nourishment as it requires from the blood and of incorporating it into its own protoplasm. Oxygen is also taken from the respiratory organs and utilized in the combustion of the various cell constituents and as a result of this cell activity carbon dioxide, water and other more complex waste products are given off. The wastes must then be carried away to be eliminated from the body through the respiratory or the excretory system. Not all cells of the body have the same metabolic requirements, but by some mysterious process each cell takes what it needs if the material is at hand. For the utilization of various food constituents by the cells, enzyme action is required, both for the building of cell constituents and for tearing them down, so that the body is a vastly complex chemical laboratory of marvelous activity. These processes cannot be discussed in detail, but the removal of wastes will be treated briefly under Respiration and Excretion.

RESPIRATION

That an animal may live, it must have oxygen. The oxygen taken into the body in respiration does not form protoplasm in the various cells as does protein but is used to combine with the materials of the cells to make simpler compounds which are ultimately eliminated from the body. This process of oxidation is the source of bodily energy and some of the products of combustion are of such a chemical character that they poison the cells unless promptly removed. The main products of combustion are carbon dioxide, water, and various complex nitrogenous compounds. Water may be and the nitrogenous products are eliminated through other systems than the respiratory organs, but carbon dioxide must pass out through the same channels through which the oxygen enters.

In man, the oxygen is taken into the lungs with air and the blood is pumped there to meet the oxygen. Bees do not have a closed circulation which will effectually carry blood to the oxygen. Furthermore, the higher animals have in their blood corpuscles a substance, haemoglobin, which is capable of taking up oxygen or carbon dioxide to be transported, but this is lacking in the colorless blood of the insects. In the bee, instead of the blood being carried to the oxygen supply, the oxygen is taken to all the organs of the body by means of tracheal tubes, small branches of which permeate all the tissues. These tracheæ receive their air supply through openings in the body-wall, the spiracles, two functional pairs on the sides of the thorax and eight pairs on the abdomen. The tracheæ are composed of delicate tubes lined with chitin, but the tracheal sacs and the finer branches lack these strengthening rings.

Active bees show a pumping motion of the abdomen by means of which air is quickly changed in the main tracheal tubes and the sacs, this motion consisting of a lengthening and shortening of the abdomen and a slight dorso-ventral movement. It is stated by Djathchenko[1] that in expiration the spiracles are momentarily closed, the contraction of the muscles thus forcing air to the minute branches, after which the spiracles are opened and the air is expelled, but detailed work by Krogh shows that the movement of gases in the finer branches is entirely by diffusion. The muscles which serve in respiration are described by Carlet.[2]

The tracheal system of the bee is shown sufficiently in Fig. 80 so that a detailed description is unnecessary. The abdomen contains the unusually large tracheal sacs (*TraSc*) connected with each other by ventral commissures (*TraCom*). They are also connected with tracheal sacs of the thorax. From the most anterior spiracles of the thorax are heavy trunks to the air-sacs of the head, above the brain. The tracheal system of the bee is more elaborate than that of most other insects and probably in no other species is there more free access of oxygen to all parts of the body.

Each constituent of the protoplasm has specific requirements for oxidation, and similarly each food consumed by an animal shows a characteristic ratio between the amount consumed and the amount of oxygen used and the carbon dioxide given off. This ratio is known as the respiratory quotient. The oxygen requirements of bees have been studied

[1] Djathchenko, Sophie, 1906. Zur Frage der Athumsorgane der Biene. Ann. de l'Inst. Argon. de Moscou, XII, pp. 1-14.

[2] Carlet, G., 1884. Sur les muscles de l'abdomen de l'abeille. Comptes Rendues de l'Acad. des Sci., Paris, XCVIII, pp. 758-759.

by Parhon [1] with bees which appear to have been stimulated to a high degree and therefore not entirely normal, and by Milner and Demuth [2] under normal winter conditions. Since the amount of oxygen used and the carbon dioxide given off can easily be known for any given amount of food consumed, it becomes possible to determine the gas exchange of bees whenever the amount of food consumed is known. This makes it possible to determine, for example, the ventilation requirements in a bee-cellar or to estimate with a fair degree of accuracy the amount of food required to bring one larva to maturity.

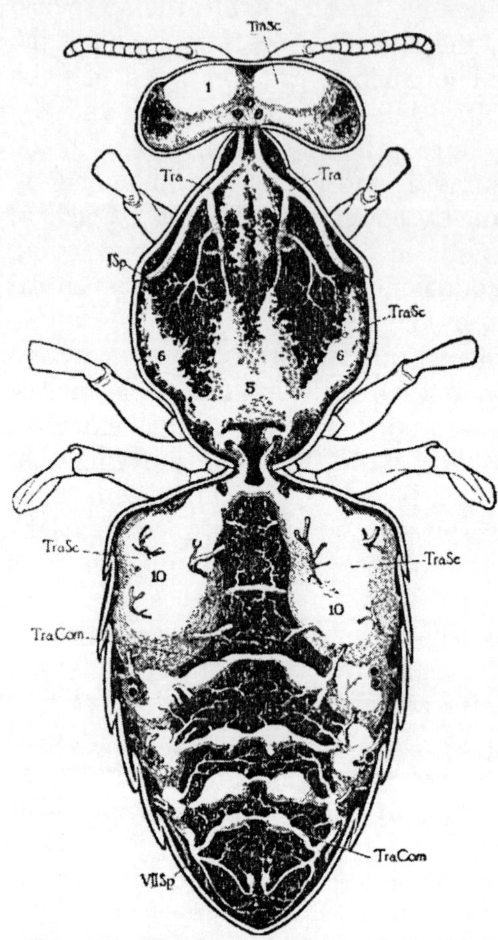

Fig. 80.—Tracheal system of worker with dorsal sacs and trunks removed, from above.

EXCRETION

The products of the breaking down of protoplasm consist, as previously stated, of carbon dioxide, water and various compounds containing nitrogen. Since the adult honeybee can live for long periods

[1] Parhon, Marie, 1909. Les echanges nutritifs chez les abeilles pendants les quartres saisons. Ann. des Sci. Nat. Zool. (9) ix, pp.

[2] Milner, R. D., and Demuth, Geo. S., 1921. Heat production of honeybees in winter. Dept. Bull. 988, U. S. Dept. Agr., 18 pp.

(especially in winter) on pure sugar, excretion must at times be reduced to a minimum. Sugar breaks down into carbon dioxide and water, both of which may pass off as gases through the tracheal system. It is only the other components of honey and the pollen which ultimately go to form nitrogenous compounds. All the carbon dioxide is expelled through the tracheæ and probably most of the water escapes as vapor by this course, although some may be ejected with the nitrogenous compounds. The excretory organs are the Malpighian tubes (Fig. 61, *Mal*), about 100 in number in the bee, which open into the alimentary canal at the junction of the ventriculus and the intestine. They are long delicate tubes which coil about the other viscera. These tubules are only one cell in thickness and the ends of these cells (*Epth,* Fig. 77 *C*) often bulge into the cavity of the tubule. The junction of the Malpighian tubules with the intestine is shown in Fig. 77 *G*. Minute crystals of urates have been found in the Malpighian tubules. The excreted products empty into the intestine and are expelled in the feces.

In the fat body (located in the body cavity) are certain large cells of rather mysterious function, called œnocytes. Koschevnikov[1] states that œnocytes of the young adult bee have a uniform slightly pigmented protoplasm, while in old bees yellow granules begin to appear in these cells. After the winter confinement, these granules are numerous and in old queens they are especially abundant. According to the view of this author, œnocytes are excreting cells which take up waste products of katabolism and, after modifying them, deliver them again to the blood to be carried to the Malpighian tubules. The changes of age may be interpreted as due to an accumulation of these products in cells which are no longer able to discharge them. This failure of the œnocytes should be investigated from the point of view

[1] Koschevnikov, G. A., 1900. Ueber den Fettkörper und die Œnocyten der Honigbiene (*Apis mellifera* L.). Zool. Anz., XXIII, pp. 337-353.

of the term of life of the bee. In some of the primitive insects the fat body is supposed to function as a permanent storage for urates.

LOCOMOTION

Bees are able to go from place to place by means of two systems of locomotor organs, the wings and the legs. Both of these are attached to the thorax and the muscles of flight are so well developed that they occupy almost the entire space in the thorax.

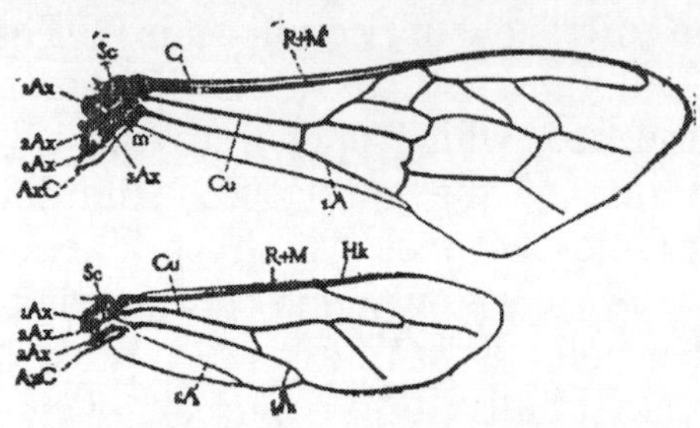

FIG. 81.—Fore- and hind-wings.

The wings (Fig. 81) are membranous structures with a definite framework of veins attached to the sides of the thorax. The details of the venations of the wings need not be considered at length. This has been investigated in a careful manner by Comstock and Needham [1] and the designations used in Fig. 81 are those decided upon by these authors after a study of the comparative venations of the various orders of insects. The symbols are explained in the appendix. The attachment of the bee's wings to the thorax has been investigated by Snodgrass.

The motion of the wings in flight is in four directions, up, down, forward and backward, and the combination of these movements causes the wing tips to describe the course of a figure 8, if the insect is held stationary. In flight, the 8 is of course modified. The hind-wings are small and are attached by hooks on their anterior margins to thickenings on the margin of the front-wings. They are not provided with large flight muscles of their own but are car-

[1] Comstock, J. H., and Needham, J. G., 1898-99. The wings of insects. Amer. Nat., XXXII and XXXIII: Reprinted, Ithaca, N. Y.

ried along by the action of the powerful muscles in the mesothorax which propel the fore-wings.

The muscles of flight are in four sets, corresponding to the four directions of wing movement. The chief muscles are not attached directly to the bases of the wings, as in dragonflies, but the wings are moved into the right position by muscles situated inside the pleura of the two thoracic segments. After the wings are in position for flight, the compression of the thorax by the vertical muscles lowers the dorsum and raises the wing while the contraction of the longitudinal muscles raises the dorsum and lowers the wing. The vertical muscles are, therefore, the elevators and the longitudinal muscles the depressors. The movements of the wings during flight are, therefore, produced mainly by changes in the shape of the thorax. The forward and backward movements are accomplished by the action of the muscles on the pleurum, acting directly on the bases of the wings.

Because of the enormous development of the two main sets of flight muscles, bees are capable of strong and rapid flight. They are also able to arrest progress suddenly or get under way rapidly. There is no reason to believe that flight is in any way dependent upon the amount of air in the tracheæ, as has been claimed, for filling the air-sacs obviously does not reduce the weight of the bee. Bees are able to fly at a considerable angle for some distance as is seen in apiaries in mountainous districts. The power of the wing-muscles is shown by the ability of a worker to fly from the hive carrying a drone, which weighs more than the worker itself.

In walking, bees use all six legs (Fig. 82). In addition to their function in locomotion, the legs constitute a rather complex set of tools for numerous other purposes, especially complex in the worker. On the front legs at the articulation of the tibia and first tarsal joint are the antennæ cleaners. The middle leg has a spur to which has been attributed the function of prying pollen from the hind-legs

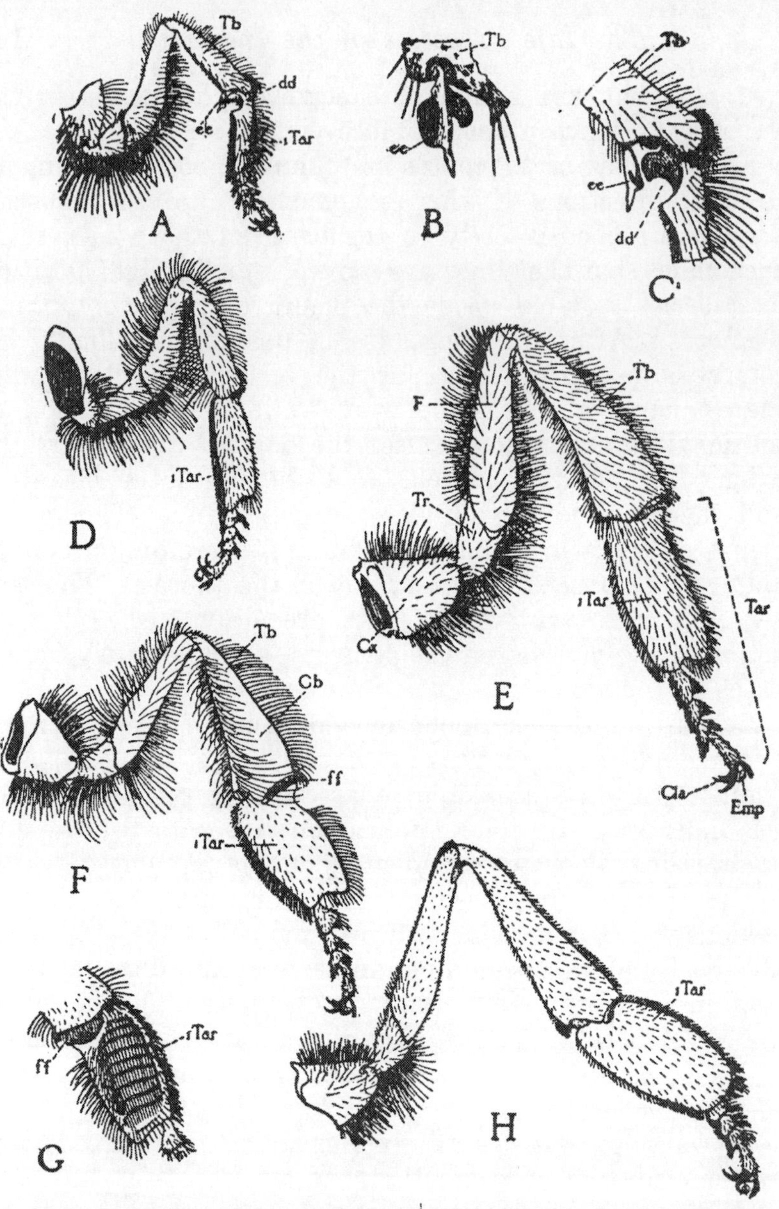

FIG. 82.—*A*, left front leg of worker, anterior view; *B*, spine of antenna cleaner; *C*, details of antenna cleaner; *D*, left middle leg of worker, anterior view; *E*, left hind leg of queen, anterior view; *F*, left hind leg of worker, anterior view; *G*, inner view of left hind leg of worker, showing pollen-combs; *H*, left hind leg of drone, anterior view.

in storing it. The hind legs of the worker-bees are highly specialized, carrying pollen-baskets or corbicula on the outer side of the flattened tibiæ and rows of spines on the inner side of the first tarsal joint. Between these two joints are the so-called wax-shears, which in fact have nothing to do with the wax, but function in pollen-gathering (p. 132). Each leg is provided with a pollen-brush for collecting pollen. The muscles for moving the legs are located inside the joints and are inserted on the chitinous walls.

The last tarsal joint on each leg carries a pair of bilobed claws (Fig. 83, *Cla*), which differ among the three types of bees. Those of the drone are bent more nearly at right angles than those in the workers and queens and those of the queen are larger than the claws of the workers. Between the claws is a lobe (empodium, *Emp*) used when the bee walks on a smooth surface. On such a surface the claws are useless and the sticky empodium is lowered and flattened, providing a good foothold.

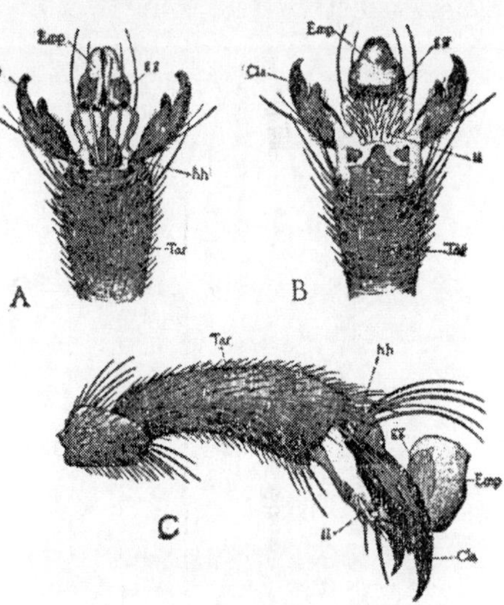

Fig. 83.—Dorsal (*A*), ventral (*B*) and lateral (*C*) views of last tarsal joint of first foot of worker.

The motion of the legs in walking is typical of all insects. The legs move in two sets; the fore and hind legs on one side move in the same direction as the middle leg on the opposite side, thus giving a triangle for support at all times. In flight the legs hang freely and are forced somewhat backward, except when they are being used as in the manipulation of pollen (p. 134).

PROTECTIVE APPARATUS

Worker-bees defend the colony by means of the sting, situated in a cavity at the tip of the abdomen (Fig. 76) but capable of marvelously rapid action when protruded. As was stated earlier (p. 109), this sting cavity is formed by the infolding of the eighth, ninth and tenth segments of the abdomen. The sting is homologous with the ovipositor of other insects. The sting of the worker-bee is straight, while that of the queen is longer, curved and less strongly barbed.

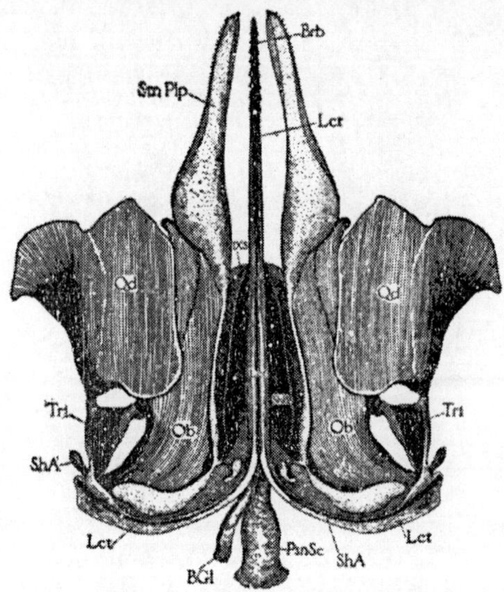

Fig. 84.—Ventral view of sting of worker and accessory parts, flattened out.

The sting (Fig. 84) and its accessory apparatus form a rather complex structure. The shaft consists of three parts, a dorsal sheath (*ShS*) along which move two barbed lancets (*Lct*). The sheath is enlarged at the anterior end into a bulb (*ShB*) and is further continued in two arms (*ShA*) which curve outward. The lancets slide on a grooved track the full length of the sheath, past the bulb and diverge along the two basal arms. The sheath and lancets combine to form a hollow tube (*PsnC*) through which the poison flows.

The arms of the sheath are attached at their anterior ends to oblong plates (*Ob*) which overlap the sides of the sting. To these plates are attached palpi (*StnPlp*), soft white projections provided with sense organs, by means of which the bee tells when she is in contact with the object which is to be stung. The lancets are attached to triangular plates (*Tri*) which in turn articulate with the quadrate plates (*Qd*). By the movements of these plates on each other the lancets are slid along the sheath when the sting is used. It has been shown by Zander[1] that the triangular plate (*Tri*) is part of the eighth sternum, the quadrate plate (*Qd*) is part of the ninth tergum and the oblong plate (*Ob*) is the ninth sternum.

The poison of the sting arises from two sets of glands. The conspicuous poison-sac (*PsnSc*) which opens into the bulb of the sting is usually seen attached to the sting when the latter is pulled from a bee. The contents of this gland have an acid reaction and it was formerly believed to be formic acid. This acid comes from two long coiled tubes (*AGlD*) on which are two small enlargements, supposed to be the secreting glands (*AGl*). Probably the tubes (*AGlD*) also have gland cells in the walls. The other poison glands (*BGl*), known as the alkaline glands, also empty into the bulb of the sting. Their secretion is supposed to have an alkaline reaction. According to Carlet,[2] the secretions of these two sets of glands must be mixed to be fully effective. The secretions enter the bulb where they are mixed and are then forced down the canal (*PsnC*) formed by the sheath and lancets.

In most books on bees, certain lateral openings in the lancets are described as paths of the poison in the process of stinging. Snodgrass showed, however, that these do not connect with the poison canal and supposed them to be ducts of some kind of subcuticular glands. McIndoo has shown them to be olfactory pores (p. 181).

The sting, as every beekeeper knows, is an effective weapon of defense. When employed, it usually cannot be withdrawn because of the barbs (*Brb*) on the lancets. The sting with the accessory plates and poison-sac are, therefore, usually torn from the body of the bee, causing

[1] Zander, Enoch, 1899. Beiträge zur Morphologie des Stachelapparates der Hymenopteren. Zeit. f. Wiss. Zool., LXVI, pp. 288-333.

[2] Carlet, G., 1890. Mémoir sur le venin et l'aiguillon de l'abeille. Ann. des Sci. Nat. Zool., 7 ser., IX, pp. 1-17.

so severe an injury to the abdomen that the worker dies within a short time. The defender is thus sacrificed for the good of the colony. The parts torn away include the muscles which operate the accessory plates and indirectly slide the lancets on the sheath. The sting may, therefore, be driven farther and farther into the wound if not promptly removed and the same reflex actions of the muscles serve to force more poison from the poison-sac. In removing the sting, care should be exercised not to squeeze the poison-sac, thus emptying its contents into the wound.

CHAPTER VII

THE NERVOUS SYSTEM AND THE SENSES

In order that bees may respond to changes in the environment these influences must be perceived, and the organs by which these stimuli are received are the nervous system and the special organs of sense. The resulting nervous impulses are then transmitted through the nervous system, by means of which the actions of the animal are also coordinated and molded in response to the stimuli received. The nervous system and its various organs of special sense are so important that a separate chapter is devoted to a brief description of the known facts.

Nowhere in the entire discussion of bee behavior is it more necessary to avoid comparisons with man. Man is capable of conscious and volitional acts while evidence of such acts in bees is lacking. The whole structure of the nervous system and of the sense organs is so unlike analogous structures in man that attempts at homologies are entirely unwarranted. Since it is impossible to comprehend senses other than those which men possess, the senses and the sense organs of the bee must be described in terms of human senses, but this should not misguide one into a belief that its perceptions are wholly comparable to those with which man is familiar. The nervous system is not yet studied with sufficient detail to permit exact knowledge of the course of the nervous impulses, and furthermore the responses of the bee are for the time more important than the mechanics of nervous transmissions.

NERVOUS SYSTEM

This system of organs consists of a series of nerve-masses called ganglia (Fig. 85, *Gng*) situated on the mid-ventral line of the body, the ganglia being connected by a pair of longitudinal cords, called connectives. The nerve-cells are located in the ganglia while the delicate processes from these cells, the nerve fibers, form the connectives and also go to all parts of the body, some serving to transmit stimuli from the sense organs and some to carry stimuli from the nervous system to the various organs of the body.

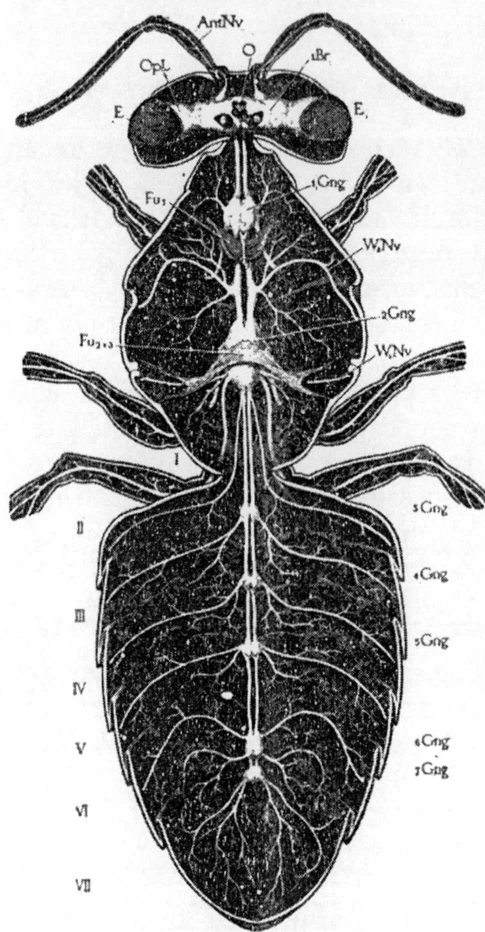

FIG. 85.—Nervous system of worker, dorsal view.

In an hypothetical generalized insect embryo one should doubtless find a ganglion for each segment of the body, probably twenty in all, but the ganglia of the bee-larva are modified from the primitive condition and in the adult still further specialization is observed, by the fusion of various ganglia.

The brain (Fig. 86), situated above the œsophagus, consists of three consecutive ganglia, recognizable in the embryo, but completely fused and not readily distinguishable in the adult. From the brain, two short connectives (circumœsophageal) pass one on either side of the œsophagus to the subœsophageal ganglion (*SœGng*) also located in the head. Continuous with the brain are the optic lobes (*Opl*) forming the nervous connection with the large compound eyes (*E*), and from the brain are nerves to the antennæ (*AntNv*) and also to the frontal ganglion (*FtGng*),

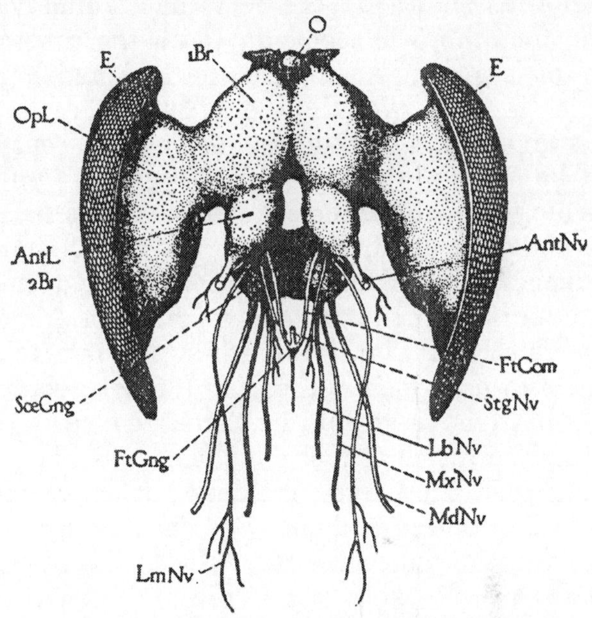

Fig. 86.—Brain and subœsophageal ganglion of worker, anterior view.

from which the stomatogastric system (sympathetic system) has its origin (*StgNv*). The subœsophageal ganglion gives off nerve branches to the mandibles (*MdNv*), maxillæ (*MxNv*) and labium (*LmNv*). For a study of the minute structure of the brain and the paths of the various nervous elements, the reader is referred to the works of Kenyon [1] and Jonescu.[2]

[1] Kenyon, F. C., 1896. The brain of the bee. Journ. Comp. Neurol., VI, pp. 133-210.

Kenyon, F. C., 1897. The optic lobes of the bee's brain in the light of recent neurological methods. Amer. Nat., XXXI, pp. 369-376.

[2] Jonescu, C. N., 1909. Vergleichende Untersuchungen über das Gehirn der Honigbiene. Jenaischen Zeit. f. Naturwiss., XLV, N. F.. XXXVIII.

In the thorax the number of ganglia is reduced to two (Figs. 79 and 85, *1Gng* and *2Gng*). The first innervates the first pair of legs while the second is a combination of four ganglia, as shown by the fact that it innervates the meso- and metathoracic segments (with the corresponding two pairs of legs and wings) and the first abdominal segment, which is fused with the thorax in the bee, as well as the first segment of the abdomen behind the construction. It should be noted that nerves (*W2Nv* and *W3Nv*) run to the bases of the wings to innervate sense organs (p. 181).

In the abdomen are five ganglia (*3-7 Gng*) which send nerve-branches to the remaining abdominal segments. The third and fourth ganglia lie one segment in front of the segments which they innervate while the remaining ones are in their own segments, the last (*7Gng*) supplying the remaining posterior segments of the abdomen, it therefore being actually a fusion of four ganglia.

The cutting of the nerve-cord does not cause death and even if the thorax and abdomen are entirely separated the parts may function independently. If the head is removed, the animal can still walk and if the abdomen is removed it can still take in food. These facts indicate that the nervous control of the body is not centralized in the brain as completely as in man and in many other animals. Proper correlation of movement cannot, however, take place unless the nervous connections are intact.

SENSE ORGANS

While much work has been done on the sense organs of bees, there are still many points of dispute, and much investigation is needed. The known organs will be described briefly, and for each organ reference will be made to papers in which further details are available.

Sight

The organs which receive light stimuli are the three simple eyes or ocelli and the two large compound eyes, all situated on the head. The compound eyes are located on the sides of the head, each eye consisting of many units. In drones, the number of these units is larger than in the two types of females and the compound eyes are so enlarged as to meet

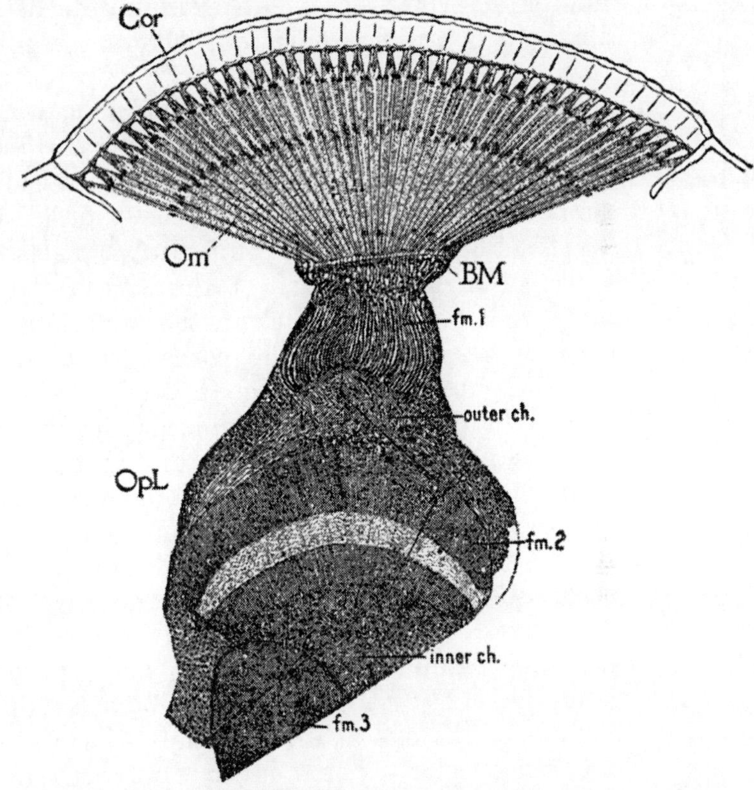

FIG. 87.—Section of compound eye and optic lobe of worker; *Om*, ommatidia.

on the vertex of the head. The structure of the units of the compound eye was described some years ago.[1] On the outer surface, these units (ommatidia) are indicated by hexagonal facets in the chitinous covering of the eye. If a

[1] Phillips, E. F., 1905. Structure and development of the compound eye of the honeybee. Proc. Acad. Nat. Sci., Phila., LVII, pp. 123-157.

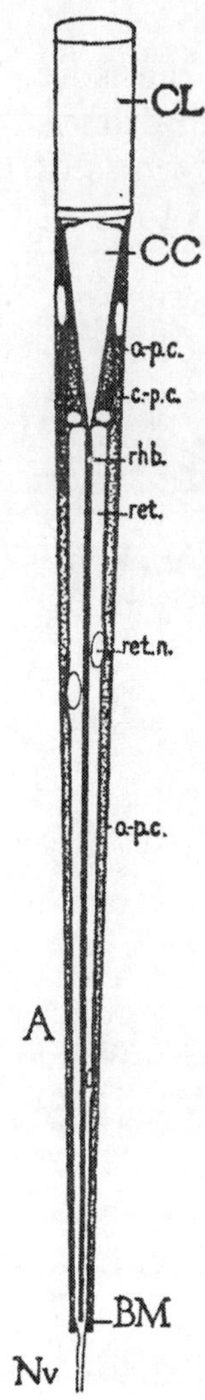

FIG. 88.—Section of entire ommatidium.

section is cut through the entire eye of a worker-bee (including the optic lobes), the structure is that shown in Fig. 87. Numerous ommatidia are shown in full length and beneath these are the optic lobes, which need not be described here. An examination of a single ommatidium (Fig. 88) shows the following details of structure: (1) an outer corneal lens of chitin (*CL*) continuous with the chitin of the head, (2) the crystalline cone (*CC*), and (3) the rhabdome (*rhb*) surrounded by eight or nine sense cells or retinulæ (*ret*). Surrounding the ommatidia are two types of pigment cells: (1) the corneal pigment cells (*c.-p.c.*), which in the pupal stage secreted the chitin of the corneal lens, and (2) the outer pigment cells (*o.-p.c.*). So far as can be determined, the functions of these parts are as follows: rays of light pass through the lens and crystalline cone cells and enter the transparent rhabdome where the stimulus is received. Any rays of light which enter obliquely or which strike the edge of the crystalline cone are absorbed by the surrounding pigment cells so that it seems probable that only those rays which strike the surface of the eye at a right angle ever reach the sense cells. There is no apparatus for changing the focus of the lens.

The type of image formed by the compound eye has been the subject of considerable speculation. The two theories on this subject are: (1) that each facet forms a separate image, and (2) that the impressions of the individual facets form a mosaic image. The latter theory has most to support it and is generally accepted. Forel[1] gives an

[1] Forel, Auguste, 1908. The senses of insects. Eng. trans. by Yearsley. London: Methuen and Co.

admirable discussion of these theories and adds considerable evidence to support the latter.

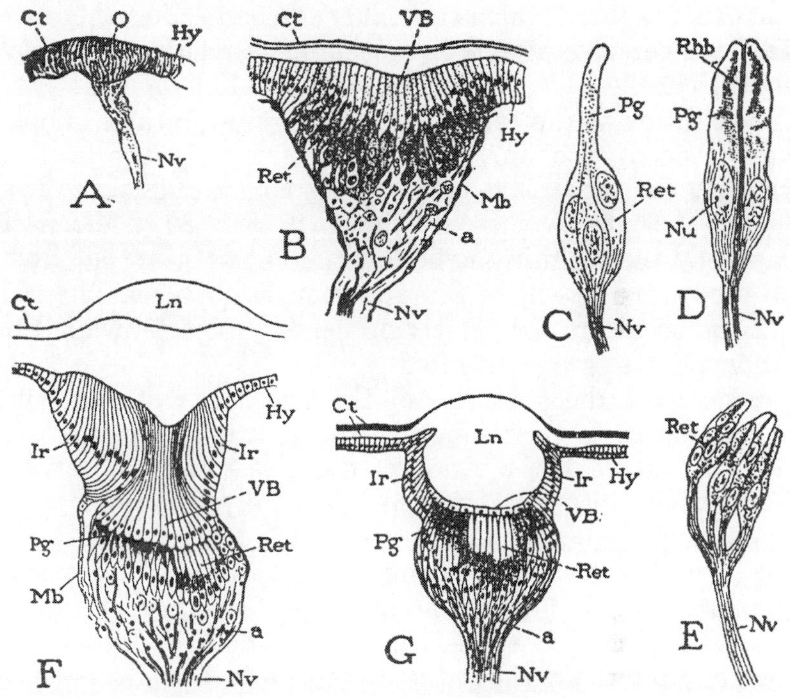

FIG. 89.—The development of a simple eye or ocellus of the honeybee (after Snodgross). *A,* longitudinal section of merian ocellus of very young pupa, consisting of thickening of hypodermis (*Hy*) with nerve (*Nv*) attached; *B,* section of lateral ocellus at later stage, cells differentiated into outer layer (*VB*) and inner layer (*Ret*), with mass of interstitial cells (*a*) at base; *C,* single group of retinula cells of young pupa, rhabdom not yet formed, small amount of pigment (*Pg*) present; *D,* retinula of two cells at later stage, with rhabdom (*Rhb*); E, four retinula cell groups connected with one nerve; *F,* transverse section of left lateral ocellus of old pupa, cuticula thickened to form lens (*Ln*), vitreous body (*VB*) and retina (*Ret*) well differentiated, hypodermis around vitreous body thickened to form iris (*Ir*); *G,* longitudinal section of median ocellus of adult, lens (*Ln*) greatly thickened, surrounded by iris (*Ir*), vitreous body (*VB*) reduced to flat layer of cells separating lens from retina (*Ret*).

As was stated earlier, it is probable that only the rays of light which strike the lens perpendicularly can reach the sensory cells. The image is probably not a distinct one. If an object in motion is within the range of vision of the bee, the image is transferred rapidly from one set of ommatidia to another, which probably accounts for the fact that bees perceive objects in motion more readily than they do still ones.

In addition to the compound eyes, there are three simple eyes or ocelli, probably derived from the same primitive organ as the individual parts of the compound eyes. The structure of the ocellus[1] is shown in Fig. 89. The part played by the ocelli in the bee's vision is not clear, but from the study of the angles of refraction it has been inferred that the ocelli are for perceiving near-by objects, while the compound eyes are far-sighted.

Aside from the structure of the two kinds of eyes and speculation as to their function, the greatest interest arises from the nature of the vision of the bees. Many observers have shown that bees perceive not only form but also color. It is frequently asserted that bees do not perceive red light, but this is an error, for under conditions of abnormal stimulation from an accumulation of feces in the winter cellar, bees respond to red light to a marked degree. It appears that the vision also extends into the ultra-violet range of colors, which are invisible to man but which are given off by various flowers. The variation in the visibility of colors appears not to be the same as that of a normal man, and the preferences for various colors appear to be well defined.

It seems certain that bees do not perceive objects distinctly and their vision is clearly far less acute than that of wasps and some other insects. When it is recalled that hairs cover many facets of the compound eyes, especially in younger bees, and that the structure of the eyes does not suggest a high degree of efficiency in vision, it is a wonder that bees are aided by vision as much as appears to be the case. Space will not permit a full discussion of the

[1] Redikorzew, W., 1900. Untersuchungen über dan Bau den Ocellen der Insekten. Zeit. f. Wiss. Zool., LXVIII, pp. 581-264, 7 figs., 2 pl.

important work of von Frisch[1] which must be consulted by every student of light responses in honeybees. He concluded that bees distinguish both form and color. Other unpublished work in this field has been done by Lineburg and by Bertholf. The effects of light on movements of bees has been studied by Minnich.[2] In summing up a discussion of vision in bees, Snodgrass says: "It is truly discouraging, however, that we must still be so ignorant about the perceptive powers of insects, considering the amount of experimenting that has been done on the subject. If we could only be insects for a short time we should know a great deal more about them than we probably ever shall know otherwise."

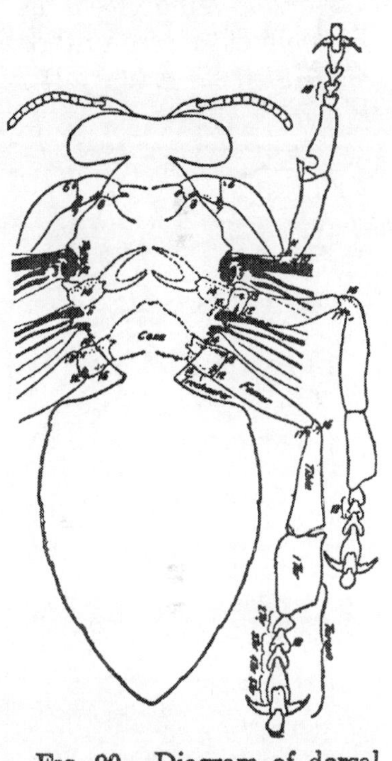

Fig. 90.—Diagram of dorsal view of worker, showing location of groups of olfactory pores.

Smell

Bees possess an acute sense comparable with the sense of smell in man, by means of which they perceive stimuli coming to them through the air, but the exact location of the olfactory organs is still a matter of dispute. McIndoo[3] has performed a service in

[1] von Frisch, Karl, 1914. Der Farbensinn und Formensinn der Biene. Zool. Jahrbücher, XXXV, pp. 1-118, 12 figs, 5 pl.

[2] Minnich, Dwight E., 1919. The photic reactions of the honeybee, *Apis mellifera* L. Journ. Exp. Zool., XXIX, no. 3, pp. 343-425, 17 figs.

[3] McIndoo, N. E., 1914. The olfactory sense of insects. Smithsonian Misc. Col., LXIII, no. 9, 63 pp.

McIndoo, N. E., 1914. The olfactory sense of the honeybee. Journ. Exp. Zool., XVI, pp. 265-346.

McIndoo, N. E., 1914. The olfactory sense of Hymenoptera. Proc. Acad. Nat. Sci., Phila., LXVI, pp. 294-341.

collecting the literature on the olfactory sense of insects and shows that this has been supposed to occur in all parts of the body. Until the work of this author, it was generally believed that the organs of this sense are located on the antennæ, but he claims that if the antennæ are removed the insect still responds to odor stimuli. He concludes that certain sense organs located on the bases of the legs and wings and on the sting of females are actually olfactory pores. The location of these organs is indicated on the diagrams from McIndoo's paper (Figs. 90 and 91), the organs being indicated by black areas and the different groups numbered. The structure of a typical olfactory pore is shown in Fig. 92. From the sense cell (*SC*), a nerve fiber (*SF*) extends to the surface of the body through the pore aperture (*PorAp*), this aperture being within a flask (*PorW*) which lies in the chitinous body wall. According to McIndoo, these organs have protoplasm exposed to the outer air, which if true is most unusual in insects. Similar organs have been found by the same writer in several orders of insects.

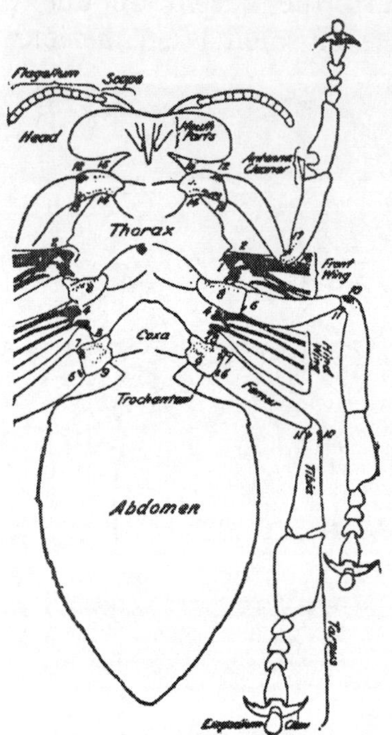

Fig. 91.—Diagram of ventral view of worker, showing location of groups of olfactory pores.

Whatever may be the ultimate decision as to the location of the olfactory organs, there is still difficulty in deciding what part odors play in the behavior of bees, although it is generally conceded that they have an acute sense of smell and that it is highly important in their behavior and especially in colony organization. Bees are attracted by the odor of honey and probably by nectar, although the finding of floral sources is not simply a response to odor. There is good reason to believe that recognition of hive-mates and enemies and the behavior toward the queen are due to responses to odors. Man's sense of smell is so inefficient that it is difficult to comprehend the responses of an insect in which this sense plays so large a part.

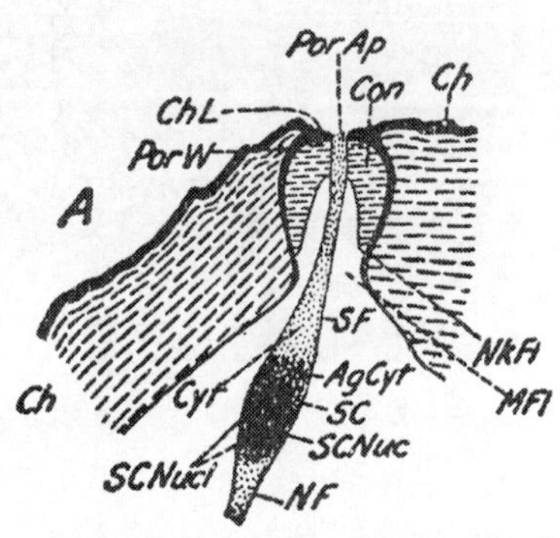

FIG. 92. — Cross-section of typical olfactory pore: *SC*, sense cell; *SF*, sense fiber; *PorAp*, pore aperture.

von Buttel-Reepen [1] from his wide experience with bees concludes that there are seven normal odors in a colony which influence the behavior. These are: (1) an individual odor, (2) an odor common to the offspring of one queen, (3) brood and larval-food odor, (4) drone odor, (5) wax odor, (6) honey odor, (7) hive odor, which is a combination of all or part of the other odors. McIndoo claims to be able to perceive some of these himself, and he adds other odors as follows: queen odor, odor emitted by guards and by fanners, odor emitted by pollen-carriers and the odor of the bee-sting poison.

On the dorsal side of the abdomen of the workers and queen on the articular membrane between the sixth and seventh terga (counting the propodium) is a transverse area which is the external portion of a scent-producing organ. This organ was described by Nassenoff,[2] later by

[1] von Buttel-Reepen, H., 1900. Sind die Bienen Reflex-Maschinen? Biol. Centralbl., XX; reprinted, Leipzig: Georgi. Eng. trans. by Mary H. Geisler, Medina, O.: A. I. Root Co. (Are bees reflex machines?), 48 pp.

[2] Nassenoff, see Zoubareff, A., 1883. A propos d'un organe de l'abeille non encore decrit. Bul. d'apic. suisse rom., V, pp. 215-216. Trans. Brit. Bee Journ., No. 136. Nassenoff's paper is in Russian.

Sladen[1] and more recently McIndoo[2] has described the structure of the glands on the interior as well as the external structure. This organ may perhaps be considered as the source of the individual odor of the females (Fig. 93).

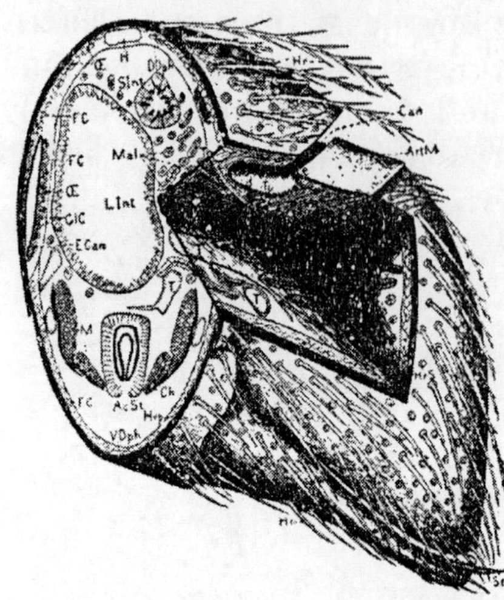

Fig. 93.—Diagram of a transverse-longitudinal view of end of abdomen of a worker honeybee, showing the internal anatomy of the fifth and sixth segments, and also the scent-producing organ composed of the articular membrane (*ArtM*), the canal (*Can*), chitinous tubes (*Tu*) and gland cells (*GlC*). The last segment is bent downward more than ever seen in the living bee. That is, in the living bee only the part marked *ArtM* is seen externally and the canal (*Can*) is never seen (After McIndoo).

If the queen is removed from a colony and a strange queen is placed among the bees in a cage, after a day or so she has acquired the hive odor and will be accepted if released. If a strange bee attempts to enter a hive, it is usually recognized at once and repelled, this being considered as due to the possession of a different hive odor, but if a field bee returns to its own hive, it is admitted, because it has the hive odor. These responses may vary according to the honey-flow and other environmental factors. In these cases and many others, there is evidence of the importance of responses to odors in the behavior of bees, so that there is justification for believing that the sense of smell is of pri-

[1] Sladen, F. W. L., 1901. A scent-producing organ in the abdomen of the bee. Gleanings in Bee Culture, XXIX, pp. 639-640; also in Ent. Month. Mag., XXXVIII, pp. 208-211.

[2] McIndoo, N. E., 1914. The scent-producing organ of the honeybee. Proc. Acad. Nat. Sci., Phila., LXVI, pp. 542-555.

mary importance. It must be admitted that the belief in this importance is based chiefly on the accumulated experiences of beekeepers rather than on careful experiments, which are sorely needed in an examination of these data in order to eliminate complicating environmental factors. Additional evidences of odor influences are given in the discussion of swarming.

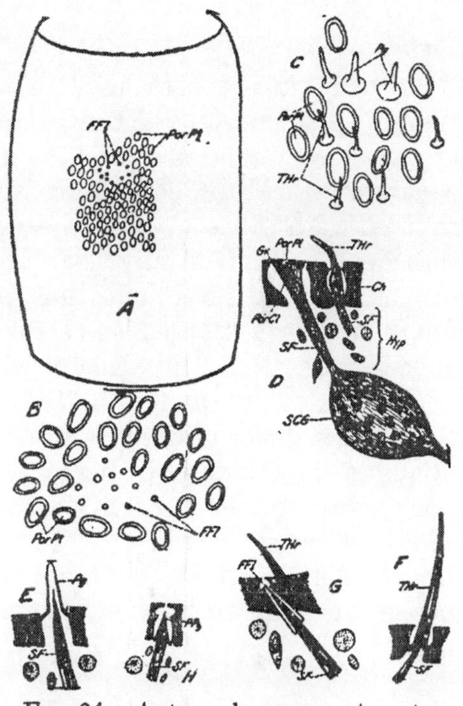

Fig. 94.—Antennal organs: *A*, antennal joint of drone, showing a few pore plates (*PorPl*) and a group of Forel's flasks (*FFl*); *B*, pore plates and Forel's flasks from drone's antenna; *C*, pore plates (*PorPl*), pegs (*Pg*) and tactile hairs (*THr*) from worker's antenna; *D*, structure of pore plate and tactile hair; *E*, structure of peg; *F*, structure of tactile hair; *G*, structure of Forel's flask; *H*, structure of pit peg.

Antennal sense organs

Before the work on the olfactory pores, just described, it was supposed that some of the sense organs on the antennæ are olfactory. Just which of the organs served in this way was not easy to decide. That these are sense organs can scarcely be doubted, but in view of the possible elimination of organs of smell from the antennæ of bees, the only course at present is to describe these organs and leave their function to be decided by later experimental work. Fig. 94 shows the distribution and structure of these organs. These are known as (1) pore plates, (2) pegs, (3) Forel's flasks, (4) pit pegs and (5) tactile hairs. In all the sensory cells are covered with chitin.

Taste

To what extent bees have this sense has not been made clear. In human experience, the senses of taste and smell are so closely related that it is difficult to determine them separately. McIndoo[1] finds that the mouth-parts are covered with sense organs of several types but their structure does not reveal any that are beyond doubt gustatory organs. While he found that bees discriminate between foods in such a manner as to suggest that they taste them, he concludes that the olfactory sense serves for gustatory perception as well as for that of olfaction. It is well known that bees show a preference in collecting nectars, since they abandon honey-dew if nectar is available and stronger honeys for milder types, but such responses may well be solely olfactory in nature. The sense of smell was at one time believed to be confined to the epipharynx chiefly because this organ is about the mouth, but this is no longer accepted.

Touch

This sense is probably well developed, and it is safe to assume that some of the antennal sense organs function in this way. The use of the antennæ by the bees suggests this. Bees are remarkably sensitive to jars and respond promptly when touched on various parts of the body. Most of the hairs which cover the body are not sensory, however.

Hearing

It is usually believed that bees can hear and many evidences of responses to sound have been described in the

[1] McIndoo, N. E., 1916. The sense organs on the mouth parts of the honeybee. Smithsonian Misc. Col., LXV, no. 14, 55 pp., 10 figs.

literature, yet it is still questionable whether they respond to sound waves. In experimenting on this subject, it is of course necessary that vibrations through solids be eliminated and that the stimulus come to the bee only through vibrations of the air. The general belief of a sense of hearing is based on the fact that bees make noises which are interpreted as purposeful. The following facts about bees lend support to this belief: Queenlessness in a colony is soon detected by the bees and they emit sounds which are interpreted as laments. If now a queen is inserted in a cage, the agitation soon ceases and the "contented hum" of the colony is renewed. The noise of swarming bees is supposed to hold the flying swarm together and the noise made by bees after finding a hive is supposed to guide them. Queens make at least two sounds, "teeting" and "quakking," and when a queen is frightened she emits a peculiar sound which is supposed to frighten the worker-bees. Of course active bees make sounds at all times.

The fact that bees make sounds is not proof that they hear and most of the statements supporting such a view may as readily be interpreted as evidences of a sense of smell: in fact, odors are known to be the dominant factor in swarming, in locating the hive and in queen recognition. von Buttel-Reepen's statement that "only a dead bee is quiet" may be answered by the statement that deaf people are often quite noisy. There is then no actual evidence of a perception of sound waves, although the experimental work so far is scarcely adequate to disprove the existence of such a sense.

Attempts to locate organs of hearing have been equally unsatisfactory. McIndoo[1] has studied this question and concludes that the pore plates, Forel's flasks, pit pegs and Johnston's organ on the antennæ do not seem to be well

[1] McIndoo, N. E., 1922. The auditory sense of the honeybee. Journ. Comp. Neurology, XXXIV, no. 2, pp. 173-199, 26 figs.

fitted anatomically to act as sound receptors. The chordotonal organs, described by Janet[1] on the proximal ends of the tibiæ are similar in structure to organs found in similar locations in crickets and katydids but have no external membranes. These seem to fill the requirements of an organ of hearing better than any others that have been discovered but their actual function is wholly unknown. One may conclude that if bees hear at all this sense is probably very poorly developed, and the evidence in support of acute hearing is without exception capable of being explained otherwise.

Temperature sense

In the discussion of the activities of bees in winter (p. 365), it is stated that at about 57° F. the bees form a cluster and, if the outer temperature drops below that point, they begin to generate heat. When no cluster is formed the bees are more active at temperatures above 69° F. than below this. In a discussion of the temperature of the hive at other seasons (p. 69), it is shown that while occupied by the bees it rarely exceeds 95° F. and that during brood-rearing the temperature of the brood-chamber is quite constant. This brief summary indicates that in some manner bees perceive changes in temperature and it may almost be believed that they have a temperature sense superior to man. The nerve endings or sense organs which function in this response to temperature stimuli are not determined and perhaps this is a function of some of the problematical organs on the antennæ.

Finding of the flowers

In a previous chapter (p. 128), a discussion is given of

[1] Janet, Ch., 1911. Sur l'existence d'un organe chordotonal et d'une vésicule pulsatile antennaires chez l'abeille et sur la morphologie de la tête de cette espèce. L'Apiculteur, LV, no. 5, pp. 181-183.

the division of labor whereby bees are seemingly able to apportion the available forage to prevent duplication. In this connection the interesting question arises as to how the bees find the flowers. Considerable detailed and painstaking work has been done on this subject. Plateau [1] and his followers, on the one hand, believe that bees are guided to the nectar by odor, this being supported by experimental evidence as well as by an array of facts concerning the gathering of nectar from inconspicuous flowers. Forel [2] and other writers assert, on the contrary, that color is the important stimulus and that flowers are found through the sense of sight. Plateau's work is open to one important criticism, since he overlooks the possibility of the return of bees to his mutilated flowers through memory. Burton N. Gates, several years ago, showed that bees visit artificial flowers and also fly to natural flowers which have been sealed in glass tubes. The reaction to these unusual objects was entirely normal. These results point strongly to the belief that odor is of minor importance in the location of nectar-secreting plants. That bees differentiate between flowers which are encountered in their flights is shown by the fact that they usually visit but one species on a trip (p. 127).

[1] Plateau, Felix, 1895-97. Comment les fleurs attirent les insects. Bul. Acad. Roy. d. Belgique, 3 sér., XXX, n. 11, XXXII, n. 11, XXXIII, n. 1, XXXIV, n. 9, 10, 11. See also Plateau, 1888. Recherches expérimentales sur la vision chez les arthropodes. *Ibid.*, part. 3-5 and other papers.

[2] Forel, Auguste, 1886-88. Recueil zoologiques Suisse, 1 sér., IV. Forel, Auguste, 1908. The senses of insects. Eng. trans. Yearsley. London: Methuen and Co., 324 pp.

See also: Andreae, Eug., 1903. Inwiefern werden Insekten durch Fabre und Duft der Blumen angezogen. Beihefte z. Bot. Centralbl., XV.

Giltay, E., 1901. Ueber die Bedeutung der Krone bei den Blüten und über das Farbenunterscheidungs vermögen der Insekten, I. Pringh. Jahrb. f. Wiss. Bot., XL.

Detto, Carl, 1905. Blutenbiologische Untersuchungen I u. II. Flora odor Allg. Bot. Zeit., XCIV.

Kienitz-Gerloff, 1898 u. 1903. Professor Plateau und die Blumentheorie I u. II. Biol. Centralbl., XVIII u. XXIII.

Finding of the hive

It is well known that bees normally return to the right hive. The fact that strange bees are not usually admitted may be explained on the basis of difference in colony odors but this does not explain the method by which they find the proper hive in most cases. Bethe [1] asserts that the bees are led back to the hive by an "unknown force" but, as von Buttel-Reepen points out in his discussion of memory of place in bees, this explanation is not satisfactory, and cannot be accepted until the known forces are eliminated. It will be recalled (p. 115) that young bees take "play flights" on warm days. If bees which have not had such flights are taken out a few feet from the hive, they fail to return. Bees that have had some experience on the wing are able to return from short distances, and, finally, old bees are often able to return if taken away two miles or more. They evidently increase in efficiency with experience. It is also known that if the hive is moved a foot or more in any direction the returning bees seek the entrance to the hive in the old place. If the hive has been moved only a short distance they may soon find it by searching, but if it is moved several feet they may fail to discover it.

If bees were attracted to the hive by odor, the field bees would probably have no difficulty in finding it if it were moved perhaps a mile. Under such circumstances a short distance would make no appreciable difference and yet the moving of the hive a foot often delays their entering it. Odor is, therefore, evidently not the guiding sense.

Bees in the field cannot always see their hive, and, in all probability, they can see neither far nor distinctly. If sight is their guide, they must remember various objects over or about which they fly as they go out and must return by known paths. This is actually the case. If bees are accus-

[1] Bethe, A., 1898. Dürfen wir Ameisen und Bienen psychische Qualitäten zuschreiben? Arch. f. d. ges. Phys., LXX, also as separate, 1898. Bonn: Emil Strauss, with different paging.

tomed to fly in only one direction to the forage and are carried off a short distance into unknown environment, they fail to return. It is evident that bees are guided back to their hives by a memory of the objects encountered, as perceived by sight. If a hive is moved, they then follow over the accustomed paths to the old location of the entrance, but having no experience over the road from the old location to the new one, they fail to make the trip unless they accidentally encounter the hive. No "unknown force" need be called in here to explain the phenomena. Evidently the play flights and the early trips to the field are the times during which bees acquire knowledge of their surroundings. If a colony is moved several miles, the bees must orient themselves anew, and in order that they may perceive the change and "recognize" the necessity for re-orientation, the beekeeper often places brush or grass about the entrance so that the change may be perceived when they first fly out.

That sight is the important sense in the location of the hive is appreciated by beekeepers who have learned that irregularities in the rows of hives, landmarks of trees or shrubs in the apiary or differences in color of the hives are beneficial in enabling the bees to find their hives quickly. These customs are well founded on the behavior of bees.

Memory

It would appear from the preceding discussion that bees are not entirely bundles of reflexes but that they actually have memory. The finding of the hive is good evidence of this fact and it is also asserted (von Buttel-Reepen) that they remember the location of the feeder in the hive and that scouting bees remember the paths to the locations chosen by them.

The best evidence of memory is found in the fact that memory is sometimes lost. If bees are stupefied by tobacco smoke, by the smoke of the puff ball (an old practice) or by some anesthetic, they are unable to return to their old location and must re-orient themselves after they revive. When bees swarm they usually do not again return to the location of the old hive (except when hived on the old stand by the beekeeper) and may be placed safely in a new location perhaps only a few feet from the old hive. The memory of the old location is not lost immediately, however, for if within a day or two the bees desert the new quarters they often return to the old hive. Here the old memories are, as it were, reserved, but they are lost in a short time. Similarly in artificial swarms, after drumming or certain manipulations in which the colony becomes "demoralized," the memory of the location is lost, either permanently or temporarily. If bees are confined for a few days they may be placed in any location and bees wintered in a cellar no longer remember their former situations. The loss of memory in these cases is not due to the formation of new associations. Bees obviously cannot lose what they do not possess and, if it is granted that memory is sometimes lost, the only conclusion is that they possess memory.

Bees show in other responses an adaptability which cannot be explained on the basis that they are merely reflex machines. They become accustomed to light within the hive which at first causes them to worry on the glass sides and in other ways show responses which are of a higher order than mechanical reactions.

Nature of bee activities

In the introduction to Chapter III, it was stated that bees are essentially creatures of instinct. While in the intervening discussions there are given evidences of the possession of memory, of limited powers of learning and association and of certain adaptations of the reactions of bees to circumstances, it should be clear that in the bee one has to do, not with human intellects and poetic passions, but with animals whose behavior is chiefly guided by mental capacities imprisoned in the chains of instinct, with animals most of whose activities are justly described as machine-like. If this discussion of the nervous responses of bees has destroyed some of the poetry of the hive, this can scarcely be considered as a serious loss, for it is not by such fancies that one can come to know the truth.

CHAPTER VIII

THE REPRODUCTIVE PROCESSES AND PARTHENOGENESIS

THE organs of reproduction are those which produce the cells from which individuals of the next generation develop and they also include the accompanying organs which serve to permit the proper disposition of the sex-cells. The continuance of the species is the function of these organs. In the larger number of species, new individuals arise from eggs which have been fertilized by sex-cells of the male of the same species. In the honeybee, certain peculiar phenomena play an important part in practical apiary manipulations. The development of the drones or males from unfertilized eggs must be considered, especially by the queen breeder.

ORIGIN OF THE EGGS

The eggs from which all the members of the colony develop are normally laid by the queen. In this individual, the only female in the colony whose reproductive organs are fully developed, the ovaries are large and, in fact, she is to a considerable extent simply an egg-producing machine. The ovaries of the queen (Fig. 95) consist of two groups (*Ov*) of egg-tubes or ovarioles (*ov*). These tubes are small at the anterior end where the eggs are beginning their growth and toward the posterior end the individual tubes, as well as the total mass, increase in diameter. At the posterior end, the tubules in each mass open into the anterior end of an oviduct (*OvD*). The oviducts from the two ovaries unite farther back into a common tube or duct, the vagina (*Vag*), which opens to the outside below the base of the sting. The posterior portion of the vagina is enlarged, forming the bursa copulatrix (*BCpx*).

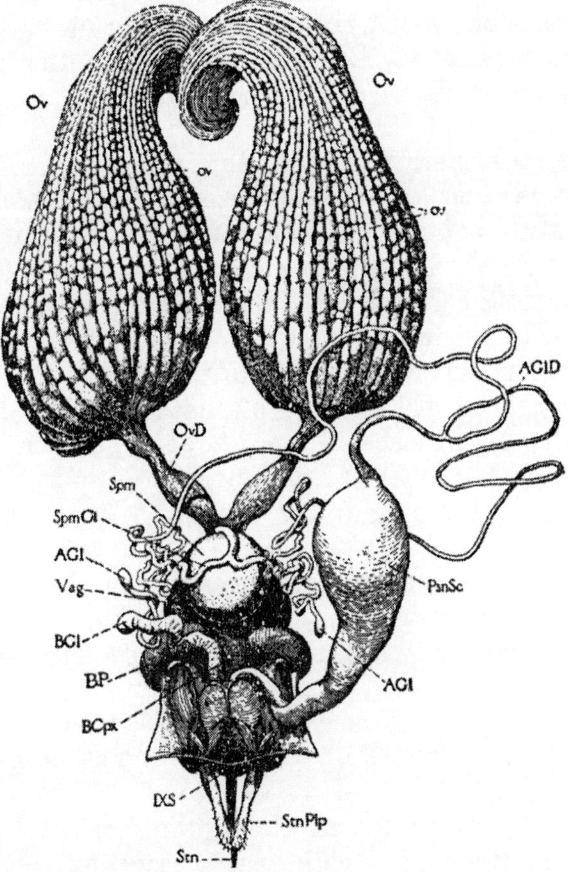

Fig. 95.—Reproductive organs, sting, and poison glands of the queen, dorsal view.

Opening from the vagina is the spermatheca (*Spm*), a saclike organ which serves to receive the male sex-cells, the spermatozoa, from the drone at the time of mating and to retain them until they are needed. Attached to this are two accessory glands (*SpmGl*) the duct of which opens into the duct from the spermatheca to the vagina. The duct from the spermatheca is S-shaped and is surrounded by muscles forming the "sperm-pump" of Breslau.[1] By the contraction of some of these muscles, the lumen of the upper end of the loop is enlarged and a small bundle of spermatozoa is

[1] Breslau, Ernst, 1905-06. Die Samenblasengang der Bienenkönigin. Zool. Anz., XXIX, pp. 229-323.

taken from the spermatheca. By the contraction of other muscles, the spermatozoa are forced on to the vagina. Cheshire[1] described this apparatus incorrectly by assuming that the muscles around the duct are sphincter muscles to hold back motile spermatozoa. The spermatozoa, according to Breslau, are not motile and no retaining muscle is needed. In copulation the spermatozoa are deposited by the drone in the vagina and must find their way to the spermatozoa by this same duct. There is no special receiving duct as described by Cheshire. The spermatheca is not composed of muscle layers, as formerly supposed.

Cheshire estimates that a normal vigorous queen may during her lifetime lay 1,500,000 eggs. Since mating occurs usually but once, those eggs which are fertilized must receive spermatozoa from the supply stored up in the spermatheca at the time of mating. Since at each expulsion of spermatozoa a considerable number pass out and all but one are wasted, it is necessary that an enormous number be stored originally. Cheshire estimates the number at 4,000,000 but it is enough to know that millions are then stored. The marvelous feature of the phenomenon is that these minute cells are able to live for perhaps five years away from the animal in which they were formed (the drone) and at the same time are so highly specialized that they can take no nourishment. There is no multiplication of spermatozoa in the queen as has been hypothecated by various beekeepers.

The formation of the eggs has been studied by Paulcke[2] and Hegner.[3] In the early stages of the formation of the egg at the anterior end of the ovarian tubes, the future egg-

[1] Cheshire, F. R., 1885. The apparatus for differentiating the sexes in bees and wasps. Journ. Roy. Micr. Soc., ser. 2, V, pp. 1-15.

[2] Paulcke, W., 1900. Ueber die Differenzirung der Zellelemente im Ovarium der Bienenkönigin (*Apis mellifica*). Zool. Jahrb. Anat. u. Ontog., XIV, pp. 177-202.

[3] Hegner, R. W., 1915. Studies on germ cells. IV. Protoplasmic differentiation on the oocytes of certain Hymenoptera. Journ. Morph., XXVI, no. 3, pp. 495-561.

nucleus is surrounded by other nuclei which later form nurse-cells. There is at first no visible differentiation, no cell boundaries being seen, but farther down the tube the nuclei are surrounded by cell-walls. Gradually the future egg-cells begin to enlarge and the individual egg-cells are separated by a number of nurse-cells, forty-eight to each egg, according to Paulcke. The egg-cell increases in size chiefly by an accumulation of yolk which serves as food for the future embryo, this yolk being supplied by the nurse-cells, which finally are exhausted and absorbed into the yolk of the egg. The egg- and nurse-cells are surrounded by an epithelium which grows thinner as the egg enlarges and which finally breaks when the egg passes into the oviduct.

The egg is covered by a thin layer of chorion secreted around it by the epithelial cells and the boundaries of the cells may be seen in the lines which persist on the chorion, forming a delicate network on the surface. At the anterior end of the egg (where the head of the larvæ is formed and also toward the head of the queen) there is a peculiar arrangement of these lines, forming the micropyle. Here the spermatozoon which fertilizes the egg enters, but the mechanism has not been adequately described. In most insects there is a definite opening for the entrance of the spermatozoon and often a complex mechanism for the closing of the opening after fertilization. There is nothing so described for the bee egg.

ORIGIN OF THE MALE SEX-CELLS

The organs of the male (Fig. 96) in which the male sex-cells originate are equally interesting. The spermatozoa develop in the testes (*Tes*), two organs homologous with the ovaries of the queen. The development of the spermatozoa probably occurs almost entirely during the pupal stage of the drone and possibly not at all in the adult. From the testes, the spermatozoa pass through the vas deferens (*VDef*) into the vesicula semenalis (*Ves*) where

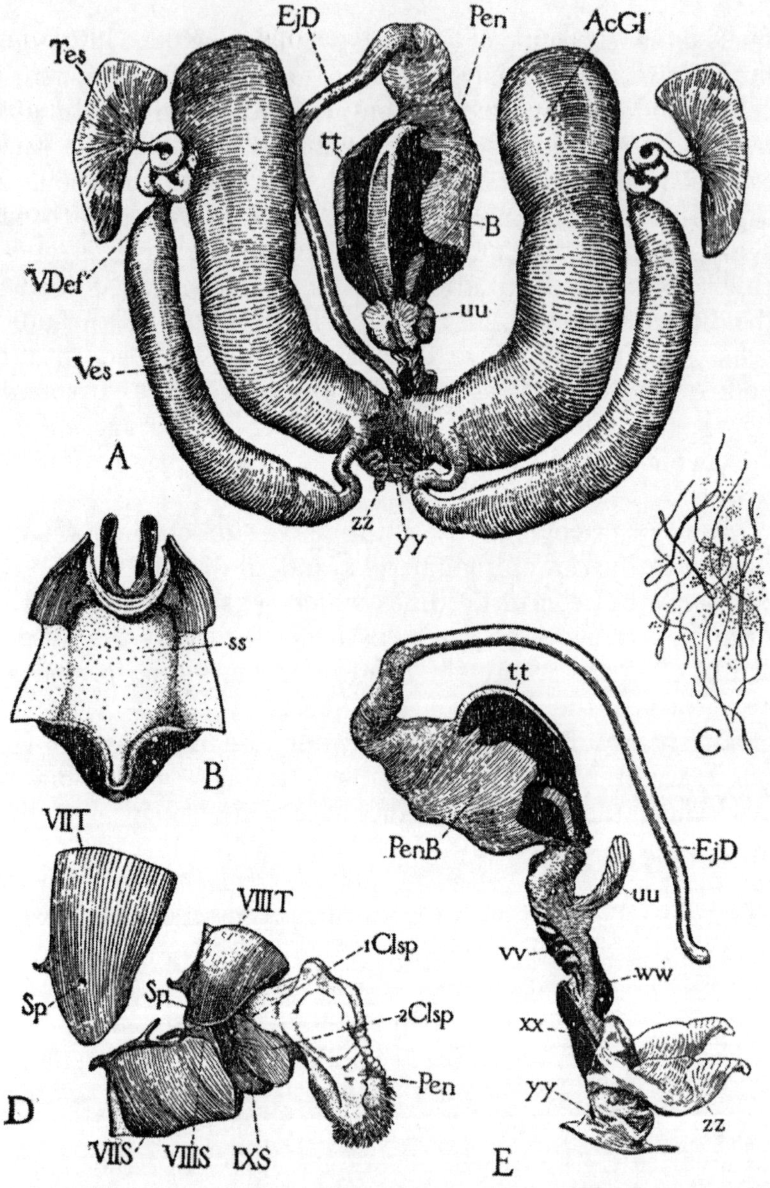

FIG. 96.—*A*, reproductive organs of drone, dorsal view, natural position, *B*, inner surface of dorsal wall of bulb of penis; *C*, group of spermatozoa and intermixed granules; *D*, terminal segments of drone abdomen with penis partly protruded; *E*, lateral view of penis as invaginated within abdomen.

they collect. The seminal vesicles open into the base of the accessory mucous gland (*AcGl*). These in turn open into a single duct, the ejaculatory duct (*EjD*), unusually large in the drone and curiously indented to conform to the structure of the vagina.

At the time of copulation, the penis, which is previously folded within the abdomen of the drone, is everted and projects into the vagina of the queen. The spermatozoa then pass through the ejaculatory duct as do presumably also the contents of the accessory mucous glands. The formation of the spermatozoa has been studied by Meves,[1] by Mark and Copeland,[2] and by Doncaster.[3]

The sudden expulsion of the penis causes the immediate death of the drone. The structure of the penis may be readily seen by gently squeezing the abdomen of a drone, by which means it is everted. In this case also the drone dies immediately so that his death at the time of mating should not be attributed to any action of the queen. As has been previously stated (p. 49), mating occurs in the air outside the hive.

PARTHENOGENSIS

The chief reason why the reproductive processes require extended discussion in a book on practical beekeeping is because of the development of the drones or males from unfertilized eggs. In most species, the sex-cells disintegrate unless they unite with the products of the opposite sex of the same species, but there are numerous instances in the

[1] Meves, Fr., 1903. Ueber Richtungskorperbildung im Hoden von Hymenopteren. Anat. Anz., XXIV, pp. 29-32.
—— 1907. Die Spermatocytenteilungen bei der Honigbiene (*Apis mellifica* L.) nebst Bemerkungen über Chromatinreduction. Arch. f. Microsk. Anat. u. Entwick., LXX, pp. 414-491.

[2] Mark, E. L. and Copeland, Manton, 1907. Some stages in the spermatogenesis of the honeybee. Proc. Amer. Acad. Arts and Sci., XLII, pp. 103-111.

[3] Doncaster, L., 1906. Spermatogenesis of the hive bee, *Apis mellifica*. Anat. Anz. XXIX.
Doncaster, L., 1907. Spermatogenesis of the honeybee. *Ibid.*, XXXI.

animal kingdom in which egg-cells are produced, which, without fertilization, are able to develop into normal adults. To this phenomenon the name parthenogenesis[1] is given.

In 1745, Bonnet described the parthenogenetic development of plant-lice and just one hundred years later Dzierzon announced his theory that the drone is likewise a product of an unfertilized egg. This later paper, published in the Eichstädt Bienenzeitung, was the beginning of a long and heated discussion in which the leading zoologists of the day took part. Briefly his theory was as follows: (1) the queen is able "at pleasure" to lay either worker or drone eggs, the drone eggs being deposited just as they leave the ovary;[2] (2) all eggs in the ovary would normally develop into males and if fertilization occurs the sex is changed to female. It is well to divide Dzierzon's theory into these two parts for they are not equally capable of proof.

The facts observed in the apiary on which this belief is based are as follows: (1) If a queen is unable to fly out to mate or is prevented from mating in some other way she usually dies (p. 79) but if she does lay eggs, as she may, after three or four weeks, the eggs which develop are all males; (2) if when a queen becomes old her supply of spermatozoa is exhausted, all her offspring are males; (3) if a colony becomes queenless and remains so for a time, some of the workers may begin egg-laying and in this case also only males develop. The author has found that many eggs laid by drone-laying queens fail to hatch and, in fact, are often removed in a short time by the workers. This makes it impossible to accept Dzierzon's statement that all eggs laid by such a queen become males and the statement

[1] For a more extended discussion, see Phillips, E. F., 1903. A review of parthenogenesis. Proc. Amer. Philos. Soc., XLII, No. 174, pp. 275-345.

[2] Onions (1912, South African fertile-worker bees. Agricultural Journal of the Union of S. Afr., May) claims that in South African bees females are also produced parthenogenetically. The claim is supported by considerable evidence. See also Van Warmelo, D. S., *ibid.*, 1913, who denies this statement.

must be modified as follows: all of those eggs laid by a drone-laying queen which develop become males. The potentialities of the eggs which never hatch are not known. In addition to the facts here stated, the theory of the parthenogenetic development of the drone is supported by investigations of the phenomena of development in the egg.

SEX DETERMINATION

The determination of sex is one of the most earnestly debated questions in zoology, but recent work has thrown a flood of light into a previously dark field. Numerous theories have been proposed, most of which are not now seriously considered. From the observations of Dzierzon and others it was concluded that sex in bees and similar forms (ants and wasps) is determined by the presence or absence of fertilization of the egg. These species appeared to be an exception to the phenomena observed in other species, especially those in which all eggs are fertilized. It is now generally accepted that sex is inherited in accordance with the same laws which govern other phenomena of inheritance. It is of course impossible to record here or even to outline the observations which lead to this theory or even to elaborate the theory. It is now held that one of the chromosomes (the assumed bearers of hereditary characters within the nuclei of the sex-cells) of the sex-cells bears a sex-determining character. Substantiation of this fact for honeybees has been given by various investigators.

While, therefore, it appears that fertilization of the egg as such is not the determining fact in sex determination in honeybees, nevertheless when fertilization occurs, the necessary sex-determining character enters and thus the egg develops into a female, which to all practical purposes is the same as saying that fertilization determines that the egg shall become a female. The determining factor is the sex chromosome rather than the act of egg fertilization.

In view of the fact that drone eggs are usually deposited in the larger cells, the theory has been advanced that the pressure on the abdomen of the queen when she is about to lay an egg in a worker-cell, by some reflex, causes the spermatheca to open, thereby enabling the egg to be fertilized. This is known among American beekeepers as the Wagner theory. Since fertilized eggs may be laid in comb-foundation when the side walls are only started and since drone eggs are often laid in worker-cells, this simple explanation cannot be accepted.

From the various phenomena observed in connection with parthenogenetic development, it appears that fertilization of the egg serves two purposes; it brings to the egg the hereditary characters of the male parent and also stimulates the egg-cell to develop by cell division. If development can occur without this stimulation, the resulting individual contains the hereditary characters from one parent only. It should perhaps be mentioned that in plant-lice both males and females sometimes develop from unfertilized eggs while in certain Lepidoptera only females come from unfertilized eggs. The male sex is not a necessary result of parthenogenetic development.

The theory that drones develop from unfertilized eggs has not been accepted without protest. From the beginning, it has been assailed by the publication of evidence and arguments which were supposed to contradict the theory. In the author's paper, to which reference has been made, the various contrary views are outlined and the interested reader is referred to this paper for references to the literature on the subject up to the date of publication (1903). Of recent critics, none is so insistent as Dickel, a German beekeeper, who claims that fertile queens cannot lay unfertilized eggs and that sex is determined by secretions of the nurse-bees. These fantastic theories with others of a similar character have been adequately overthrown by Dickel's critics and need not be discussed at length here.

Practical applications

The development of males from unfertilized eggs is a fact of importance in various phases of apiary work. If, for example, an Italian queen mates with a black drone, the workers and queen offspring are hybrids, while the drone or male offspring is pure Italian. This fact is important to the breeder, for drones from mismated queens are just as good for breeding purposes as those from purely mated queens. It is true that this has been denied by various writers, but the denial is based chiefly on variation in the color of the drones, it being overlooked that color is not a safe criterion for the purity of race of either queens or drones. Color is a much more stable characteristic in workers. The parthenogenetic development of drones must be considered in planning any breeding work with bees. In the selection of breeding material it does not necessarily follow because the workers of a colony have the quality desired that the drones will be best for breeding purposes, since the hereditary characters of the workers come from two parents while those of the drones come from only one of the two.

HERMAPHRODITE BEES

Many cases are recorded [1] of bees which show both male and female characters. These hermaphrodites or androgynous bees may have male characters on the head and female characters in the abdomen or they may be divided longitudinally in various combinations of characters. There is a mixture of male and female characters, varying in different individuals, in both external and internal organs. It is a peculiar fact, not easy of explanation, that when such cases occur there are often many in the same colony. Boveri [2] suggests that in such cases fertilization is delayed until after cell division has begun and that only part of the

[1] von Della Torre, K. W. u. Friese, H. 1899. Die hermaphroditen und gynandromorphen Hymenopteren. Berichte d. Natur.-Med. Ver. Innsbruck, XXIV.

[2] Boveri, Th., 1901. Ueber die Polaritat des Seeigel-eies. Verh. Ges. Wurzburg (N. S.), XXXIV, pp. 145-176.

cells receive the male chromosomes. While this theory would readily explain the great variation in such hermaphroditic bees, it is based on the assumption that sex is determined by fertilization, which may be questioned.

EGGS WHICH FAIL TO HATCH

In some cases, one of which came under the author's observation, queens are normally mated and lay eggs, but all the eggs fail to hatch. This is perhaps due to some abnormality of the queen, and in the case examined it appeared that the failure to hatch might have been due to the evaporation of the water in the protoplasm through the unusually thin and soft chorion of the eggs. Similar cases were described by Claus and von Siebold [1] and also by Leuckart.[2]

[1] Claus u. von Siebold, 1873. Ueber taube Bienen-eier. Zeit. f. Wiss. Zool., XXIII, pp. 198-210.

[2] Leuckart, R., 1875. Ueber taube u. abortive Bieneneier. Arch. Naturgesch., XL.

CHAPTER IX

RACES OF BEES

THE honeybee, so well known to beekeepers, has certain near relatives which are of interest, and it is quite probable that a careful study of the various phases in the behavior of these bees would throw considerable light on similar phenomena in the honeybee. The honeybee is usually considered as representing the apex of the evolution of the bees (Apidæ), in that the social organization is the most complex in this family of insects. The ants (Formicidæ) and wasps (Vespidæ) represent lines of parallel evolution in social life which has resulted in insect communities, comparable, but by no means identical, with that of the honeybee.

TYPES OF SOCIAL BEES

Among the Apidæ are three great types of social bees, the bumblebee (Bombus or Bremus), the stingless bees (Melipona and Trigona) and the honeybees (Apis). The simplest forms, the bumblebees, have smaller colonies which die out in the winter, leaving the species to be continued from fertilized queens which hibernate. The stingless bees are tropical insects which store their honey and pollen in spherical vessels and rear their brood in "combs," one cell in thickness. In the honeybee colony, the architecture is the most perfect and the honey and pollen are stored and the brood is reared in hexagonal cells, which combine to form a comb two cells in thickness. The bumblebees and stingless bees fill a cell with pollen and honey, the queen then deposits an egg on this mass and the larva is not further fed or cared for. On the other hand, the queen honeybee lays her eggs in empty cells and the larvæ are fed a specially prepared larval food at first in one quantity and later as they require. For a further discussion of the more primitive bees as well as of the probable evolution of the Apidæ, the reader is referred to the interesting paper of von Buttel-Reepen.[1]

SPECIES OF THE GENUS APIS

In the genus Apis there are other interesting honeybees but which have no special practical value. It is of interest to note first that specimens of Apis have been found in fossil form, preserved in amber. von Buttel-Reepen mentions *A. adamitica* and *A. meliponoides*, the latter transitional between Melipona and Apis. Among recent species of this genus are *A. dorsata,* the giant bee of India, with its varieties *zonata* and *testacea* of the Philippines and the Malay Peninsula, *A. florea,* a dwarf bee of India with several varieties, and finally *A. mellifica,* the honeybee with the numerous varieties to be discussed later. Unsuccessful efforts have been made to introduce the giant bees into Europe and America, among which may be mentioned the trips of Benton, 1880 and 1905, and Dathe, 1883. Dathe succeeded in getting living *dorsata* bees to Germany but the effort was fruitless. The last mentioned trip of Benton was at the expense of the United States Department of Agriculture. *A. dorsata* builds a single comb in the open air, usually suspended on the limb of a tree; there is no distinction between drone and worker cells and these bees do not take kindly to confinement in a hive.[2]

[1] von Buttel-Reepen, H., 1903. Die stammesgeschichtliche Entstehung des Bienenstaates sowie Beitrage zur Lebensweise der solitaren und sozialen Bienen (Hummeln, Meliponinen, etc.). Leipzig: Thieme.

[2] For further data concerning the various species of the genus Apis, consult the above mentioned paper by von Buttel-Reepen as well as the following:

Gerstacker, 1862. Ueber die geographische Verbreitung und die Abanderungen der Honigbiene nebst Bemerkungen über die auslandischen Honigibienen der alten Welt. Reprinted in von Buttel-

VARIETIES OF THE SPECIES MELLIFICA

In the classification of insects, differences in structure and color are the characters on which classification is usually made, but in the differentiation of the varieties of honeybees there are no constant differences in these characters to guide the student. The varieties are established by beekeepers because of recognized and well-marked differences in the behavior of the bees from various regions. They are, however, valid biological varieties. While there are color differences, these are of little value in attempting a classification. Since beekeepers usually refer to these divisions of the species as races, this term is here adopted. Roughly the races are divided into three groups, (1) the eastern, (2) the European and (3) the African races. Certain characteristics of these groups are valid but the grouping is somewhat artificial. The principal races are here discussed in the order suggested by this grouping, the names given the races being indicative of their origin. None of the races of the honeybee is native to America. The German bees were introduced early in the history of the country and are often designated native bees, but this is an error. After their introduction they multiplied rapidly and were soon found in the woods.

Egyptian

These bees are somewhat smaller than the races best known to American beekeepers, the abdomen is slender and pointed and the cells of the comb are also said to be somewhat smaller. The first three segments of the abdomen are light yellow to reddish-yellow with black border, being brighter than Italians. The abdomen is covered with grayish-white hairs. The abdomen of the queen is marked

Reepen's Apistica. Partial English translation by Dallas, Ann. and Mag. of Nat. History, 1863, III series, vol. II.

Koshewnikov, G. A., 1900-1905. [Material for the study of the genus Apis.] Russian.

Additional references are given in the von Buttel-Reepen papers.

with reddish-brown on the first segment and the color areas are variable. Queens and drones are small and the queens are prolific. These bees sting furiously and are not subdued by smoke. They do not, according to von Buttel-Reepen, form a winter-cluster and, therefore, cannot withstand cold weather. Drones are reared in large numbers; the cappings are "watery";[1] the queen-cells are small, very numerous, clustered and smooth. Fertile workers are abundant and are said to be present even when there is a laying queen. These bees were introduced into Germany in 1864 and to England and America in 1867. Here they attracted considerable attention but were promptly abandoned as worthless.

Syrian

There are two races of bees in Palestine, one of which is, according to von Buttel-Reepen, identical with the Egyptian. The other is known among American beekeepers as the Holy Land bees. The Syrians are larger than the Egyptians and in color they resemble Italians. These bees swarm excessively, build many queen-cells and winter poorly. Many virgin queens go with after-swarms and do not kill each other until one is mated. Young queens lay drone eggs in the first month. These bees were introduced into America in 1880 by Jones and Benton but were soon abandoned as valueless. They were introduced by Hopkins into New Zealand in 1883.

Cyprian

This bee has been given a thorough test by American beekeepers. It is somewhat smaller than the Italian and

[1] Some races of bees fill their honey cells more completely than others and when the honey is in contact with the capping it gives the honey an appearance that is described as watery. When the capping is separated from the honey by an air space the capping appears white (or yellow, depending on the color of the wax). In general the black races seem to produce whiter comb cappings than more yellow bees.

the abdomen is pointed, with three yellow bands, similar to that of Italians but somewhat lighter in color. The queens are small and very prolific. These bees winter well unless the colony wears itself out by breeding in winter. The workers are exceptionally cross, are not subdued by smoke and do not run on the combs. They build many queen-cells (less than Syrians). They were sent (unsuccessfully) to America by Gravenhorst in 1877 and first imported by Stahala in 1879; additional shipments were made by Jones and Benton in 1880. They have been widely advertised and tested but were abandoned because of their unmanageable qualities.

Grecian

These bees resemble a hybrid between Italians and Germans. So far as known they have not been shipped to America. They were sent to Germany in 1860 by von Roser.

Caucasian

These bees vary in color from three bands of yellow on the abdomen to black or gray according to the region from which they come. The ones introduced into America have shown virtually no yellow color, having come from the more northern parts of the Caucasus. The yellow examples are said to resemble Italians markedly. This is the most gentle race known, although they defend their hives well against robbers. They seldom enter the wrong hive, winter well, cap their honey-cells white and are, in the main, desirable bees. The hybrids are not gentle. They were first taken from their native country by Butlerov in 1877 and were shipped to Germany in 1879 to Vogel, who described them carefully. The first exportations were chiefly the yellow strains. In 1880 Julius Hoffman, Ft. Plains, New York, received two colonies of these bees but condemned them because they did not work on buckwheat! Later, Rauchfuss Brothers, Denver, Colorado, imported queens of this race and recommended them. Following this, additional queens were imported and American-bred queens were distributed by the United States Department of Agriculture several years ago.

The gentleness of this race is universally admitted, but Caucasians have some faults which have caused them to be abandoned by most beekeepers who have tried them. They use propolis most lavishly and in the autumn often build a wall at the entrance, leaving holes only large enough for single bees to pass (Fig. 97). They also build many burr and brace combs. The dark color makes it difficult to tell when the queens are purely mated and the dark queens are difficult to find on the combs. An additional factor which has led to the lack of interest in this race is the rapid spread of European foulbrood within recent years. This has virtually necessitated the use of Italian bees in many localities and has discouraged experimentation with other races. There are still several prominent American beekeepers who are enthusiastic in praise of the Caucasians.

FIG. 97.—Propolis at entrance, built by Caucasian bees. The entrance block on one side made a propolis wall unnecessary there.

Italian

This is the most popular race among the best American beekeepers. The bees of Italy vary considerably in color, those in the north being virtually identical with the German bees in color. The typical "three-banded" Italians are found farther south and in Sicily there is a still lighter strain. Some investigators believe Italians to be a cross between the German and Egyptian bees. Typically, the yellow color covers three segments of the abdomen, the head and thorax and posterior segments of the abdomen being black with some traces of yellow on the mandibles, and the hairs have a yellow cast. The legs are brown. Queens and drones are variable in color from solid black to the yellow found on workers. Italians are gentle (but not equal to Caucasians in this respect), less prolific than the eastern races but usually better than black bees, build few queen-cells, rarely develop fertile workers, keep the hive clean, drive out wax-moths, winter well, do not run on the combs, swarm less than Carniolans and some eastern races and cap their honey less white than Germans, Carniolans and Caucasians. The rearing of brood is quickly curtailed in a dearth of nectar and they cease rearing brood in the autumn sooner than most races. An important characteristic of Italians is the resistance to European foulbrood. In this respect, they have been compared chiefly with German bees, to which race they are vastly superior.

Italian bees were sent to Switzerland (by von Baldenstein) in 1843, to Germany in 1853, to England (by Neighbor) in 1859 and to France about the same time (by Hamet), to Australia in 1862 and again in 1880, to German Guinea in 1887, from California to New Zealand in 1880, from Germany to Ceylon in 1882 and from Italy to New Zealand (to Hopkins) in 1883, to Guam in 1907 (from Hawaii by Van Dine).

The first importation of these bees to America has been a matter of some dispute and was the basis of a sharp controversy. Their introduction marks an important milestone in American apiculture, almost equal to the invention of the movable frame-hive. About 1855, Samuel Wagner and Edward Jessop of York, Pennsylvania, made an unsuccessful importation of an Italian colony, which died en route. In the winter of 1858-59, Wagner, Langstroth and Colvin (Baltimore) sent an order to Dzierzon (Germany), which was not delivered. Later in 1859, they received seven living queens[1] from Dzierzon and reared two or three queens that fall, but the imported queens all

[1] A cage dated May, 1859, in Dzierzon's handwriting was found by C. H. Lake after he purchased the Colvin apiary (Beekeeper's Instructor III, No. 12, 1881).

died the following winter. On the same steamer that brought these queens, Mahan (Philadelphia); who had made a trip to Europe for these bees, brought over "one or more" queens (of doubtful purity). In June, 1860, Wagner and Colvin received another consignment. In the meantime, S. B. Parsons (Flushing, New York) was commissioned by the Agricultural Division of the Patent Office to procure ten colonies, which he purchased from Hermann of Tamins (reported by him January 3, 1860) and shipped from Havre, reaching the United States in May. In the annual report of the Division of Agriculture submitted January 29, 1861, the Superintendent reports that the effort was unsuccessful "owing to inattention to the instructions given by the agent of the Office." C. J. Robinson later asserted that he and Mahan had solicited an order from the Commissioner of the Patent Office in 1859 authorizing Mahan to proceed to Italy and procure bees. This request was refused but it was claimed that this instigated the movement to have Parsons (an agent of the Division then in Italy) get the bees. Robinson states that Parsons bought ten for the Government and ten for himself (this second purchase is denied by the friends of Parsons) and that he reported that all the bees consigned to the Government died. At any rate, Parsons in 1860 placed at least some of his stock in the hands of Cary, Langstroth, Quinby and others and the sale of Italian queens began in 1861. Riley, then Chief of the Division of Entomology, in 1892 claimed for the Government the credit of the first importation direct from Italy. Rose (New York) received colonies in 1861 and Colvin continued shipments from the Dzierzon apiary in 1863-64. Various other early shipments were made, and now queens are imported annually. In the early days of the enthusiasm over Italian queens they often sold for twenty dollars each. Italian bees are now found everywhere that beekeeping is conducted and are usually considered preferable to all others. In the United States, special attention has been given to the breeding of Italian bees and it is probably true that better Italian stock can now be obtained in America than in Italy.

To distinguish differences in strains of Italian bees and in part to provide trade names, various names have been given by American beekeepers to certain types. The five-banded or "golden-all-over" bees have been bred specially for an increase in the yellow color on the abdomen. The red-clover Italians sold several years ago were supposed to have a tongue-length above the average, sufficient to allow them to get nectar from the red-clover blossom. Various strains are distinguished by the name of the breeder. The specially yellow bees are not usually considered as desirable for commercial beekeeping as the typical Italians, which are commonly designated as three-banded or leather-colored.

German

These bees are black in color and are generally known among American beekeepers as "black bees." It is of interest to note that according to Dzierzon there were yellow bees in Germany before Italians were introduced and this helps to explain the variation in the German bees. von Buttel-Reepen, following distinctions made by Dzierzon and other early writers, divides the German bees into two varieties, the typical and the heath bees. The typical variety is native to Germany, Russia, Scandinavia, Denmark, Holland, England, Switzerland, Austro-Hungary and parts of other European countries. The heath bee is darker than the typical variety, swarms excessively and is especially adapted to honey-flows coming in late summer (buckwheat, heather); young queens in after-swarms lay drone eggs abundantly the first season. This variety is found in Hanover, Holstein, Oldenburg and Holland. There is a possibility that there are two varieties of German bees in the United States, as is so often claimed, and that these have arisen from these two natural varieties.

The German or black bees in the United States seem to

combine many of the undesirable qualities of all other bees. They are less prolific than Italians, they (and especially crosses with Italians) are cross but respond to smoke, they build more queen-cells than Italians and develop fertile workers more readily (less in these last respects than the eastern races), they do not clean the hive well or resist moths completely, they run badly on the combs and fall off from the corners of the combs during manipulation and they swarm more than Italians. Their greatest fault is that they succumb so rapidly to European foulbrood that it is most difficult to rid a colony of black bees of this disease. They cap comb-honey white and winter fairly well, but their nervousness is against them in this respect. While these bees are condemned by the best American beekeepers, some of the leading beekeepers of Europe (especially in Switzerland) claim them to be superior to Italians. Since no effort has been made to improve these bees in America, this may account for the difference of opinion.

The German or black bees were introduced into New England (probably from England or Holland) in 1638. In 1644, John Eales was brought to Newburg from a neighboring town to instruct the people in beekeeping, indicating an early interest in the industry, but he later became a town charge. Black bees reached west Florida not later than 1763, Kentucky in 1780, New York in 1793, west of the Mississippi River in 1797, Cuba in 1764, San Domingo in 1781, New South Wales in 1822, Tasmania in 1831, New Zealand in 1839, Brazil in 1845 (or earlier), Chile about 1848, California in 1853, Colombia about 1855 and Argentina in 1857. Harbison took 116 colonies (with a loss of only six) from Pennsylvania to California via Panama in 1857. The same year (August 20th) the first bees were shipped from San José, California, to Hawaii.

Carniolan

These bees are grayish-black in color and the claim that yellow bees were native to parts of Carniola is often questioned. Francis Jager is authority for the statement that the bees of the Wippach valley (Vipavska dolina) are yellow. Carniolan bees are large, gentle (second only to Caucasians), prolific, swarm excessively, are good honey-gatherers, build numerous queen-cells, collect little propolis, winter admirably, cap their honey white and do not run on the combs during manipulation. It is claimed by some beekeepers that they resist European foulbrood as well as Italians: this appears not to be true but the subject should be thoroughly investigated by disinterested persons. They are native to Carniola, Jugoslavia.

These bees have been shipped repeatedly to Germany and other European countries and to America. While they have some ardent advocates in the United States, they are losing ground, especially on account of their swarming proclivities and the black color, which American beekeepers do not fancy. Queen breeders have distinguished other races, which are not distinct from the Carniolan, among which are the Banat (Banater) race, of recent importation into America, and the Dalmatian which appeared in American literature in the eighties. The names of other provinces have been used as trade terms for different breeders.

African races

While several races of bees have been distinguished from Africa, in addition to the Egyptian previously discussed, very little information is at hand concerning these bees in the hands of beekeepers. A yellow race, described as *Apis adonsoni*, is found in parts of Africa, having the abdomen a darker reddish-yellow than the Egyptian. On the north coast of Africa is found a black bee, known among beekeepers as Tunisian, Punic or North African. This race extends well into the continent. The bees of this origin that have been tried in the United States are extremely cross, propolize excessively and winter badly. They are not now known to be present in the United States. A separate race of black bees is described from Madagascar and other islands and still another from Togoland. It is well known that honeybees are abundant in parts of Africa and careful exploration would doubtless reveal many interesting facts concerning these bees. Onions [1] claims that in the South African race the unmated workers lay eggs which develop into female bees. As the continent of Africa becomes more settled by white men and as apiculture advances, some interesting additions to knowledge of the African races of bees may be expected. Baldensperger (Nice, France) has recently described bees from the African desert which appear to be a distinct race, to which he gives the name Saharian.

Asiatic races

von Buttel-Reepen (Apistica) places *A. indica* as a variety of *A. mellifica.* It is a smaller bee, which is said to bite rather than sting. It crosses with previously described races. Several sub-varieties are indicated.

Chinese-Japanese

These bees are placed by von Buttel-Reepen as sub-varieties of *A. indica.* The Chinese bee has a heavy coat of long dirty gray hair; the Japanese bee lacks this.

BEST RACE OF BEES

To answer the question as to which race of bees is best is difficult. For comb-honey-production, the German, Carniolan and Caucasian races have the advantage of capping the honey white, but the German bees are especially subject to European foulbrood, Carniolans swarm excessively (especially in comb-honey-production) and Caucasians propolize badly. Without going further into the merits and demerits of the various races, it may be as well to give the almost unanimous verdict of American beekeepers,

[1] Onions, G. W., 1912. South African "fertile worker-bees." Agricultural Journ. of the Cape of Good Hope, May. See also Van Warmelo in the same journal, 1913.

which is in favor of the Italian race. It is probably true that the tests made cannot be considered as free from prejudice but the decision was made years ago and no special reason has been presented for changing it. Since this race became popular it has been carefully bred and it is easier to obtain good stock of this race than of any other in the United States. It was the first race brought to America in the effort to improve the early introduced black bees and proved so vastly superior that it soon took a firm hold on American beekeepers. It is doubtful whether any other race will be accepted as better or even as good by the majority of beekeepers and certainly no markedly better race has been tried in this country.

CHAPTER X

REGIONAL DIFFERENCES WITHIN THE UNITED STATES

Before discussing the different methods of manipulating bees in the successful production of honey, it may be helpful to point out some of the fundamental differences between various parts of the United States in regard to the sources of honey and in climatic conditions, which influence the choice of the proper system of manipulation. In the American literature on beekeeping, these differences are frequently mentioned and the word "locality" in the beekeeper's vocabulary has come to be used as an all-inclusive argument or excuse for his particular practice and often partially to cover his ignorance of the actual reasons for differences observed. This term "locality" is the subject of the present chapter. As will be shown later, two apiaries a few miles apart may give quite different results, not only in the amount or source of crops but in the effect of certain manipulations, and the facts here presented help to explain these differences. Since migratory beekeeping is practiced only between two unlike regions, this subject is also discussed in the present chapter.

The system of manipulation to be followed and the manner in which honey may best be prepared for market depend on its color and quality. The methods of wintering, spring management and perhaps especially those of swarm control depend on the time of the beginning of the main honey-flow in relation to the time of the beginning of spring brood-rearing and on the length and intensity of the nectar-flow. While the chief sources of nectar and pollen are discussed in another chapter, it may be helpful here to present in outline the combination of floral and climatic conditions which so strongly influences the business of honey-production and guides the beekeeper in choosing suitable locations for his apiaries.

CLIMATIC CONDITIONS AFFECTING BEEKEEPING

Variation in intensity of honey-flows

In general, the nectar-flows increase in rapidity or intensity as one goes northward and with this rapidity in the honey-flow usually comes a shortening of the period during which nectar is secreted. As a rule, the northern honeys are lighter in color, although there are many exceptions which will be pointed out later. In the more northern localities, the beginning and end of the honey-flows are usually sharply marked, while in the South there is a gradual increase in the honey-flow to the maximum and a correspondingly gradual cessation of the honey-flow.

Variation in the value of plants

There is a striking difference in the value, from a beekeeper's standpoint, of plants according to locality, and the causes of these phenomena are in most cases not understood. A few of the more striking examples will serve to illustrate this variation. White clover yields nectar most abundantly in the northern range of this plant, while farther south the flow of nectar is less intense and the honey is often somewhat darker. Alfalfa yields nectar freely in the irrigated districts of the West, but is usually of no value to the beekeeper east of the Mississippi River. Buckwheat is the source of large honey crops in parts of southern New York and Pennsylvania, while in Indiana and Illinois it secretes much less nectar, again increasing in value to the beekeeper in Michigan. Exceptions to these general statements sometimes arise because of abnormal climatic conditions. For example, a heavy honey-flow from alfalfa is sometimes obtained in the vicinity of Syracuse, New York. This was probably not due to the plants becoming acclimated but occurs in dry seasons. In some seasons white clover yields well much farther south than the limits previously given. Other examples are given later.

Sources of information

There are unfortunately few bulletins and articles dealing with the variation in beekeeping conditions in the different parts of North America, although the conditions most favorable for the growth of honey-plants are rather well known. Some papers discussing differences in various parts of certain states have within recent years appeared in the bee-journals and there is an increasing interest in this phase of beekeeping, so long neglected. The beekeeper will at present find it desirable to go to original sources for most of his information, rather than to depend on the beekeeping literature. In establishing out-apiaries, it will be found of inestimable value to consult soil survey maps which have now been prepared for a goodly portion of the counties of the various states. The terminology used in naming the soil types may at first appear confusing, but after some study of the descriptions of the soils and after learning under what conditions within a county successful apiaries are now maintained, it becomes relatively simple to locate other desirable locations. Some states also have reconnaisance soil maps covering the entire state area and these are preferable to detailed county maps in that the finer details are usually valueless to the beekeeper. In addition to these maps, data on meteorological conditions are readily available from the many stations of the United States Weather Bureau, and these will be of great value in determining such factors as hours of sunshine, average temperatures for summer and winter months and similar data which greatly help the beekeeper in determining his best practice for any given place. Additional material is often available from state geological surveys, natural history surveys and other official sources, and bulletins dealing with specific honey-plants, such as the clovers, alfalfa or buckwheat, will often contain interesting facts which have a practical bearing on beekeeping. As a rule most of this material may be obtained without charge from state and federal offices.

BEEKEEPING REGIONS

It helps to an understanding of the differences in the practices of beekeepers in various parts of the United States if the country is divided into honey regions. This, as any experienced beekeeper will at once recognize, is a more or less arbitrary division and many exceptions might be cited to the following classification. In the main, however, the nature of the honey-flows justifies such an arrangement, and this plan is still more permissible if the systems of manipulation most advantageous by beekeepers are considered. These regions may first be divided into general and restricted, depending chiefly on their area. The general regions are those not only of considerable extent, but of greater influence on the choice of manipulations.

General regions

These are five in number and the division is based on differences in climatic conditions found in the United States. The placing of the sage region in the rank of a general section is justified mainly by the size of the crops obtained there in favorable seasons.

(1) *The white clover region* includes eastern Canada, the New England states, except along the coast, and a belt along the northern United States as far West as the Dakotas. It is limited to the west by the arid country and again reappears on the Pacific coast, both in the United States and Canada. The southern boundary is approximately Mason and Dixon's line and the Ohio River. In this region, in addition to white clover, alsike clover, sweet clover, basswood, tulip tree and locust contribute to the honey crops and, with the exception of tulip tree, the

honeys from these sources are light in color. Alsike clover is steadily increasing in importance with its wider planting for forage, while basswood is rapidly disappearing because of the extensive cutting of this tree for lumber. In this region the honey-flows are rapid and relatively short and the main honey-flow is usually preceded by one from spring flowers (fruit bloom, dandelion) followed by a dearth. In the more northern localities this interval is brief or entirely absent. After the main honey-flow there is usually a period when no nectar is available, followed again by a late summer or fall honey-flow (buckwheat, asters, goldenrod or Spanish needle, according to locality). This region is more suitable for comb-honey-production than any other part of the United States, on account of the intensity of the honey-flows and the light color of most of the honeys. The necessity for a rapid building up of colonies in the spring and the difficulty of swarm control make necessary special systems of manipulation in this region. The wintering problem is naturally most acute here also. Most of the American literature on beekeeping in both books and journals is based on systems applicable to the white clover region. The honeys of this section are in great demand, probably because the honey-consuming public is better educated to the flavors obtained here. In this region are thousands of beekeepers with only a few colonies, although the number of specialists is increasing satisfactorily.

(2) *The alfalfa region* is located in the West, where this plant is chiefly grown for forage. Alfalfa is at its best as a nectar-producer under irrigation and usually at high altitudes. Colorado, Utah and Idaho are now the largest producing states in this region. Sweet clover is also an important contributor to the nectar supply in most sections. The honey of this region is usually of fine flavor and light in color, but alfalfa honey quickly begins to granulate and in consequence would seem best adapted to extracting. The honey-flow is not so rapid as in the white clover country, which also makes this region less favorable for

comb-honey-production. However, many beekeepers produce comb-honey extensively. The system of manipulation is different from that in the white clover region because the honey-flows are usually longer and swarming is less difficult to control. The number of honey-flows depends on the number of crops of alfalfa that are harvested in a season. This region is steadily increasing in importance, and a market is rapidly being built up for alfalfa honey. In this region, honey-production is conducted chiefly by extensive beekeepers.

(3) *The southeastern region,* which varies greatly in the sources of honey throughout its extent, and which is an area of abundant rainfall, lies south of the white clover region and extends west to eastern Texas. The various rather distinct subdivisions of this territory might well be placed among the restricted honey regions, except that certain things in common in the honey-flow make the same type of manipulations necessary. Among the important plants of this district are sourwood, cotton, tulip tree, tupelo, manchineel, mangrove, titi, palmettos, citrus trees, gallberry and partridge pea, with nectar from clovers in some sections in favorable seasons. Sweet clover is valuable in some localities. Most of the honeys are amber, and the chief characteristic of this region is a succession of honey-flows, often intergrading. The honey-flows are usually not rapid. This region is, therefore, best adapted to extracted-honey-production. Swarming is much less troublesome than in the North. Beekeeping is developing in this section, but there is opportunity for many more beekeepers, there being now relatively few who rank as professionals. Colonies of bees may usually be bought at low prices in box-hives. This region is perhaps the best in the United States for commercial queen-rearing, except in parts of Florida where dragon-flies are troublesome.

The diversity of conditions in this region is well shown in Fig. 98, which was prepared by E. G. Baldwin, formerly of De Land, Florida, who studied the beekeeping possibilities of that state thoroughly. It will be seen that the sources of nectar are distinct geographically. The geographical position of this state and the diversity of soil and climatic conditions strongly influence the growth of the honey-plants. In Florida two localities only a few miles apart may be quite unlike, when viewed from the standpoint of the beekeeper. This is also true in many other parts of the United States.

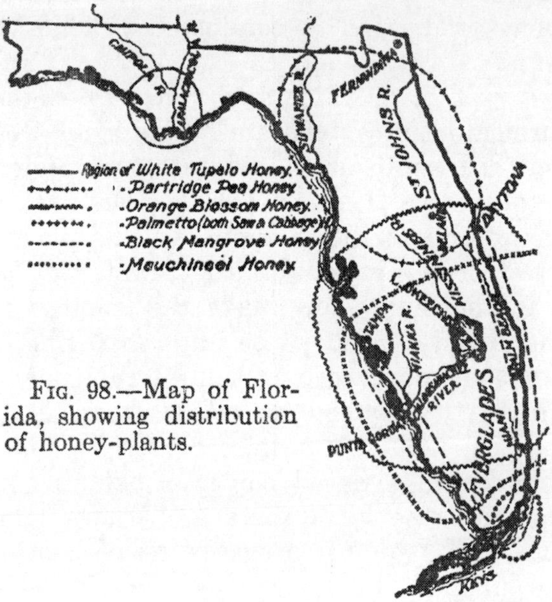

Fig. 98.—Map of Florida, showing distribution of honey-plants.

(4) *The semi-arid region of the Southwest* is located chiefly in the arid and semi-arid parts of Texas, New Mexico and Arizona, and here also the honey-plants are of somewhat restricted distribution. Among the plants which are important to the beekeeper are mesquite, horsemint, catclaw, huisache and guajilla. Most of the honey produced in this region is extracted, although a large number of beekeepers produce bulk comb-honey (chunk honey), cut from large combs (without sections) and placed in cans in which extracted honey has been poured to fill the spaces. Such honey is usually sold locally. Beekeeping in this region is largely in the hands of professional beekeepers.

(5) *The sage region* is confined to the cañons of southern California and should be considered restricted except for the fact that sage honey wields so important an infiuence

on the honey market that the region may justly be placed among those of major importance. All the various sages are heavy yielders under favorable conditions and there is usually no other honey source of primary importance where this honey is produced. The influence of rainfall on the honey crop of this region is discussed in the chapter on honey sources. If the crops of sage honey were uniformly heavy, this would be an ideal region for comb-honey-production, for sage honey is mild in flavor, water-white and does not easily granulate. However, successful comb-honey-production necessitates a rapid flow, which often fails to appear in this region and most of the honey is extracted. Here, also, there are many professional bee-keepers.

In addition to the geographical limits ascribed to these main regions, other localities situated outside the prescribed boundaries might well be included with certain of the general regions in discussing the type of flow. For example, California, north of the sage region, is comparable with the South, and along the Pacific coast to the north are localities which belong to the white clover region.

Restricted regions

In addition to the more general divisions named, there are other localities with special advantages for the bee-keeper, but more limited in extent, which lie within the boundaries of the main divisions. As previously mentioned, the southeastern region is virtually composed of a number of such restricted sections. The list here given will be recognized as incomplete and is intended merely as a suggestion. Many more restricted regions will be recognized from the discussion of the sources of nectar. Among the more important limited regions may be mentioned those in which the following plants secrete nectar.

(1) *Buckwheat.*—The honey of this plant is dark and of strong flavor, suitable chiefly for manufacturing purposes

or for the foreign population. The variation in the secretion of nectar from buckwheat has been mentioned.

(2) *Sumac.*—Valuable locally in New England. Another species of the same genus yields a surplus in limited areas in Georgia.

(3) *Spanish needle* (numerous species).—Heavy yielders of amber honey in the autumn in swamps. Among the best-known regions in which these plants are of value may be mentioned the lower Delaware River and Illinois River valleys and the Kankakee swamp.

(4) *Willowherb.*—Important in northern Michigan and in Washington and Oregon, west of the Cascade Mountains in burned-over forest areas. This region extends into the far north, where this plant thrives.

(5) *Sweet clover.*—In regions having soils rich in lime, this plant is exceptionally abundant and is spreading rapidly, due to an increased use in agriculture. On soils rich in lime it is the source of large crops of honey of excellent quality, showing at times a slightly greenish color where the secretion is slower. It is especially valuable in northern Kentucky, southern Indiana, part of Alabama and Mississippi and especially in the north central states. The last-named area is rapidly developing and must soon be considered as a major region. Sweet clover contributes considerably to the crop in the alfalfa region, but in this case the methods of beekeeping are chiefly determined by the alfalfa.

(6) *Blue thistle.*—Important in the Shenandoah Valley.

(7) *Raspberry.*—Northern Michigan where the forests have burned over and in parts of New York.

(8) *Beans.*—In southern California, where beans of various kinds are grown in great quantity, beekeepers find it profitable to move their apiaries to the bean fields after the sage honey-flow. The honey is white, of excellent flavor and granulates quickly.

(9) *Heartsease.*—Mississippi Valley. A heavy yielder of nectar in late summer.

(10) *Sourwood.*—Important in southern Appalachian Mountains.

(11) *Citrus.*—Important in Florida but especially in California where orange honey is light in color and excellent in flavor.

Variation within a region

It must not be understood that the territory within either a general or a restricted region as here defined is equally good throughout. The cutting of forests, the extensive cultivation of some plant which restricts the growth of honey-plants, local differences in soil or drainage, the presence of large towns and a multitude of other factors may so reduce the number of individual honey-plants where they would normally grow as to make extensive beekeeping unprofitable. On the other hand, the cutting of forests may make a region better by allowing a honey-plant to spread (*e.g.* willowherb) or the planting of some nectar-yielding species, either under cultivation (*e.g.* alsike clover, alfalfa) or in waste places (*e.g.* sweet clover) may greatly increase the value of a locality to the beekeeper. In fact, the entire alfalfa country is a man-made honey region These factors, many of which are due to human interference with the natural environment, must be considered in choosing locations of apiaries and in manipulating colonies.

Climatic influences may change an area from year to year. A lack of sufficient rainfall, for example, may kill white clover in certain areas and not in others. This occurred during 1914, when a severe drought killed clover over much of Illinois, while an abundance of rain fell in northern portions of the state, there being marked differences in localities only a few miles apart.

DISTRIBUTION OF BEES IN THE UNITED STATES

The relative importance of the various honey regions is indicated by the number of colonies of bees in each one, although care must be exercised in examining these data to avoid misinterpretation. The only source of information on this subject is the United States Census, and data from this source are utterly unreliable for beekeeping, since only bees on farms are enumerated. While the number of colonies reported is far too low, within certain limits one is justified in assuming that approximately the same percentage is omitted throughout the country. Fig. 99 was prepared in the Bureau of Agricultural Economics of the Department of Agriculture from data furnished by the Census of 1920, each dot representing 500 colonies. A comparison of such maps for the earlier census dates shows some changes from one decade to the next, but in the main the distribution remains much the same as formerly. The relative importance of the leading states in honey-production is shown in Fig. 100, the states listed being those which furnish approximately 80 per cent of the nation's honey crop.

The white clover region is rather uniformly stocked with bees, with some concentration in the included buckwheat area. The alfalfa section has less bees while the geographically limited sage region is heavily stocked. The amount of honey produced in the eastern states doubtless greatly exceeds that of the western states, but in the West the honey is usually produced by specialists who ship to wholesale markets, and as a result western honey is relatively more important in determining the wholesale prices for honeys.

The enormous number of colonies in the southern states is a surprise. In the fifteen states usually included in the division of southern states are 45 per cent of all the colonies in the United States. In this region the box-hive and the farmer-beekeeper are still found in large numbers, there being few specialists except in Texas. Because the industry has not developed on modern lines, most of the honey from the South does not reach the larger centers of distribution and, therefore, has little influence on the wholesale honey markets. The number of colonies of bees in the South is

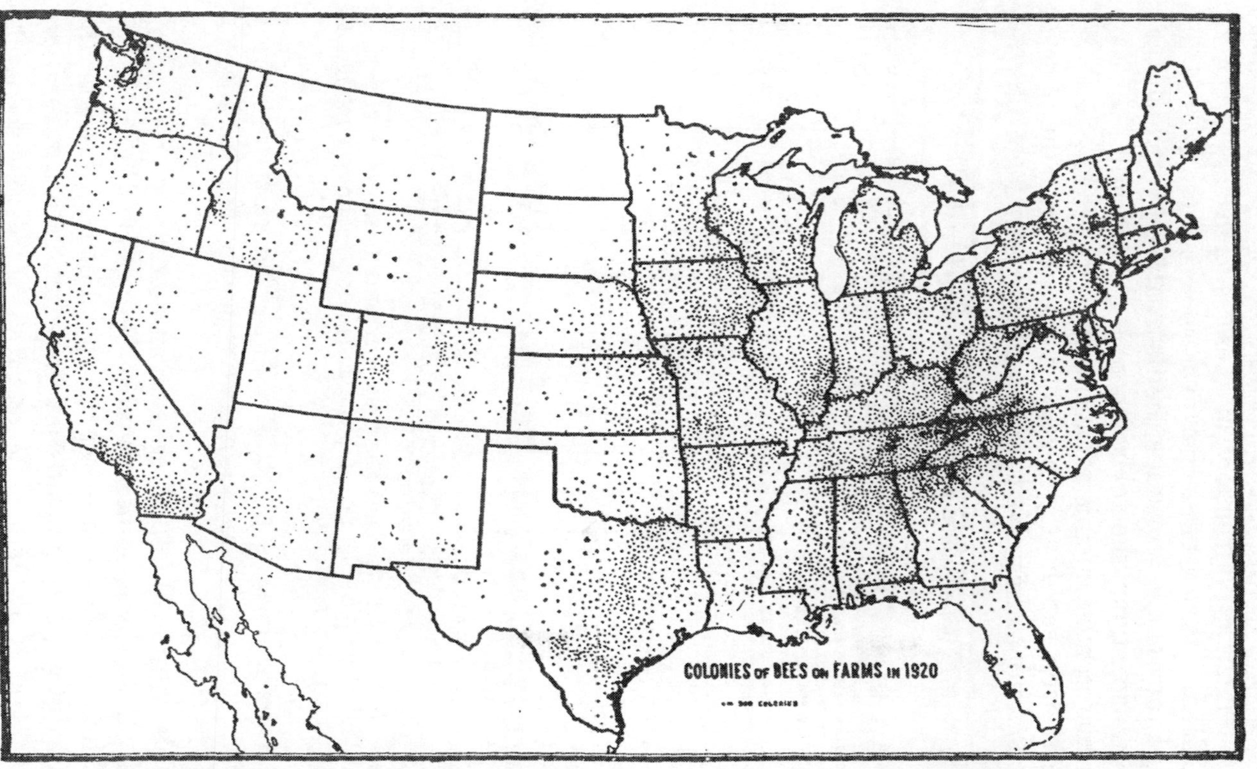

FIG. 99.—Map of the United States showing distribution of colonies of bees on farms according to the Census of 1920.

proof of the remarkable opportunities for the development of the industry, for many of these colonies are given no attention. As one beekeeper expresses it, these bees would die, if they could, to escape the ill-treatment to which they are subjected, but the environment is so favorable that they increase in spite of mismanagement.

Attention should also be called to the larger number of colonies in southern New York and northern Pennsylvania,

HONEY PRODUCTION AND DISTRIBUTION BY STATES FOR EACH 1000 POUNDS PRODUCED IN THE UNITED STATES

BASED ON NUMBER OF HIVES REPORTED BY THE BUREAU OF THE CENSUS AND AVERAGE YIELDS PER COLONY REPORTED TO THE UNITED STATES DEPARTMENT OF AGRICULTURE BY CORRESPONDENTS MANY OF WHOM ARE COMMERCIAL BEE KEEPERS

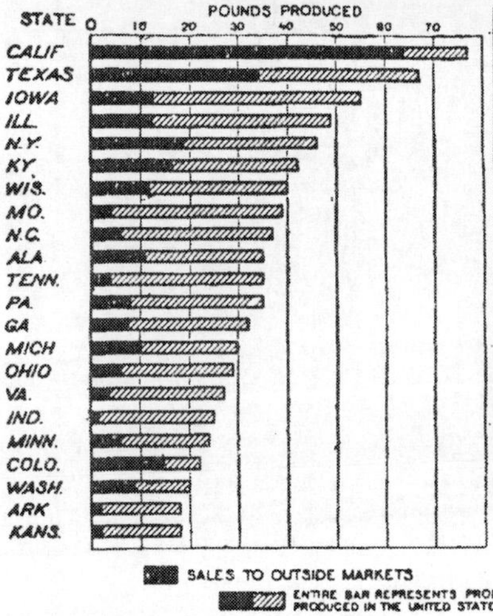

STATE	PRODUCTION POUNDS	SOLD TO OUTSIDE MARKETS POUNDS	SOLD LOCALLY OR USED AT HOME POUNDS
CALIF.	77	63.91	13.09
TEXAS	67	34.17	32.83
IOWA	55	12.10	42.90
ILL.	49	12.25	36.75
N.Y.	46	18.86	27.14
KY.	42	16.38	25.62
WIS.	40	11.60	28.40
MO.	39	3.90	35.10
N.C.	37	5.92	31.08
ALA.	35	10.85	24.15
TENN.	35	3.85	31.15
PA.	35	8.05	26.95
GA.	32	7.68	24.32
MICH.	30	10.20	19.80
OHIO	29	6.09	22.91
VA.	27	3.78	23.22
IND.	25	1.50	23.50
MINN.	24	6.00	18.00
COLO.	22	14.52	7.48
WASH.	20	8.80	11.20
ARK	18	1.98	16.02
KANS	18	1.98	16.02

FIG. 100.—Chart showing the relative importance of the various states in honey-production and the amounts of honey supplied to home and other markets.

where buckwheat is plentiful. The other restricted honey regions seem to have less influence on the number of colonies.

This map will repay considerable study in connection with other phases of beekeeping. To one familiar with the distribution of the diseases of the brood of bees in the United States [1] it is clear that there has been a severe loss

[1] Phillips, E. F., 1911. The occurrence of bee diseases in the United States (Preliminary report). Circ. No. 138, Bur. Ent., 25 pp.

from this cause, as indicated by the smaller dots in regions where diseases are most prevalent. New England was formerly well stocked with bees, but many colonies have been destroyed by disease. Certain areas in Pennsylvania, Ohio, and Indiana, where disease is abundant, are inadequately provided with bees. One important reason for the larger number of colonies in the South is probably the scarcity of disease.

MIGRATORY BEEKEEPING

By this expression beekeepers designate the moving of apiaries from place to place during a single summer to take advantage of two or more honey-flows which do not occur in a single locality. This has been practiced since ancient times, and most extensive beekeepers cherish the hope that some day the subject may be sufficiently understood so that they may move their bees several times a season and thereby keep them working almost all the year. Some elaborate plans have been made for moving bees from south to north as the seasons advance, but most of the trials have been failures. Since success in beekeeping depends on an intimate knowledge of the honey sources of the locality and of the best manipulations to obtain maximum crops, such migratory beekeeping would necessitate detailed knowledge of many sections, so that the beekeeper may know when and where to move his colonies to advantage.

The Mississippi River has long been considered an ideal avenue for transporting colonies in migratory beekeeping, especially since there is no better way to ship colonies than by boat. It has been proposed that the beekeeper place his apiary on a flatboat in the South in early spring and move northward by night, allowing his bees to gather nectar by day, and following the season as it extends northward. This plan so well illustrates the limitations of migratory beekeeping that it may be examined critically. One of the chief difficulties is the fact that the beekeeper must know just where to anchor after each move so that his bees will be in range of the best forage and this would involve too careful a study of the valley to make the plan practical. This objection might be overcome but there is a more fundamental difficulty which has not been sufficiently considered by those who have cherished this dream. If one species of plant furnished the main nectar-flow throughout the Mississippi Valley, the beekeeper could move northward to prolong the gathering period, but this is not the case. Many plants furnish nectar in the various portions of the valley and if the apiary were moved northward the bees often would leave behind them a honey-flow from another source. If migratory beekeeping from south to north and then back south with the closing season proves successful it will probably be within the nectar-secreting area of a single species of plant or perhaps of two species, one for each direction of the journey. The Mississippi River plan was tried several years ago on a rather extensive scale without success.

The experiment of moving an apiary south for the winter for the purpose of making increase has recently been tried. If one is raising bees for sale and has a heavy demand for colonies, it may pay, but the chances of success in following this plan for honey-production are small.

The limitations of migratory beekeeping, in so far as present successes indicate them, have not been previously pointed out. They are approximately as follows: The movement of bees must not be from one general region to another, as from the white clover to the alfalfa region, but from a location where the flora is that of the general area to a restricted locality where the honey-flow comes at a different time, usually later. For example, it has been profitable to practice the following plans in migratory beekeeping: (1) from white clover to sweet clover, buckwheat, Spanish needle or heartsease; (2) from sage to bean; or (3) from one of the restricted regions in the

South to another. As previously mentioned, the honey-flow at the temporary out-apiary usually comes after the main honey-flow at the permanent apiary. In most such cases, the conditions demand the production of extracted honey, as comb-honey-production and migratory beekeeping are not well suited to each other.

In considering the possibility of migratory beekeeping it must be decided whether it is desirable to move the bees or simply the beekeeper. In other words, if the trip is a long one involving considerable expense and danger of loss in moving a large number of colonies, it may be cheaper and easier for the beekeeper to own two or more lots of bees and supplies. The expense of transportation and the danger involved are probably the factors which determine the feasibility of moving from south to north or from sage in California to alfalfa in Utah or Colorado. In the South, especially where bees can be purchased at a low price, it would not seem profitable to move apiaries over long distances. The shipping of bees in wire-cloth cages may in the future remove the present limitations.

It would certainly seem that a northern beekeeper is not embracing all his opportunities if he stops work when his bees can no longer obtain nectar, while there are still hundreds of places in the South or even in the tropics where he might maintain apiaries with profit in the winter. When it is recalled that the professional is a relatively new factor in beekeeping, it may still be expected that the future development of the industry will show an increase in migratory beekeeping, or at least in migratory beekeepers.

OVERSTOCKING

The bugbear of the specialist beekeeper is the fear that he will overstock his localities, that is, place in each apiary so many colonies that there will not be enough nectar available to permit the colonies to store approximately the maximum profitable surplus. Since there are few places in the United States that are now overstocked, this subject worries the beekeeper more than the facts warrant. Some beekeepers have found it practical to keep several hundred colonies in one apiary. E. W. Alexander, Delanson, New York, found it more profitable, in an exceptionally good buckwheat region, to keep over 700 colonies in one yard than to establish out-apiaries. In the South and West large apiaries are not infrequent.

While it is desirable to keep bees in as few places as possible to avoid duplication of apparatus and time lost in transportation, there is another factor to be considered. The size of an apiary should be determined chiefly by the number of colonies that the beekeeper can manipulate in a single day during the honey-flow. If he finds that he can usually care for seventy-five colonies in a day under his system of management, then that number is ideal for his apiaries. He can then arrange his out-apiaries so that each will receive a visit as frequently as the conditions demand. The amount of work that can be done in a day will increase with experience and the out-apiaries correspondingly may be increased in size, for they should be large enough to furnish a full day's work, unless some means of rapid transportation is available. With modern transportation facilities the distance to out-yards is of less importance than formerly and many beekeepers now have motor trucks to carry an extracting outfit and other apparatus and supplies from one apiary to another. Considering the day's work as the determining factor in the size of the apiary, the out-apiaries may be more numerous and closer together than would be the case if each yard were increased to the maximum. In the present undeveloped condition of the beekeeping industry and with so many localities almost untouched by bees, it is not wise to run any risk of overstocking. The location of out-apiaries should be determined by the available forage, the minimum distance between them usually being decided by the distance that bees can fly.

DADANT OUT-APIARIES

To illustrate the problem which confronts the beekeeper in the establishment of out-apiaries there is here reproduced a map (Fig. 101), made from one by C. P. Dadant, Hamilton, Illinois, of the apiaries near his home in 1891. Since that time the operations of this beekeeper and his sons have greatly increased [1] but this map may be used for the present purposes. Dadant then owned the Home, Sherwood, Villemain and Sack apiaries, the other four shown belonging to other beekeepers. All are located on land sloping toward the Mississippi River. The Sherwood apiary was the best, giving crops in the spring and fall. The Villemain apiary appears to have been in the poorest location, the range of the bees being restricted by the river, but it was near the only basswood grove in the country and the bees gathered honey in the fall from the islands. The Sack seems to have been too near other apiaries but was actually second only to the Sherwood yard. The bees did not work more than a mile along the bluff but went three miles to the river, having the bottom lands covered with fall flowers within their range of flight. They were separated from the adjacent apiaries by hills and timber. The two small circles

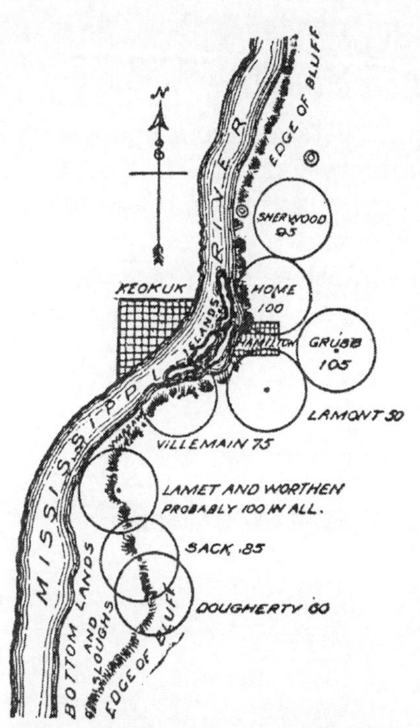

FIG. 101.—Map showing distribution of Dadant apiaries, Hamilton, Illinois.

[1] Dadant, C. P., 1917. Locating your apiaries [Description of the Dadant apiaries]. Amer. Bee Jour., LVII, pp. 306-7.

show sites of former apiaries, used before the Sherwood was established. The bees in the home apiary were only a mile and a half from abundant pasturage on an island but did not reach it, although they sometimes went two miles or more in another direction.

This description of conditions in 1891 does not at all represent those of the Dadant apiaries today, but this map shows the locations decided on in that region by an experienced beekeeper who had kept bees in that district for twenty years. It shows that distance from one apiary to the next is not the sole consideration, but that contour of the land, timber tracts and other barriers must be taken into consideration. Probably it would profit any extensive beekeeper who has several out-apiaries to make a similar map of his region, especially if he includes the honey sources.

CHAPTER XI

THE FIRST STEPS IN BEEKEEPING

Many persons begin beekeeping accidentally. The interest of many of the present beekeepers in the honeybee has first been aroused by a swarm passing over the premises or perhaps lighting on a tree near by. The desire not to allow anything to go to waste or not to allow a valuable article to elude him, coupled perhaps with a dare-devil impulse to risk a combat, has induced many a man or woman to attempt to hive the stray swarm. Or perhaps there is a temptation to exhibit one's prowess before the other members of the family. Having hived the swarm in a box or barrel with no loss of life or limb—and bees are never easier to handle than when swarming—it is by easy steps that one goes on until an attack of what is commonly known as "bee-fever" has developed, from which recovery seems hopeless. If a swarm is caught and put into a box, the owner should obtain a modern hive as soon as practical and lodge his new possession in a home where they may be manipulated. The necessary equipment is discussed in Chapter II.

PURCHASE OF COLONIES

Others, however, decide to begin beekeeping without this accidental impulse. The desirability of beginning on a small scale may be emphasized again here. Colonies should, if possible, always be purchased near at hand to prevent the loss which may follow, especially if colonies must be transported by inexperienced persons. The further advantage in this procedure is that the former owner usually may be induced to assist in the moving and he will also prove helpful in the early days with the bees. It is best to have the bees already housed in the hive which is to be adopted, but if this is not possible then colonies in any hive or in boxes or barrels may be purchased and transferred (p. 259). Transferring is a difficult operation for a novice, in fact it is not relished by an experienced beekeeper, and is to be avoided. Early in the summer is usually the best time for making the start, although the price charged for colonies is usually higher at that season. There is less opportunity for making such mistakes in management as will result in loss of bees during the first few months of ownership if these come during the summer. It matters little what race or strain of bees is obtained at the beginning except that it is desirable to avoid bees with too great a percentage of black blood in them, such bees being difficult to manipulate. After the apiary is established any desired race may be obtained by removing the queens and replacing them with mated queens purchased from commercial queen breeders. If these are introduced to replace the old queens of the colonies, the progeny of the new queens will rapidly replace the offspring of the discarded ones as they die from natural causes.

Purchase of bees to be shipped from a distance

Another method growing in favor is to buy bees by weight, without frames. Bees are now easily shipped in cages specially constructed for the purpose, even though the journey requires several days. By this method the possibility of carrying some brood disease is obviated and there is less likelihood of damage to the bees by breaking or melting of combs or by suffocation during the journey. Nuclei or small colonies with frames may also be shipped a considerable distance. These will usually build up to full colonies during the season if bought early, but of course surplus honey can scarcely be expected the first year from such a small colony. Still another plan is to buy an empty hive and leave it with some beekeeper so that a swarm may be hived in it, after which it is removed to the desired location.

Requirements in purchased colonies

If there is opportunity to examine the colonies before purchasing, several important things should be insisted upon: (1) Get as little drone-comb or crooked or defective comb as possible; (2) see that the colony is free from disease (p. 421); (3) the colony should be provided with plenty of honey; and (4) the amount of brood should be adequate for the time of year. It is perhaps asking too much of the beginner to expect him to determine whether disease is present in colonies purchased. In many states and counties there are official apiary inspectors whose duty it is to give advice on the subject of disease and these men may be asked to assist in this work. At any rate, even the novice can tell whether there is any dead or discolored brood and it is at least safe not to accept colonies in which any discolored brood is found, normal brood being pearly-white. Formerly the sale of bees was believed to bring ill-luck and the customary way to acquire colonies was to go at night to the apiary and, after the removal of the colony, to leave coins to the value of the bees on an adjacent hive. The possibility of an insufficient pile of coins or perhaps none at all is probably a factor in causing modern beekeepers to prefer to sell bees according to present-day methods. The beginner can scarcely be advised to adopt the ancient manner, for the custom might be found faulty when explained to a magistrate.

HOW TO LEARN BEEKEEPING

To acquire skill in manipulating bees and to learn the proper management of the apiary so as to obtain maximum results, it is best to spend some time in the apiary of an experienced beekeeper. If one contemplates making beekeeping an important part of the occupation, this is especially to be desired. It is usually possible to arrange for employment at a small wage in the apiary of a specialist for a season. Not all extensive beekeepers, however, manipulate their bees well and many fail to get the maximum returns through faulty systems, especially in comb-honey-production, but after some experience in such an apiary the prospective beekeeper is better able to read the details of manipulations understandingly, and he can correct in his own practice the mistakes which may have been taught him by his teacher.

Value of reading

The many books on bees have points of merit and reading the various journals devoted to beekeeping is to be commended. Reading alone does not make a beekeeper. The "book-beekeeper" may be well informed concerning the behavior of bees and may know the different systems of management so that he can discuss them in detail, but only by practice do these become an actual part of his beekeeping equipment.

Merits of beekeeping courses

A good way to learn beekeeping is to attend some school where a thorough course in this subject is given. Until recently beekeeping was not included in the work of the agricultural colleges in the United States, but interest is now being aroused in this work and it is spreading in a manner to give deep satisfaction to those interested in the development of the industry. In the apiary of an experienced beekeeper, the beginner perhaps gets more personal attention than he does in a class, but usually in the rush of honey-production, the theoretical side of the work is neglected and frequently the beekeeper is not able to offer much help to his student on such subjects. Consequently when he begins to keep bees for himself, he may find local conditions quite unlike those in the apiary in which he worked and, not knowing the fundamental facts about bees, he may be at a loss to know what to do. In a regular course of study, the proper emphasis may be placed on the various subjects, although naturally there is less opportunity for practice with the bees. The ideal plan is to take the prescribed course and then spend the following summer in the apiary of the best beekeeper available. The student is then able to understand more clearly what he sees and hears and is better able to recognize and perhaps mentally to condemn the little peculiarities which one encounters occasionally in the manipulations of practical beekeepers. If the teaching of beekeeping is conducted wisely, it should result not only in increased knowledge of bees, but in the training of more professional beekeepers.

BEGINNER'S OUTFIT

It is only with experience that one is able to judge of the comparative merits of different hives and other equipment, but the beginner usually desires definite information concerning the equipment which should be purchased. The giving of such advice is attended with some risk, for one hesitates to advise an equipment which may be discarded when the beekeeper becomes more familiar with the business. In the following lists, the choice is made on the basis of the equipment which is preferred by the larger number of good beekeepers and not alone on the author's personal preferences.

General equipment:—

Bee veil.
Smoker—medium size.
Gloves (for the beginner only).
Some kind of hive-tool—a screw-driver will answer.

For each colony:—

Bottom board of ⅞-inch material.
Two 10-frame Langstroth hive-bodies—preferably single-walled. The colony will be reduced to one hive-body if comb-honey is produced.
Self-spacing frames, punched for wiring.
Medium brood-foundation, 1¼ pound for each hive-body.
Telescope cover.

For comb-honey-production (minimum):—

3 supers for 10-frame hive (if possible one made up for sample). The 4¼ inches square section, 1⅞ inches wide, is usually preferred. The purchase of only one super to the colony is to be condemned.

Thin foundation, 2 ounces to super. For the beginner the use of small starters of foundation is sometimes preferable. If full sheets are used, 8 ounces to the super should be provided.

For extracted-honey-production:—

2 extra hive-bodies identical with those used in brood-chamber, with full sheets of comb-foundation (see p. 35 concerning spacing devices in surplus chambers).
1 2-frame non-reversible extractor.
1 Bingham uncapping knife.

For bulk comb-honey-production:—

3 10-frame supers with shallow extracting frames.
½ pound thin-super foundation for each super.

CHAPTER XII

THE APIARY SITE

In the establishment of a commercial apiary, the chief requisite is proximity to the sources of nectar. To fulfill this, it is essential that the honey resources of the region be studied carefully. While it is possible to keep bees in almost all of the habitable parts of the United States, it is not everywhere profitable to practice extensive beekeeping, so that if one contemplates making honey-production a major portion of one's business, it is wise to go to the best available location rather than to struggle along in a mediocre locality. A second requisite is ease of transportation to the apiary and to market.

APIARY GROUNDS

In the North, a plot of ground sloping to the south or east is usually preferable and in any region it is advisable to face the apiary so as to protect the hives and especially their entrances from the prevailing winds. If the contour of the land or a near-by forest does not afford protection from the wind, a windbreak may be planted. A row of evergreens is sufficient in the North and is serviceable in winter when it is most needed. A solid fence or building is less desirable, since such a windbreak, instead of breaking the force of the wind, often simply deflects the currents into the midst of the apiary with disastrous results. In moist regions, a slope is desirable for drainage. The hives should be so placed that they receive sunlight in the early morning. This is helpful in winter and perhaps equally so in summer as it starts the bees to the field earlier, so that they get the nectar from plants which furnish it only in the mornings. If possible, the apiary should not be near the public road and should be situated where the bees will not prove a nuisance to passers-by or sting live-stock. If the only convenient location is near the road, the line of flight of the bees may be deflected upwards by a high hedge or a solid fence, for after they fly over such an obstruction they will keep above the line of travel on the road and will not molest teams or pedestrians. This is an important consideration as bees sometimes sting horses fatally. Preferably the apiary should be located away from the clothes-drying yard so that they will not spot the clothes with their feces. This applies especially in the North, and this objection may be overcome largely by removing the cellar-wintered bees when no clothes are to be hung out. Perhaps it would be more in keeping with the usual practice to advise that no clothes be hung out just after the bees have been placed on their summer stands.

The hives should, if practicable, occupy the higher ground of the plot chosen for the apiary, so that in carrying heavy supers to the apiary house the load will be carried downhill and the empty supers uphill. Such an arrangement will materially reduce the labor in a commercial apiary.

Exposure to the sun

While exposure to the sun is advised in the early morning, it is often well to protect the hives from the sun in the middle of the day, so that the bees will not hang out in front of the hive and to prevent the melting down of combs. On the other hand, too dense a shade is not advantageous and usually it is not best to locate an apiary in woods. To provide shade, the hives may be placed in two rows under a shed or arbor with the entrances to the outside (Fig. 102). Such sheds usually run north and south, but in hot dry countries an east and west direction is sometimes better. In temperate climates, sheds are not in favor, but many beekeepers use shade-boards, so constructed that they extend about a foot in all directions from the nive except to the north. These must be held in place by a heavy weight and are rather objectionable because they have to be removed each time the colony is manipulated.

As the extreme of protection from the sun's rays may be mentioned the house apiary, in which the entrances to the hives are through holes in the wall of a specially constructed house. Such arrangements meet with little favor among American beekeepers because of the difficulty of manipulating the colonies inside the house. In Europe, however, the beekeepers often construct elaborately designed and decorated house apiaries (Fig. 14) in which an American commercial beekeeper would find himself seriously hindered.

Fig. 102.—Apiary in the West, shaded by thatched shed.

Care of the apiary grounds

The ground on which the hives are located should be smooth so that a wheelbarrow or cart may be utilized in carrying supplies or honey. This is also desirable if a lawnmower is used to keep grass and weeds from obstructing the entrances. High grass about the entrances is a hindrance to the bees on returning to the hive and should be avoided. Few commercial beekeepers find time to use a lawnmower during the rush season, but prefer to lay boards in front of the hive or to kill the grass with salt. It is sometimes convenient to pasture one or more sheep in the apiary inclosure. Raising the hives above the grass on high stands is another solution of the difficulty, but is not desirable in a heavy flow of honey, since bees often fall to the ground with their loads and since the stands may break down under the weight of honey.

ARRANGEMENT OF HIVES

The hives may be arranged variously according to the preference of the beekeeper. Each hive should be inclined so that the entrance is about an inch lower than the back of the hive to prevent water from collecting on the bottom board. It is usually desirable that the hives be so placed that the beekeeper will not need to pass in front of the entrances as he goes about his work. The usual practice is to place hives in rows either close together on a slightly raised platform or singly on individual stands. The placing of hives in pairs on a common stand is also common. Where economy of space is a consideration, it is advantageous to place hives close together in groups of four (Fig. 103), back to back, two facing east and two west. Such an arrangement is especially desirable when the bees are wintered outdoors in quadruple cases (p. 372). This allows a space beside each hive for the beekeeper while manipulating and is greatly preferred to hives in long rows close together. Where space permits, many beekeepers prefer to place the hives singly (Fig. 104), but it should be remembered that it is undesirable to move the colonies when packing for winter.

Fig. 103.—Colonies in summer position in groups of four. This arrangement is advantageous whether or not the bees are wintered in four-colony packing cases.

NUMBER OF COLONIES IN ONE APIARY

The number of colonies which may be kept profitably in one apiary depends entirely on the nectar supply. In the white clover region, it is considered best to have not more than one hundred colonies in an apiary, with apiaries located at least two miles apart. This number can be

Fig. 104.—Former apiary of the Bureau of Entomology, College Park, Md. The use of this apiary for experimental work accounts for the divergence in the height of the hives. The hives were here arranged singly about four feet apart.

increased in many localities. In the other general honey regions of the United States, it is usually profitable under favorable local conditions to keep from 200 to possibly 500 colonies in one apiary. There are so many factors to consider in determining this point that no general rules may be laid down. Since this is not a question which the beginner is called on to answer, it may be advised that the beekeeper decide each case individually from a study of the honey flora, the experience of other beekeepers and his own experience.

Out-apiaries

In locating colonies away from the central apiary, usually called an out-apiary or out-yard, easy transportation, especially to the main apiary, is most desirable. It is also an advantage to have the out-yard, especially one in which comb-honey is produced, near to the home of some person who can hive swarms which may issue in spite of precautions taken, and to protect the colonies from depredation. If these precautions are not practical, it is better to have the bees where they are not easily seen from the highway.

In establishing an out-apiary, the points previously mentioned should be considered as desirable but not essential. Since bees may be kept on roofs, in woods and in other places lacking many desirable features, it will be seen that it is not profitable to consider the desirable features too seriously. Another distinction should be made. If the out-apiary is permanent, it will pay better to plan the location thoroughly. However, many commercial beekeepers, especially those outside the white clover belt, think it wise to change the locations of their out-apiaries to meet changing conditions in the region and they, therefore, do not find it profitable to consider the conveniences in equipment in apiary planning to any great extent. To the commercial beekeeper the only essentials are the things which bring the greatest return. The amateur can better afford to spend time cutting grass and arranging hive-stands since his living does not depend on the crop and he has fewer colonies for which to plan.

CHAPTER XIII

THE MANIPULATION OF BEES

THE work which the beekeeper does with his bees has for its object an increase in their productiveness. Bees gather nectar and pollen when they are available in response to their own instincts to gather; they build wax when it is needed if space and food are available. The duties of the beekeeper are not concerned with creating these impulses. However, bees do not always work so as to accomplish the most efficient results, when measured by the commercial standards of the beekeeper, and the care which he bestows on his bees serves to provide conditions suitable for the turning of their natural instincts into those channels which will yield the greatest profit

COMMON MANIPULATIONS

Disturbance to be reduced to a minimum

Bees should be handled so that their work will be disturbed as little as possible, for the manipulations of the beekeeper are only accessory to their labors. Stings should be avoided. This is not so much because they are painful, but chiefly because the odor of the poison irritates bees and makes them difficult to manage. A veil (Fig. 27) and a good smoker (Fig. 25) are practically indispensable. By the use of smoke, the bees may be quieted so that they may be handled readily, the guards are disorganized and the bees gorge themselves with honey, after which they are not easily provoked to an attack. Too much smoke must be avoided as it disorganizes the entire colony and considerable time elapses before the bees fully return to their normal activities.

Hasty movements and the jarring of the hive are to be avoided. The organization of the bee's eyes enables it to see movement more readily than still objects. On seeing bees flying about the face, the beginner often strikes at them or moves quickly to escape the sting, thus provoking an attack. It requires quiet nerves not to jerk a frame or even to drop it when the hand in which it is held is stung.

Equipment for manipulation

Aside from a smoker, veil and hive-tool, the beekeeper needs no other equipment in opening a hive, but the beginner may find gloves (better those with the fingers removed) desirable. If special clothing is worn in the apiary, and it is desirable for both comfort and economy not to wear one's best; white suits are most satisfactory. They are the most comfortable in the heat of summer and the beekeeper has a good excuse for this comfort because they are best for apiary use.

When to handle bees

The best time to open hives is in the middle of warm days, especially when the bees are busily engaged in collecting nectar. Bees should never be handled at night nor on wet cold days. It is not always possible for the extensive beekeeper to choose the ideal time but it is well to plan to open hives in favorable periods, not only for the comfort of the operator but principally because it interferes least with the work of the colony.

Opening a hive

Before opening the hive, a little smoke should be blown in the entrance. When the cover is slightly raised, a little more smoke should be directed over the frames before the bees have an opportunity to escape. If the frames are covered by a mat or oilcloth, which is not desirable but often used, the outer cover may be removed entirely and one corner of the mat lifted to admit smoke. The covering then may be removed and the manipulation begun. In case the bees become troublesome at any time during the work, as they probably will if it is continued, more smoke may be blown over or directed down between the frames to disorganize new guards. No directions need be given as to the way to recognize trouble and it need only be stated that the most common fault is to use smoke too freely. During all manipulations the operator should stand at the side or back of the hive and not in front of it, to prevent interference of bees leaving and returning to the hive.

Fig. 105.—Hive-body resting on cover during manipulation.

If one wishes to examine the brood-chamber when the colony is in two or more hive-bodies or has comb-honey supers, the hive-cover serves as a good support for the removed bodies. They are placed diagonally on the cover (Fig. 105) with only four points of support, thus avoiding the crushing of bees. If a second body is removed, it may be placed out of line on the first in the same manner. If the bees show signs of robbing, combs in removed bodies should be protected more carefully.

Remedies for stings

Various remedies for stings have been advocated but all are valueless. The puncture made by the sting is so small that no liquid can enter it after the sting is removed and the opening has closed. As soon as practical, immediately if possible, the sting should be removed, care being taken not to squeeze the attached poison-sac. This can be done by scraping the sting out with a knife-blade or the fingernail. After this is done the injured spot should not be rubbed and the usual advice of the beekeeper is to "forget it." Bathing with liniment or any other irritation serves only to spread the poison through the tissues. The intense itching soon disappears. As a comfort to the novice, it may be stated that repeated stings usually cause an immunity to the poison to develop, after which no after-swelling occurs. In case of severe stinging, the injured parts may be covered with an ice-bag or with cloth wet with ice-water.

Removing frames

After the frames are exposed, the propolis which often fastens them may be loosened by prying gently with a hive-tool and the frames may be crowded somewhat closer together to permit the removal of one of them. It is immaterial which frame is removed first, unless the special object for opening the hive determines it. In cool weather the propolis may be brittle and care should be taken not to jar the hive as this is broken.

During manipulation, a side frame is often removed and leaned against the hive to allow more room for moving the other frames. In leaning a frame against the hive, it should be in a nearly upright position to prevent breakage and leaking of honey, and should not be placed in the hot sun. The frame on which the queen is located should not be left outside the hive unless necessary, for she may crawl away and be lost. The frame should be leaned against the hive on the side away from the operator so that he will not be annoyed by bees crawling up his legs. In all the handling of the colony, bees should not be crushed, for this excites the others, and if frames are crowded too closely together the queen may be killed.

Handling frames

In examining a comb, it should be held so that if any bees fall they will drop into the hive, except when it is necessary to carry away a frame for some purpose. Freshly gathered nectar sometimes drops out if the comb is improperly handled. If this falls into the hive the bees clean it up, whereas outside the hive it may cause robbing and is at least untidy. The beginner should early form the habit of keeping combs in a vertical position. While sometimes it does no harm to tip a frame, it is rarely necessary and may cause honey to leak or the comb to break, especially if the frame is not wired. As a comb is taken from the hive, it should be lifted by the ends of the top-bar, two hands being used. This brings the comb up vertically with one side toward the operator (Fig. 106). To examine the reverse side without tilting the comb, raise one end of the top-bar until it is perpendicular (Fig. 107), turn the frame on the top-bar as an axis until the reverse side is brought into view, and then lower to a horizontal position with the top-bar below (Fig. 108). In actual practice these steps are not taken successively but the turning on the top-bar is simultaneous with the raising and lowering of the end of the frame. This is a good operation for the beginner to practice a few times.

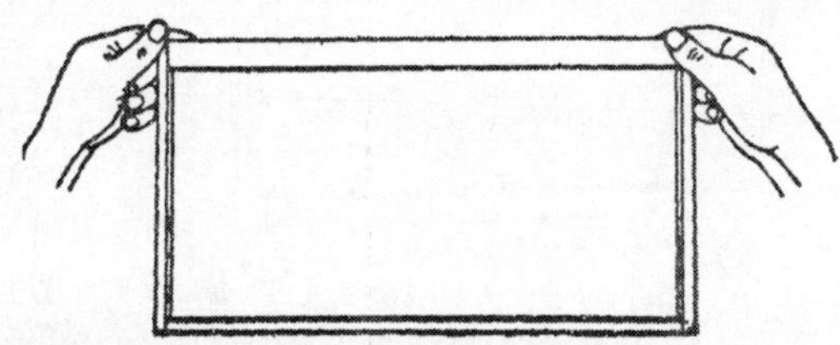

Fig. 106.—Handling a frame, first position.

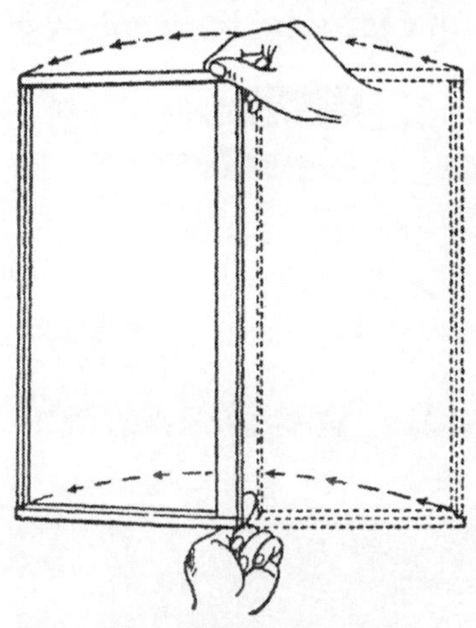

Fig. 107.—Handling a frame, second position.

Desirability of straight combs in manipulation

The use of comb-foundation in the frames is desirable to insure uniform comb, all of worker-cells, except in places where the foundation may sag or become torn. Drone-comb is undesirable for either brood-combs or supers except

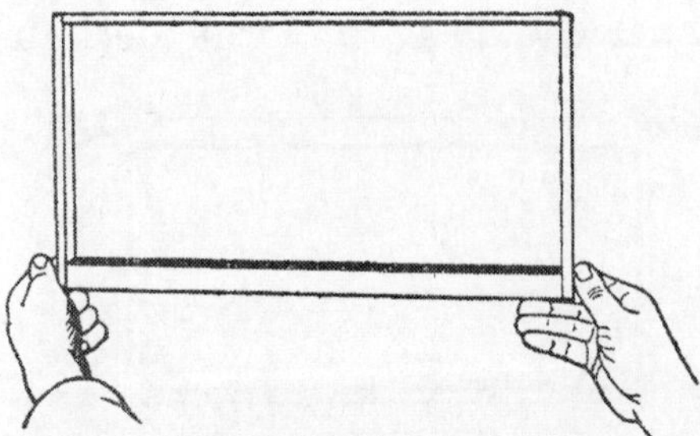

FIG. 108.—Handling a frame, third position.

in raising drones for queen-rearing. The use of comb-foundation in wired frames insures straight combs and reduces the danger of bees being crushed in removing or in returning frames. A frame-hive with combs built crosswise is more difficult to handle than a box-hive and this should never be permitted. The entrance of the hive should be exactly horizontal so that the combs will hang parallel with the sides of the hive and so that the outer ones are not fastened to the hive-body, if they are properly spaced at the top. The back of the hive should be about one inch higher than the front to allow condensed moisture to escape. A hive leveling device shown in Fig. 109 needs no description. The extensive beekeeper will not care to be bothered with such leveling, but this can usually be done adequately without a level. When colonies are in groups of four, the entire platform should be level.

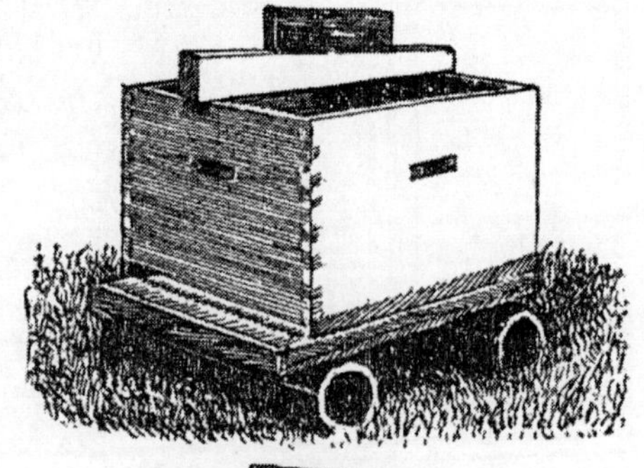

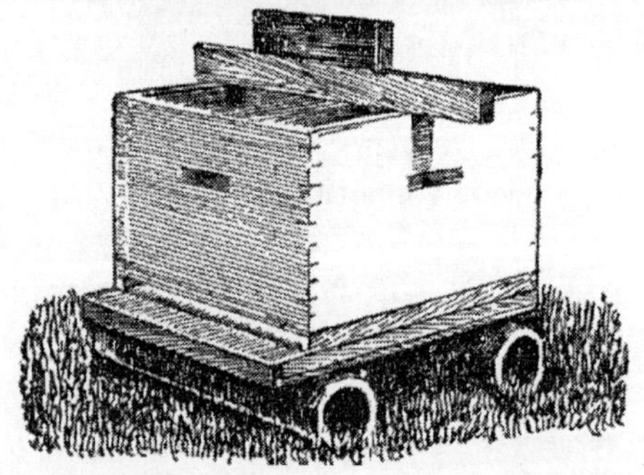

FIG. 109.—Hive leveling device. In the upper figure the wedge-shaped piece is on edge so that when the top is level the hive entrance is one inch lower than the back. In the lower figure the wedge is on its side.

Closing the hive

In closing a hive, after the frames are replaced and spaced properly, the cover should be put on in such a way as to crush no bees. If necessary the bees may be driven down by the use of smoke, but if bees are on the top edges of the hive, the cover may be slid on from the end or side so that none will be crushed.

OCCASIONAL MANIPULATIONS

In the following discussions manipulations will be described which may be useful at almost any time or at different times in the season but which are not part of the regular work of most apiaries. The plan is to give the various manipulations in the order in which they are used during the season. The manipulations discussed under this heading are most frequently useful in the spring.

Feeding

To stimulate brood-rearing or to provide stores in the spring, in preparing colonies for winter and at other times during a shortage of stores, it may be necessary to feed the bees. Obviously, it is desirable to allow the bees to keep sufficient honey and if this can be done it is always preferable to feeding. No better stimulation to heavy breeding in the spring can be found than adequate protection and an abundance of honey-stores, but a large amount of food is needed at this season and the beekeeper should feed if he finds that he has failed to leave enough. In small hives, the giving of additional stores in the spring is usually desirable, either in the form of combs of honey or as a sirup.

The feeding of sugar sirup to produce comb-honey has of course been tried and some beekeepers have believed that the product is honey. This is not the case and the fraud may readily be detected. Fortunately, even at the lowest prices of granulated sugar, the sections actually cost the beekeeper more than he gets for pure comb-honey and this fact effectually keeps adulterated comb-honey off the market.

What to feed

Honey from an unknown source should never be fed, because of the danger of introducing disease. Beekeepers usually feel that it is cheaper to feed sugar sirup because of the higher market value of honey, but no food for bees better than honey has yet been found. If extracted honey is fed, it should be somewhat diluted. The best plan is to give combs of honey, but one must make sure that the honey given to bees has not come from a colony infected with American foulbrood.

As a substitute for honey, a sirup made of granulated sugar is best. For spring feeding, a thin sirup may be used, even as dilute as two parts of water to one of sugar (by volume). Ordinarily equal parts of each are used. For supplying winter stores, a thick sirup, $2\frac{1}{4}$ to $2\frac{1}{2}$ parts of sugar to one of water, is preferable. To prevent granulation of the sugar in the thick sirup, it is inverted (changed chemically to levulose and dextrose) by the addition of a teaspoonful of tartaric acid to 20 pounds of sugar while the sirup is being heated to dissolve the sugar crystals. In early spring and late fall, sirup may be fed while warm and fall feeding should be done as rapidly as the bees will take the sirup. In making sirup, the greatest care must be taken not to allow it to be discolored by scorching the sugar; it should be as clear as if made with cold water. Glucose, other cheap sirups or molasses and the cheaper grades of sugar should not be fed to bees, especially for winter stores, since they contain substances indigestible to bees, causing dysentery.

Candy and cube sugar are sometimes used for supplying bees in winter after their stores are exhausted. These should be employed only in emergency and nothing but granulated sugar should be used in making candy for this purpose. A soft white sugar, known in the trade as "coffee A," placed in a division board-feeder is sometimes utilized as a stimulant to brood-rearing.

Slow feeding to prevent robbing is sometimes desirable during extracting or other manipulations or while rearing queens. A thin sirup of one part sugar to nine of water is used, being fed in large feeders in the open.

Feeders

There are numerous types of feeders, used for different purposes, and they are pictured and described in dealers' catalogues. The division board-feeder is hung in the hive like a frame. It may be filled without being removed and a float may be used to prevent bees from drowning. The Alexander feeder is useful mainly for stimulation. It may be placed under the rear of the brood-chamber if the bottom board is moved forward, but this often causes robbing and a better plan is to place it in a collar under the brood-chamber. For feeding small quantities, a "pepper-box feeder" may be inverted over the brood-frames and in an empty hive-body. Mason jars may be used in the same way, special pierced covers being sold by dealers in beekeeping supplies, and five-pound honey-pails with pierced covers are common. For rapid feeding in the fall, a large pan in an empty super (Fig. 110) is perhaps best. Green grass should be thrown in the sirup to give support to the

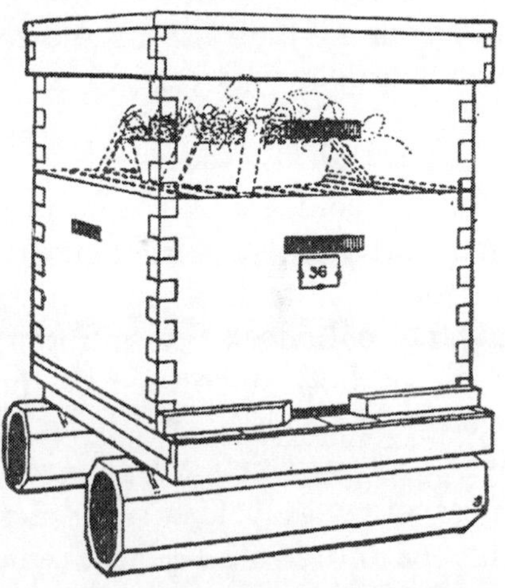

Fig. 110.—Pan in super arranged for feeding.

bees while feeding, this being better than excelsior or chips as it does not absorb the sirup. The empty super and pan may be placed under the brood-chamber for late feeding, in which case the bees take the sirup more rapidly.

Uniting

If a colony becomes queenless in late fall, it is usually not profitable to give it a queen, but it may be united with a normal colony to save the bees. It is not wise to try to winter weak colonies, but if two or more are united to make a strong colony, keeping the best queen, the risk in wintering is reduced and better results are obtained in the spring. It is also more profitable to unite weak colonies in the spring than to build them up, the usual method being to place one hive on top of another with about two thicknesses of newspaper between.

Influence of hive odor

Every colony has a distinctive odor by which bees recognize individuals from their own group, normally resenting the entrance to their hive of those from other colonies. In uniting colonies, the different odors may be hidden by smoking both vigorously. Tobacco smoke may be used, but if too much is employed the bees become stupefied. If bees are stupefied by tobacco smoke, chloroform or other anesthetics, they lose their memory of former locations and may be united and placed wherever desired, but American beekeepers rarely have occasion to use such methods. During a honey-flow, when the field bees are coming in heavily laden with nectar, the field bees of two colonies that are close together may be allowed to enter one hive and they do not molest each other. The queen to be saved should be caged for a day or two to overcome the danger of the strange bees killing her. When brood-rearing is reduced, as in the fall, the colony odor is apparently less influential, for less precaution is necessary in uniting.

Learning the new location

Field bees return to the location of their hive and they remember the old location and return to it if the hive is moved. If two colonies to be united are not close together, they should be moved gradually nearer, perhaps a foot every day that the bees can fly, until they are side by side. The bees learn each location in succession and after uniting they will not return to the original position and be lost. If it is necessary to move the colonies faster, they may be put into the new place and a pile of brush or weeds or a slanting board placed in front of the entrance so that when the bees fly out they will perceive a change and learn the new location. If it is desired to unite two weak swarms this may be done simply by placing them together, either in the hive or on the hive entrance. Swarming bees abandon the memory of the old location (p. 191); they are full of honey and may be placed anywhere. The better queen should be saved and the other removed or the bees may separate into clusters. Swarms may be added to newly established colonies if desired.

If queenless colonies are found in early spring which are to be united with normal colonies, the usual practice is to place them on top of the latter. Few bees return and there is usually no trouble as such bees seem ready to go to any colony.

Transferring

In increasing the apiary, it is sometimes profitable to buy colonies in box-hives because of their small cost. They should, of course, be transferred to movable-frame-hives as speedily as possible, for bees in box-hives are of small value as producers, because of the impossibility of manipulating the combs. The advice is often given to beginners to buy colonies in box-hives and transfer them, but this advice is questionable. There is no more trying work connected with beekeeping, unless possibly it is the moving of a large apiary, and if a beginner can transfer a colony from a box-hive successfully he has proved his right to become a beekeeper.

The best time to transfer colonies, if there is opportunity for choice, is the spring (during fruit bloom in the North) when the amount of honey and the population of the colony are at a minimum. However, the work can be done at any time during the active season, but there should be nectar coming to the hives so that while combs are exposed robbing will not be induced. If necessary, transferring may be done in a tent or cage of netting or wire to keep robbers away, but the odor of honey may cause excitement in the apiary. If the field bees are out of the hive, the work is lessened.

There are several methods of transferring and one may be chosen according to the plans and wishes of the beekeeper. Full descriptions of methods are given in Farmers' Bulletin 961 which may be obtained free from the Department of Agriculture, Washington, D. C.

Plan 1.—The box-hive is set a few feet to one side and in its place is put a hive with movable frames, containing full sheets of foundation or drawn-combs. As the field bees return, they go at once to the new hive. The box-hive is turned upside down and a small box is inverted over it. The box-hive is now pounded continuously (the operation being known as drumming or driving) in such a manner as to transmit the jar to the combs and the bees desert their combs for the upper box. They cluster in this box like a natural swarm and they may then be thrown in the new hive. If possible, the queen should be seen so that the operator may be sure that she is off the old combs. It is necessary that she be obtained, unless one desires to requeen at this time, in which event the old queen should be captured and the new one may be run in with the bees and will be accepted promptly. The box-hive containing the brood is now placed right side up in a new location. In twenty-one days all of the worker-brood will have emerged and possibly some new queens will be reared. These bees may be driven out and united with their former hive-mates by allowing them to run in the entrance. They should, however, be compelled to go through perforated zinc or a queen- and drone-trap (Fig. 31) to keep out the young queens. The old combs may now be melted after removing the honey. By this method straight combs are obtained. If nectar is not being collected, the newly established colony should be fed.

Plan 2.—Wait until a swarm issues from the box-hive and then move the old hive to a new location. The swarm is then placed in a new hive on the old stand and it is further increased by returning field bees. After twenty-one days the bees which have emerged are united with the bees in the new hive, as described under Plan 1.

Fig. 111.—Cutting combs from a box-hive.

Plan 3.—If the beekeeper desires to save the combs in the box-hive, the bees may be drummed into a box, after which the brood-combs and any other good combs are cut out (Fig. 111) and fitted into frames, being fastened with string, rubber bands or strips of wood until the bees have an opportunity to repair them. These frames are hung in a hive on the old stand and the bees are then allowed to run in. The cutting of combs, especially those containing brood and honey, is disagreeable and, since combs from a box-hive are usually of little value, this method is not recommended.

Plan 4.—Another method which is in some respects better than those just given is to place the box-hive with its largest surface uppermost. If the bottom is now open, it is closed except for an entrance and a piece is removed from the upper side of the box-hive. The hive in which the colony is to be located is now put over the large opening and all cracks and openings around it are closed. The upper hive is filled with drawn-combs or, if these are not available, with sheets of foundation. When the queen needs more room for egg-laying, she will go to the upper hive and, after she is located there, a queen excluder is put between the box-hive and the new hive to prevent her return. As the brood emerges below, the colony becomes established above. If there is difficulty in getting the queen to go to the new hive, the box-hive may be drummed. After the brood in the old combs has all emerged, the bees may be drummed from the box-hive and it may be treated as desired.

Transferring from walls of houses

Swarms often locate in the walls of houses and it is sometimes necessary to remove them to prevent damage from melting combs. If the cavity in which the combs are built is accessible, the method is the same as in transferring under the third plan, except that drumming is impractical and the combs must be cut out with the bees still adhering to them. A liberal use of smoke will subdue them. If it is impossible to open the cavity without doing considerable damage to the building, a bee-escape (Fig. 21) may be put over the entrance so that the bees can leave but cannot return, any other openings to the combs being carefully closed. Even better than a bee-escape is a cone of wire-cloth about eight inches high with a hole at the apex just large enough for a single bee to pass. This is tacked on the house and the bees issue through the hole in the apex but do not find it again to return. A hive (with drawn combs in it if possible) is then placed so that its entrance is as near as practical to the entrance which the bees have been using. A queen should soon be introduced to the bees in the hive. The old queen does not desert her combs and continues laying eggs, but, as her colony is depopulated, the amount of brood rapidly diminishes. As brood emerges, the young bees also leave through the wire-cloth cone and join the bees in the hive until in four or five weeks the queen on the old combs is left practically alone. When nearly all of the bees are out of the cavity and there is little or no brood, the bee-escape is removed, the entrance to the cavity is made larger if possible and if there is no honey-flow, the bees rob their old home and carry the honey to their new hive, leaving only the empty combs. These will usually do no damage as wax-moths soon destroy them. The entrance to the cavity should now be closed carefully to prevent another swarm from taking up quarters there and the hive is removed. This method takes considerable time, but is often best where the cavity is inaccessible. It is often difficult to close the cavity to prevent the bees from establishing a new entrance when a bee-escape is placed over the one to which they are accustomed.

Transferring from hollow trees

The method will depend on the accessibility of the cavity and the value of the tree. Usually the bees cannot be drummed out and the combs must be cut out after subduing the bees with smoke. If the colony is high and the tree is felled, the bees are disorganized by the jarring so that they can be handled easily. The hunting of colonies in the woods is interesting and the cutting of a bee tree is an experience which everyone interested in bees should have, but the time consumed is considerably more than the value of the bees and honey justify. It does not pay to build up the apiary in this way if the beekeeper's time is valuble.

Preventing robbing in the apiary

At any time during warm weather, bees are inclined to rob other colonies, if there is no honey-flow. Every precaution should be taken to prevent this. Feeding often attracts other bees and if there are indications of robbing, it should be deferred until late in the day. Honey left where bees can get it or combs left out of the hives during manipulations may at times lead to serious robbing.

As soon as robbers are noticed, manipulation should be discontinued and the hives should be closed. If serious robbing occurs, the entrance should be contracted and the hive-fronts wiped with a cloth moistened with kerosene or carbolic acid. If brush is thrown at the entrances, robbers are less likely to enter. Outdoor feeding to prevent robbing is described in a previous section (p. 257).

A wire-cloth cage, five feet square and six feet high, may be used if manipulations are necessary during a time when robbing is probable. This cage should not be closed at the top and bees which fly from the colony under manipulation escape, while robbers will rarely enter. A folding tent or cage made of mosquito-netting may also be used. A smaller wire cage closed at the top may be set over a colony that is being robbed.

If the cause of robbing is suddenly removed, this may produce more excitement than if the robber bees were allowed to complete their work. For example, if a colony is being robbed and is suddenly removed to save it, the robbers turn their attention to other colonies, or if a piece of exposed comb has attracted robbers, its removal may divert them to more serious devastation.

The beginner in beekeeping may mistake the play flights of young bees for robbing, but after the latter has once been observed this error will not be repeated. Bees appear old soon after they begin robbing; they are dark and thin, their actions are nervous, and the hairs on the body are lost, probably by being torn off by defending bees and by squeezing through narrow openings.

When a colony is abnormal, as in queenlessness or disease, it may be robbed of its stores slowly, without any excitement, usually by the bees of a single colony.

Moving bees

In migratory beekeeping, in bringing purchased bees to the apiary and under various other circumstances the beekeeper will find it necessary to move bees. The frames must be fastened firmly in place. If self-spacing frames are used, especially if there is considerable propolis on them, no precautions need be taken to prevent the swinging of the frames, but it is often desirable to nail a ⅜-inch strip in the bee-space over the tops of the frames so that they cannot fall out of place if the hive is tipped. Abundant ventilation should be given, the amount depending on the temperature. In cold weather, the entrances may simply be closed with a block and the cover fastened securely, but in extremely hot weather it is desirable to remove the cover or both the cover and the bottom board and nail on wire-cloth (Fig. 112). A 2-inch collar may be fastened to the top of the hive-body and wire-cloth put above this, to give clustering space for the bees. Colonies rarely suffer from exposure during moving so that the beekeeper should not err by giving inadequate ventilation. In transporting colonies on a truck or wagon, the length of the frames should be across the wagon-bed, while on a train they should be parallel with the length of the car.

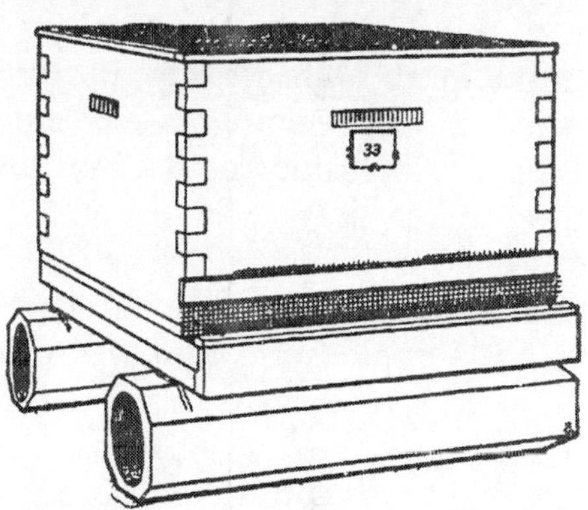

Fig. 112.—Hive ready for moving. In this case the bottom board is left on.

It is customary to ship colonies in hives with combs, but recently the shipping of bees in wire-cloth cages without combs has been practiced. This has much to commend it, especially in reducing the danger of introducing bee diseases into new locations. The cages contain numerous slats on which the bees hang, and they are provided with food for the bees en route. The bees are put into the cage by means of a funnel, either with or without a queen. Bees are now regularly sold by the pound in such packages and shipped to all parts of the United States. It is probable that as this method is perfected it will be used in migratory beekeeping, thus avoiding danger of carrying disease to the home apiary and reducing the transportation charges.

ELIMINATION OF NON-ESSENTIAL MANIPULATIONS

While it is necessary in any discussion of beekeeping which aims at completeness to describe the various manipulations which may be needed during the course of the year, the beekeeper should early in his experience establish a system for the care of his bees so that unessential movements and manipulations may be avoided. If bees are solely for pleasure, it matters little whether they are disturbed in their work, and the time of the beekeeper need not be considered an important consideration, but when bees are kept for profit, these factors become vital. Every manipulation which does not benefit the beekeeper by increasing his profit should be eliminated ruthlessly, and every time a colony is opened it should be for some definite purpose.

Two essentials

Two factors are necessary to the production of the maximum honey crop over which the beekeeper has no control. He cannot govern the weather or produce honey-plants with profit. There are, on the other hand, two other factors with which his work must deal. His efforts should be for the purpose (1) of getting plenty of bees of the right age in time for the harvest and (2) of keeping these bees in proper condition for gathering the maximum crop. The first essential is far-reaching and obviously includes the entire care of the colonies to prevent starvation or loss from other causes. It applies especially to the work in the preparation period from early fall until the honey-flow of the following year. The second essential applies chiefly to the control of swarming. It is well for the beekeeper to keep these two essentials always before him and to ask himself, when he plans any work with the bees, whether it comes under one of these heads.

The beekeeper may profitably go one step further in the analysis. For example, stimulative feeding in the spring is mentioned earlier in this chapter. He should first of all determine whether stimulative feeding is more profitable than the giving of abundant stores. If he finds that he gets more bees by stimulative feeding, he should then determine whether he obtains enough more to justify the expenditure of time and money, or whether he can get a larger total crop by keeping a few more colonies, combined with the giving of abundant stores. An example taken from life may not be amiss, the names being here omitted. Two beekeepers are located in exceptional situations which may be assumed to be equally good. One of these men is skilled in the improvement of his stock and has made significant progress, but the work occupies considerable time. The other beekeeper feels that he has not the time for this (and he may not have the skill), but he keeps one hundred colonies more than his co-worker. In the case just cited the beekeeper with the larger number of colonies makes more money, but this illustration is by no means given to discourage breeding. It shows, however, that for that particular region the greater profits come with extensive beekeeping, while in other sections more intensive work might yield better financial returns. Both men have the same object in view—to produce workers on time for the harvest. Both are successful while all about them are beekeepers with indifferent or poor success, attributed probably to bad luck.

Increase in efficiency through system

Not only must these essentials be emphasized, but the necessary manipulations must be systematized. After some effort in this respect, the beekeeper is usually astonished at what may be accomplished. This may be illustrated by another case. This beekeeper began work with bees on a business basis after keeping a few colonies for pleasure for several years. At the beginning of his experience he taught school, thus having his Saturdays for the bees as well as the summer vacation. At first the vacation was six months, but later the school year was increased, giving him only three months. By systematizing his work, he was able to do as much as formerly and gradually increased his colonies to 250 in three apiaries, all run for comb-honey. He then gave up teaching and accepted a position which kept him away from his bees except during thirty days' vacation in the summer. At first he was frequently near his bees so that if any work was necessary he could arrange to have it done by others. Finally he accepted another position which took him entirely away from his old home and he now goes back just before the honey-flow and leaves as soon as it is over. He still produces comb-honey and is still successful. He has probably almost reached the maximum number of colonies that he can run for comb-honey in so short a time. It is obvious that many manipulations usually considered necessary must be eliminated in these apiaries. By leaving plenty of stores and by giving the bees abundant protection many of these are rendered unnecessary. This case is not by any means recorded as ideal, but it illustrates what the elimination of superfluous manipulations may accomplish.

Anyone can produce honey in a time of plenty, but only the good beekeeper gets an adequate return in less abundant seasons. The ideals toward which the beekeeper should work are: (1) to handle the bees as little as possible; (2) to manipulate them only when he has some definite object in view; (3) to follow a definite system, not based on rules but on a knowledge of bees, capable of modification as occasion may arise, but working for one end—maximum honey-production.

CHAPTER XIV

SPRING MANAGEMENT

In attempting to give the work of the apiary in chronological order, it is difficult to decide where to begin. To a large degree, success depends on the results obtained in wintering, so that preparation for winter might be considered the first step in the annual cycle, and practical beekeepers usually so consider it. However, winter is a period during which the beekeeper has little work with his bees, and it is perhaps better to begin the cycle with the first evidences of activity outside the hive. As has been shown, bees do not hibernate, and consequently their early flights are not evidences of an awakening after a period of inactivity. With their first return to the open air in the spring, the beekeeper knows that the active season with his bees has arrived.

As will be shown in the chapter on wintering (see also p. 157), bees are often compelled to retain their feces for long periods in winter. This, together with the excessive generation of heat, may deplete the colony, causing conditions known as spring dwindling and dysentery, one or both of which may be present.

It will also be shown later that it is not desirable to manipulate bees in winter. Brood-rearing may begin during the severe weather of January or February in the North in colonies wintered out-of-doors, but this can scarcely be considered as an activity of spring.

With the opening of the earliest spring flowers and the accompanying rise in temperature, the bees venture forth to get the small amounts of nectar and pollen thus provided.

As the weather becomes warmer the supplies rapidly increase and the bees are greatly stimulated to build up the colony. The old bees that emerged the previous autumn have, under ordinary winter conditions, expended considerable energy, and their ability to do the collecting and the inside work in the spring is in general in inverse ratio to the expenditure of energy in the winter. Brood-rearing, however, begins before or as soon as new supplies come to the hive, provided, of course, that the colony is normal, and as the first bees emerge they in turn increase the capacity of the colony for brood-rearing, so that with a good queen and other favorable conditions the amount of brood is rapidly increased.

ACCEPTED SPRING MANIPULATIONS

The main object of the work in the spring is to insure an abundance of bees in time for the harvest. In the more northern localities, summer comes on with a rush and often the principal nectar-secreting plants are in bloom so soon after cold weather that the colony is frequently not in condition to obtain the maximum crop; or there may be a period in the spring when, from lack of nectar, the bees are not stimulated to the maximum breeding. If left to themselves and if honey is already present in the hive, bees will naturally rear brood and thereby rapidly increase the size of the colony, and the work of the beekeeper is to provide within the hive the most favorable conditions for the manifestation of this instinct.

Prevention of drifting

Colonies which are wintered in the cellar need not be put in the same locations that they occupied the previous year, when they are removed. In setting them out, some care is necessary to prevent mixing. If they can fly as soon as they are set out, they may rush forth and then be unable again to locate the proper hive, in which case they often "drift," that is, bees enter the wrong colonies with the result that some colonies will be increased in size at the expense of others. If bees can be set out at night or on a cloudy or chilly day, this is generally avoided. The entrances may also be reduced or, if necessary, may be closed with wet cloths.

Spring protection

If the colonies have been wintered in the cellar, breeding normally will not begin so soon as in colonies that were left outside. When the hives are carried to their summer stands, the bees are subjected to sudden changes in temperature and to low temperatures and, unless the wintering has been exceptionally good, they may be less able to withstand adverse conditions than colonies that were wintered in the open. It is, therefore, preferable to provide packing for these colonies, even if it is only a wrapping of waterproof paper over the hive. After colonies are removed, the bees need a cleansing flight to rid themselves of the accumulated feces and they should be put out at a time when this will probably soon be possible.

First examinations

During early breeding, the beekeeper ought to have no occasion to open a hive, but if he finds that certain colonies are not up to standard, he may choose a warm day to open them. After a winter away from the bees, the keeper is usually anxious to look at them. On a fine warm day when the bees are flying freely, he should make his first general examination of the apiary but, if he has previously supplied the colonies with abundant stores and has protected them from changes of temperature, this may well be put off. If he desires to learn whether the bees have sufficient stores he can determine this by lifting the hive, or the size of the cluster may be determined, without breaking the propolis which seals the cover, by looking at the combs from below.

On the first examination, the beekeeper should look especially for queenless colonies. If any are found, it is best to unite these with normal colonies, although queens may now be obtained early from southern breeders. He should also examine the stores, for bees require large amounts of food during the spring and, while they usually get considerable nectar, it rarely is enough to provide stores for excessive breeding. If food is needed, it may be given rapidly in the form of a thick sugar sirup, or it is even better to provide combs of honey. If hives are soiled with the spottings of dysentery or if dead bees are present, the hives may be cleaned out somewhat, but the first examination should be brief, unless the weather is exceptionally warm.

Spring dwindling

The old bees die rapidly and are replaced by young ones, which, in a good colony, emerge more rapidly than the old ones disappear. If, on the contrary, mortality among the old bees exceeds the rate of emergence, the condition arises which is known as spring dwindling. Obviously, prevention is better than treatment, but by giving extra protection and by making the collection of stores unnecessary by feeding, the energy of the old bees may be conserved so that it is utilized chiefly in rearing brood and the colony may often be saved. The brood-chamber may also be reduced to conserve the heat of the cluster.

Need of water

Bees need water for brood-rearing and it sometimes happens in the spring that they are lost in trying to obtain it. If there is no water close at hand, it is often advantageous to provide a watering place in a warm sheltered spot in or near the apiary.

Uniting

If exceptionally weak colonies are found, it is economy not to attempt to build them up, but to unite them. In uniting in the spring, two weak colonies should not be placed together, but a weak colony should be united with a strong one. If desired, the number can be restored by subsequent division. This is one of the most important points in spring management.

Cleaning the hives

When the weather becomes settled, it is desirable, especially when comb-honey is produced, to subject the hive to a spring house-cleaning. If the bottom board is cleaned of débris and the propolis is scraped from the frames and rabbets, it will not only facilitate future manipulations but, when the sections are put on, there will be less propolis to discolor them. While Caucasian bees were kept in the apiary of the Bureau of Entomology the removal of propolis in the spring was practically a necessity. This may be done quickly in the spring, while the propolis is brittle. Miller used a hoe to remove propolis and burr combs from the top-bars of the brood-frames.

Equalizing the colonies

Not all colonies increase in population equally fast, even with the best management. The differences may be due to a variety of causes. If some colonies have more stores than they need, thereby reducing the space available for brood-rearing, combs of honey may be removed and given to colonies that need more stores, returning to the rich colonies empty combs removed from those to which honey is given. Similarly, if some hives contain more brood than the average, colonies may be equalized by taking combs of emerging brood with the adhering workers away from those abundantly supplied, giving them to weaker colonies, care being exercised not to transfer the queen. The weakest colonies in the apiary should be assisted in this way only after all the others are equalized; then they are given any frames of brood still available, and are thus built up as rapidly as possible. Another method of equalizing is to shake bees from the frames of a strong colony in front of the entrances of those to be helped. The young bees go in and are accepted, while the field bees return to their original hive. The queen must, of course, not be shaken in this way. The advantages of having colonies develop at about the same rate and of reaching the honey-flow equally strong in bees, are as follows: (1) the colonies are ready for a given manipulation at the same time, thus allowing the work to be well systematized; (2) less hive-bodies are needed than if strong colonies are given supers in accordance with their individual needs; (3) when properly done, equalizing probably results in an actual increase in the total number of bees in the apiary, since every queen is more nearly capable of egg-laying to her full capacity and no queen is restricted by having only a small number of workers to feed her brood; (4) less manipulation is necessary when the honey-flow begins (especially in comb-honey-production) in sorting combs of brood and in reducing the brood to one hive-body, if this is practiced; (5) the brood is compact and this is especially desirable in comb-honey-production.

The work of equalizing colonies is considerable and the beekeeper must determine for himself whether it is profitable. In the management of out-apiaries, this work necessitates extra trips which come at a time when the average beekeeper has all the work that he can do. Making colonies in one mold often fails to bring to light the deficiencies of some queens and the superior qualities of others for breeding stock. If a brood disease is present or is even known to be in the neighborhood, there is danger in moving combs about so freely.

Clipping queens

The clipping of the wings of queens is advantageous in the control of swarms, as will be shown, and to find queens in the spring is easier than later. In clipping the queen, she is lifted from the comb, held securely but gently between the thumb and index finger of the left hand and a wing is cut off with fine scissors. The queen may be held with her wing against wood, when it may be cut with a sharp penknife, but scissors are safer, at least for the beginner. Some beekeepers clip the queen's wing when she is introduced, in case queens are mated from nuclei, but some colonies may rear queens without the knowledge of the owner and an examination for unclipped queens in the spring will greatly reduce swarms which issue with queens capable of flight. Some beekeepers, so that they can tell a queen's age, clip opposite wings on alternate years or make a distinctive cut each year. It may perhaps be well to warn the beginner against clipping the wings of an unmated queen. If egg-laying is progressing regularly the queen is of course mated.

Summary of favorable spring conditions

The conditions favorable to the rapid increase in the size of the colony in the spring may be restated as follows: (1) a large number of vigorous workers, due to successful wintering; (2) a prolific queen; (3) abundant stores properly located in the hive so as to be easily accessible to the bees; (4) favorable weather conditions; (5) fresh pollen and nectar and water for the bees; (6) a prolific race or strain of bees; (7) good brood-combs of worker-cells in quantity sufficient for the needs of the colony.

QUESTIONABLE MANIPULATIONS

The manipulations previously discussed are not practiced by all beekeepers but they are not the subject of controversy. On the other hand, two spring manipulations have been the subject of much discussion by beekeepers and are still in dispute. These are spring stimulative feeding and the spreading of the brood.

Stimulative feeding

So long as nectar is coming to the hive in abundance, the colony is stimulated to the maximum brood-rearing possible in proportion to the population. Frequently, however, there are periods when from a lack of nectar-secretion or inclement weather, no fresh supply of food is obtained. It is asserted by some that the feeding of a thin sugar sirup at this time in small quantities acts just as a natural honey-flow, stimulating the bees to greater activity in brood-rearing and resulting in the maximum strength of colony at the time of the honey-flow. Since feeding requires some manipulation of the colony which is not beneficial in inclement weather, many beekeepers believe that by providing an abundance of food in the fall or by giving stores rapidly in the spring the colony received all the stimulus to brood-rearing that it should have and that stimulative feeding is not desirable. This is obviously a question especially for the northern beekeeper. If a colony is short of stores, combs of honey may be given. If a colony has wintered well, has a good queen, is in a large hive abundantly supplied with stores and is well protected from changes in temperature, it is doubtful whether it can be stimulated to any greater brood-rearing. Even if stimulating feeding results in increased brood-rearing, as it may under some circumstances, the beekeeper may still find it to be unprofitable. If he is managing several apiaries, the work of going to all of them daily, or even less frequently, is considerable, and he may find it more profitable simply to operate more colonies to make up for the difference. If stimulative feeding is practiced, it is usually best to feed warm sirup in the evenings so that the bees will not fly as a result of the feeding and so that robbing will not be started.

Spreading the brood

Spreading brood is an even more debated question. If the brood-cluster is divided and an empty comb is inserted, the bees will attempt to cover all the brood and, in so doing, that part of the empty comb which intervenes will be kept warm enough so that the queen will lay eggs therein. When this new brood is well started, the manipulation may be repeated and still more eggs will be laid. This is attractive in theory but in practice is attended with extreme danger. The bees may not attempt to cover both portions of the divided brood, resulting in loss, or, because of exceptionally cold weather, they may contract the cluster and leave the outside brood to die. The beginner should by all means leave the amount of brood to be determined by the bees, confining his work to the supplying of protection, stores and room for the expansion of the brood.

If the giving of abundant protection, stores and room for the maximum advantageous expansion of the brood will cause the colony, from its own instinct, to reach its maximum strength in time for the storage of the crop, then additional manipulations in stimulative feeding and in spreading of the brood, even though they may do no harm, are non-essential. They are, therefore, to be condemned for the commercial apiary. If the favorable conditions enumerated do not bring the necessary strength of colony and if stimulative feeding will, then these manipulations are justifiable. If the period for brood-rearing previous to the beginning of the honey-flow is short, rapid brood-rearing becomes more important. This is usually the case in northern localities. It is safe to say, however, that stimulative feeding and spreading of the brood should not be practiced early in the spring but should be confined to a period of not more than six weeks just previous to the particular honey-flow for which the beekeeper is building up his colonies. If the main crop is in late summer, the beekeeper need not force his bees in the spring. In some localities, the season is made up of a series of honey-flows of about equal importance. If there are long intervals between honey-flows, the beekeeper must see that brood-rearing is at its best during a period of six or eight weeks before each flow.

Substitutes for pollen

Beekeepers sometimes notice that during a shortage of pollen bees will pack meal or sawdust on their legs, just as they do pollen, and will carry it to the hive. There are also reports of coal-dust being carried in this way. After observing bees gather rye flour from a neighboring mill, Dzierzon put some in his apiary where the bees could get it readily, and they carried it in eagerly. Based presumably on his recommendation, beekeepers have for some years been in the habit of supplying rye, pea, corn or oatmeal finely ground in the spring. Since pollen has long been recognized as the source of protein food for the bees, it has been the aim of beekeepers to obtain for this purpose flours or meals which have a high protein-content. The best material for pollen substitutes is not chemically much like pollen and all contain a large percentage of starch which the bees cannot utilize as food. There seems until recently to be only one actual trial in brood-rearing on such materials, but not long ago R. L. Parker tested all of the commonly used materials on bees in a greenhouse and found that they could not rear brood to the pupal stage on any of them. The use of pollen substitutes cannot, therefore, be recommended.

CHAPTER XV

SWARM CONTROL AND INCREASE[1]

AT the close of the chapter on the manipulation of bees, it is pointed out that success in honey-production depends (1) on getting bees in time for the harvest and (2) on keeping them in the proper condition for storing. The first requirement is discussed in the chapter immediately preceding. However, if a colony of bees builds up rapidly to full strength, the beekeeper is confronted by the problem of preventing it from dividing its forces, thereby causing him to fail in getting the maximum crop, or even to get no surplus from it. This second problem is mainly involved in swarm control, but also includes the providing of other conditions favorable for storing.

THE PROBLEM OF SWARM CONTROL

Loss from division of the working force

In the days of the box-hive, success in beekeeping was measured by the number of swarms that issued, but the beekeeper now knows that he cannot increase the number of his colonies during a honey-flow without curtailing his crop, unless the increase is made from brood that would emerge too late for the resulting bees to assist in gathering nectar. Success in manipulation is now measured by the results the beekeeper attains in preventing swarming. If swarms issue, as they will at times in spite of every known

[1] For a more complete study of the management of bees during the swarming season, the reader is urged to consult Farmers' Bull. 1198 of the U. S. Dept. Agr., "Swarm Control" by Geo. S. Demuth, 46 pp., 12 figs.

precaution, the beekeeper then aims to use the bees so as still to keep them together and thus to overcome the danger of a reduced crop. Because the experienced beekeeper so well knows that swarming endangers his crop and also that swarms may be lost, the usual statements concerning the beauty of a swarm fail to meet a ready response from him. To him, swarming is the one great handicap in beekeeping.

The necessity of keeping the bees together cannot be overestimated. If a colony is divided just before or during the honey-flow, the two parts fail to produce as much surplus honey as the same bees would if they had remained in one colony and in normal condition. Furthermore, when bees are preparing to swarm, their condition is not so favorable for gathering. Whether there is some physiological difference or whether the lack of concentrated effort in gathering is due to an unbalanced condition of the colony population is not known, but the results of the swarming preparations are shown in a decrease in the crop. In successful honey-production it, therefore, becomes essential that every effort be made to reduce and to overcome the tendency to swarm.

Variation in swarming

It is interesting to note that, in any region, swarming usually occurs at a certain season and rarely throughout the entire active season. It is most common in those sections of the North in which the main honey-flow comes in early summer. If there are two heavy honey-flows, swarming may occur in connection with each one, although it is usually less troublesome in the later one. The crowded condition of the hive in the production of comb-honey is favorable for the development of the swarming tendency and, since the early summer honey-flows of the North are the best for comb-honey, the control of swarming is most difficult in northern comb-honey apiaries.

That many comb-honey-producers crowd their colonies more than is necessary or desirable will be shown in a later chapter, but, even with the most skillful manipulation of the supers and with the proper manipulations throughout, there is always more crowding than is necessary in extracted-honey-production. Swarm control is, therefore, chiefly a problem for the northern comb-honey-producer, and from these men have been obtained the best systems for controlling swarming and also the most information on its cause.

In the South, where the honey-flows are longer and less intense, swarming is less frequent, and this is also true in the irrigated regions of the West. In those sections of the tropics where the honey-flows are practically continuous, there may be a kind of swarming season, but swarms are so much less frequent that the northern beekeeper would not consider the control of swarming a serious problem in such a locality.

Variation in colonies in respect to swarming preparations

In any apiary and in almost any season, colonies differ greatly in their propensity to swarm. (1) Some show no indication of swarming. These are the very best for honey-production and the beekeeper should aim to increase their number. (2) Other colonies show a tendency to swarm by starting queen-cells, but may be deterred either by cutting out the newly started queen-cells or by taking away some combs of brood. (3) Still other colonies are more persistent and will swarm if the honey-flow continues unless they are subjected to some radical manipulations (4) Some colonies whose queens fail swarm in connection with the supersedure of the old queen.

"Of 160 colonies run for comb honey that were fair subjects for comparison, 13¾ per cent went through the season without ever offering to start queen-cells; 12½ per cent started cells one or more times, but gave it up when their cells were destroyed; and 73¾ per cent seemed so bent on swarming that they were treated by being kept queenless 10 or 15 days. The colonies that were left with their queens all the time averaged 36½ per cent more sections than those that were treated. But that's better than they would have done if left queenless for 21 days, which would be the case practically if swarms were shaken."[1]

Direction of the beekeeper's efforts

The work of the beekeeper in swarm control may be divided into two phases, for his manipulation of a colony depends on his recognition of the degree of persistence in swarming which a colony exhibits. He may try to increase the number of colonies which make no preparations to swarm and may prevent swarming in the colonies which respond to simple measures. To these manipulations may be given the name preventive measures.

However, the beekeeper finds some colonies which he knows from experience cannot be kept from swarming by cutting out queen-cells, by the removal of a frame or two of brood or by other simple expedients. To describe the difference which the beekeeper recognizes is somewhat difficult, but, in general, if the larvæ in the queen-cells are still small, preventive measures may be used. In cases of the building of queen-cells obviously due to supersedure or when the working force is relatively not so strong as the brood, an artificial swarm should not be made. To the more drastic measures, used on colonies with advanced larvæ in the queen-cells which will persist in their preparations to swarm, the name remedial is proposed.

PREVENTIVE MEASURES

Whatever the system of management, the earliest manipulations in swarm control will usually be preventive measures, for the beekeeper cannot know very far in advance which colonies will fail to respond to the less drastic manipulations and in any event these will deter swarming in the larger number of colonies.

[1] Miller, C. C., 1905. Gleanings in Bee Culture, XXXIII, p. 1174

Breeding

Some beekeepers make a practice of requeening colonies which swarm with young queens which are the progeny of queens whose colonies have not swarmed, in an effort to eliminate swarming by selection of non-swarming stock. In a sense, this work has failed, for after years of such selection the bees still swarm under favorable conditions, but the testimony of many practical beekeepers indicates that the percentage of colonies that swarm under proper management is reduced by selection of non-swarming stock. Since the men who are making this selection are, at the same time, improving the manipulations in swarm control and are becoming more skilled in this work, it is somewhat difficult to measure the value of this effort. Since requeening from good stock is a highly commendable practice for other reasons, it seems advisable to choose breeders from those which have not swarmed, wherever possible. If breeding queens are chosen from the colonies which show the best results in honey crops, they will usually be from colonies that have not swarmed during the season.

Mechanical devices

Efforts have been made to devise a hive which will give to the bees an environment in which the swarming tendency will usually not be developed, a well-known example of which is the Aspinwall hive, with slatted frames between the combs. Similar slats between the frames of ordinary hives have been used. Since a non-swarming hive is needed especially in the production of comb-honey, it would appear that there should be provision for more crowding of the bees than is given in the Aspinwall hive, but it is perhaps too early to pass judgment on the efforts in this line. A deep (two-inch) bottom board with a large entrance (Miller, "Fifty Years Among the Bees") leaves space under the frames in which may be placed a slatted rack during the active season. This provides abundant ventilation and room for bees and may act as a preventive of swarming, although it was not so claimed by Miller. The use of large hives in the production of extracted honey, which so successfully reduces swarming, may be considered as the giving of an environment unsuitable for the development of the swarming tendency rather than the control of swarming by manipulation.

Preventive manipulations

The most common methods of preventing swarming are by manipulation, probably because success, if attained, is immediately recognizable. Greater progress has been made in the devising of manipulations for this purpose than is shown in breeding or in the invention of mechanical devices. The manipulations used by the beekeeper in swarm prevention fall into the following classes: (1) the introduction of young queens (preferably from superior stock, possibly the progeny of queens whose colonies have not swarmed); (2) the prevention of crowding in the brood-chamber previous to the honey-flow, the crowding incident to comb-honey-production being brought about only after supers are put on. This is often accomplished by giving an extra hive-body for early brood-rearing, so that there is abundant room for brood and stores; (3) the use of bait sections or extracting combs (Fig. 135) in the first super in comb-honey-production, thus inducing the bees to begin work in the supers promptly to avoid excessive and unnecessary crowding in the brood-chamber; (4) the proper manipulation of supers in comb-honey-production (p. 328) to reduce crowding as far as possible (possibly also to remove young bees from the brood-chamber); (5) the use of only good worker-comb in the brood-chamber to reduce the number of cells unavailable for worker eggs; (6) ventilation (by raising the hive on blocks, or by large entrances); (7) shade, to prevent overheating; (8) the removal of combs of brood which are replaced by empty combs or sheets of foundation to relieve the congestion (see also this manipulation under remedial measures); (9) the removal of queen-cells soon after they are started, since if queen-cells are well advanced, their removal is not so effective in preventing swarming. This usually requires an examination of the brood-chamber once in seven to ten days.

Miller's methods

To make these manipulations clear, it may be well to recapitulate by describing the system used by the late C. C. Miller. To provide abundant bees in time for the harvest, as well as to eliminate any tendency to early swarming, strong colonies were given an extra hive-body, during the rapid spring breeding, all the combs being built to the bottom bar of the frame so far as practical. Colonies were requeened whenever a queen showed signs of inability to keep up the full strength of colony, these queens being from mothers whose colonies had not swarmed. When the honey-flow began, a single hive-body for each colony was filled with full combs of brood (any additional combs of brood being used in other less populous colonies, for increase or for other purposes) and each colony was given a super containing one or more bait sections, into which the bees went at once, if the honey-flow permitted. Miller was a master in the manipulation of supers and the system used by him is described in a later chapter (p. 328). His hives had wide entrances (2 inches deep) and were protected by trees from the heat of the sun. Frequent examinations were made to remove newly started queen-cells. The crops which Miller obtained were so much greater than those of other beekeepers similarly situated, or even than those in better locations, that his methods should be studied carefully. He used the 8-frame Langstroth hive, but did not especially recommend it. It should also be added that Miller was a firm advocate of the improvement of stock by selection and he attributed much of his success to his efforts in this line.

REMEDIAL MEASURES

The preventive measures previously mentioned are usually sufficient to control swarming in a colony used in extracted-honey-production but, in the crowded conditions of the comb-honey hive, in a good season, there will probably be some colonies that will persist in their preparations to swarm. In a poor season, when the colony lacks the stimulus of nectar coming to the hive, it has not the conditions nor the number of bees necessary for swarming, but when conditions during early brood-rearing are favorable and when there is abundance of nectar in the main honey-flow, there is also usually a larger population, and preparation for swarming may be begun and often completed in most of the colonies in the apiary. It then rests with the beekeeper so to manage these colonies that, by keeping the bees together and in working condition (p. 91), he may obtain practically as large a crop as if swarming had not occurred. He now aims not so much to prevent swarming as to satisfy the instinct and to overcome the evils incident to division of the working force. The method adopted depends largely on the size and location of the apiary. If all the bees are in one apiary, where they are under the immediate care of the beekeeper every day, they may be permitted to swarm naturally but, in comb-honey-production especially, colonies in out-apiaries can be expected to produce more, without the loss of swarms, if by some remedial manipulation the swarming tendency is controlled to suit the convenience of the beekeeper. If an assistant is kept at each apiary, it becomes essentially like the home apiary but it rarely pays to keep so much help.

Control of natural swarms

Swarms which issue may be managed in several ways. (1) They may be allowed to fly into the air and cluster on some support, after which they may be hived and placed in the desired location. When the bees have clustered they may be shaken into a box or basket and then placed in front of the hive that they are to occupy. They should be placed so that some of the bees find the entrance promptly, otherwise they may begin their characteristic march in the wrong direction (p. 76). If the bees cluster on a limb which can be cut, this may be removed and carried to the hive and the bees shaken off. If the cluster forms on the trunk of a tree or post or in some other place from which they cannot be removed readily, a box containing a piece of comb may be placed above and preferably in contact with the cluster and the swarm will soon move into the box, where it may be handled. Care should be taken to get the queen, as otherwise the bees may again take wing and return to her.

(2) If the queen's wings are clipped (p. 274), she is unable to fly with the swarm and, after leaving the hive, she falls to the ground. The swarm generally does not cluster if the queen is not with it or, if it does cluster, it soon takes wing and returns to the old hive, provided it does not have a virgin queen with it as is sometimes the case if swarming has been unduly delayed. In the meantime, the beekeeper should find the queen on the ground and place her with the returning bees, after adjusting the hives as described later.

(3) If a queen- and drone-trap (Fig. 31) is placed over the entrance, workers can leave, but when the queen attempts it she is retarded by the trap. She then, in her attempts to escape, usually goes into the upper part of the trap and is unable to return. The swarming bees then behave as they do when the queen's wings are clipped, and soon return. To allow the queen to go below with the bees it is necessary only to pull the tin slide which is shown partly drawn in the illustration. Here, also, the hives are adjusted as when the queen is clipped and of course the swarm is not left in the old brood-chamber. The inexperienced beekeeper should perhaps be warned not to leave a queen-trap on the entrance at all times for it will prevent virgin queens from leaving the hive to mate. Drones of

course are also prevented from leaving and if they are abundant they may crowd the entrance, with disastrous results.

(4) As the swarm issues, a wire-cloth cage may be placed over the hive or fitted over the entrance. The bees then cluster in the top of the cage, without causing confusion in the apiary, and may be hived when convenient.

Automatic hivers

Several years ago the desirability of some automatic hiving device was much discussed and numerous efforts were made to invent apparatus which would deposit or lead the issuing swarm to a new hive. These arrangements were devised to place the swarm in a new location and beekeepers now prefer that it be returned to the old spot.

Location for the swarm

After a swarm has issued, the old practice was to hive it in a new location, thus dividing the working force. The beekeeper should manipulate the two parts of the original colony so as to prevent such a division. A method sometimes used is to return the swarm without the queen to the old hive and about a week later (before the developing queens emerge) the queen-cells are cut and the colony is requeened later. The usual method is to remove the hive-body containing the brood while the swarm is out and to return the swarm to a new hive on the old stand. By either of these methods, the swarm is augmented by the returning field bees and, if there were supers on the colony before swarming, they are kept with the swarm and the bees promptly return to their work. The most common error of the inexperienced beekeeper in swarm management is to put the supers on the "parent colony" (the one which retains the brood). The population of the parent colony is reduced by the loss of the field bees and the casting of after-swarms is thereby made less probable. These manipulations make it necessary that the beekeeper be present when the swarm issues, or soon after, and they are therefore not suitable for out-apiary management.

Disposition of the brood after swarming

The so-called parent colony may be sufficiently populous to cast an after-swarm, and should, therefore be managed so as to prevent this and also so that the emerging bees shall be useful, especially if the honey-flow will probably be of long duration.

Fig. 113.—Manipulation to reduce population of parent colony — first position. Previous to swarming.

The parent colony may be broken up at once by the distribution of the brood to other colonies, while the adhering bees are added to the swarm. Another method is to destroy all queen-cells except one and to allow the parent colony to remain intact. If the parent colony is left to requeen itself by the mergence of the developing queens, it often casts an after-swarm, so it is safer either to remove all queen-cells except one or to remove them all and give a laying queen or virgin queen.

Fig. 114.—Manipulation to reduce population of parent colony — second position. Parent colony is now in hive without supers.

Still another method is to reduce the population of the parent colony just before the young queens emerge and to add the emerging bees to the swarm. If the parent colony is put back beside the swarm after the latter is hived, left there for a week and then removed to a new location, it is so reduced when the virgin queens emerge that an after-swarm is not cast. A modification of this method, preferred when the clipping of queens is practiced or when the queen-trap is used, is to set the parent colony to one side with its entrance about 90 degrees from its former location (Figs. 113 and 114), so that all returning field bees join the swarm. As the brood emerges, the young bees become accustomed to the location of their hive. In a few days the parent colony is turned about halfway around toward its former position (Fig. 115), and, after the bees again become accustomed to the change, it is moved to a position parallel to that of the new colony (Fig. 116). If within seven or eight days of the issuing of the swarm, the parent colony is removed to a new location, the young bees in flying out join the swarm, thereby considerably reduc- the parent colony.

Fig. 115. — Manipulation to reduce population of parent colony—third position.

When the parent colony is moved, part of the bees may be brushed in front of the entrance of the swarm, leaving some to care for the brood but not enough to induce an after-swarm. The parent colony may be used for increase or the bees as they emerge may still be added to the swarm or to some other colony. Other methods of using some young bees or sealed brood to advantage will be found by the beekeeper. They may be used to build up weak colonies, or, if the honey-flow will probably be long enough to warrant it, two parent colonies may be placed side by side. By giving one a queen and removing the queen-cells from the other, they may be united about two weeks after the swarm issues, when most of the brood has emerged from the queenless colony, and they are then ready for supers.

Fig. 116.—Manipulation to reduce population of parent colony—fourth position.

What to use in the brood-chamber in hiving swarms

The use of full sheets of comb-foundation in the brood-frames has the marked advantage of resulting in straight combs of worker-cells. The comb is built up rapidly, in fact so rapidly as to be considered a disadvantage at times, in that brood is so quickly reared that the increase in population may again induce swarming. The use of full sheets of comb-foundation may increase the work done in the brood-chamber, at the expense of the surplus.

Narrow strips of comb-foundation, perhaps an inch wide or less, may be used, and this usually results in slow progress in the construction of combs in the brood-chamber. The bees then do more work in the supers, if they have been started, and it is so long before the colony can rear much brood that they rarely attempt to swarm again in the season. However, combs built on strips of comb-foundation often contain many drone-cells, especially if the comb-building in the brood-chamber progresses faster than the cells are filled with eggs by the queen or when comb is built outside the space needed for brood. If the parent colony has a brood disease, the use of strips of comb-foundation is preferable, thus combining swarm management and disease treatment. When either strips of comb-foundation or full sheets are used and partly drawn combs are present in comb-honey supers, the queen may go above to lay eggs and this should be prevented by the use of the queen-excluder (Fig. 117) for a few days or until there is room for egg-laying below, when the excluder may be removed. If the supers are left off for a time, work will progress in the brood-chamber so that space for egg-laying

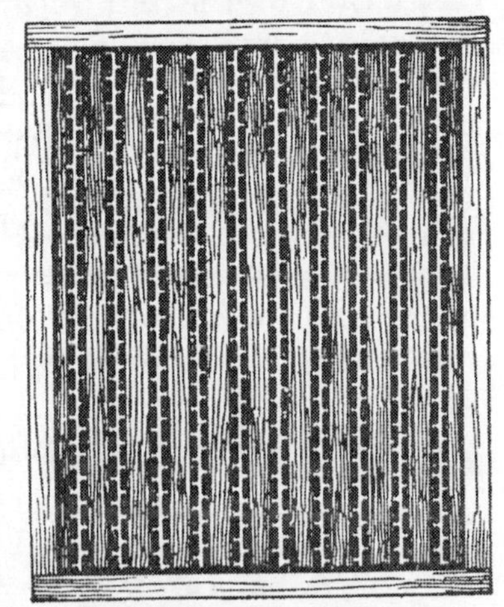

FIG. 117.—Queen-excluder ("honey board").

will be available there and the queen will not go to the supers.

One or two empty combs may be used in the brood-chamber, the remaining spaces being filled with frames containing full sheets of comb-foundation. This prevents the storage of pollen in the supers and gives the queen a place to lay eggs at once, so that an excluder is not necessary. Swarms sometimes desert a hive containing only comb-foundation, but some empty comb or a comb containing some unsealed brood will prevent this. The placing of comb-foundation next to full comb often results in an unusual extension of the side walls of the comb and a restriction of the building out of the comb-foundation.

Empty combs, or comb filled with honey or sealed brood, are also sometimes used. It is claimed by some that, just after swarming, bees secrete wax with a minimum expenditure of energy and with the least consumption of honey, and it is therefore believed that it is wasteful not to give the swarm an opportunity to secrete some wax in building comb. If the swarm is only moderately strong, the bees may confine their efforts chiefly to the brood-chamber, if empty combs are used.

In extracted-honey-production, these questions do not arise, for the beekeeper can use whatever is most convenient and, by giving plenty of room for storage, the colony will rarely swarm again. It, therefore, does not pay to use strips of comb-foundation in the extracted-honey apiary.

In comb-honey-production, a swarm may be hived in the usual way and then in a day or two the brood-chamber may be contracted temporarily by substituting thick division boards for four or five of the frames (in a ten-frame hive), thus so reducing the room in the brood-chamber that the bees are driven to the supers. This method may be used during a honey-flow of white honey, which is preferable for comb-honey, and when there will probably be a later honey-flow of honey of a lower grade, which is good enough to use in building up the brood-chamber but not of fine enough quality for sections. If this contraction is practiced, and it is less frequent now than formerly, it should be to about five frames, rather than a slight contraction to perhaps seven frames.

Remedial manipulations

The remedial measures so far discussed are useful for colonies that have swarmed, in making the most of the parts of the divided original colony. However, these require almost constant attention in some seasons and this is necessary just when the beekeeper can least afford to give it, if he is managing a large number of colonies. Because of the desirability of the manipulations being in accordance with the plans and schedule of the beekeeper, rather than at the whims of the bees, as in natural swarming, beekeepers, especially producers of comb-honey, have tried many ways virtually to create the conditions which are found after swarming, but to do this with advantage to the crop. By such a system the comb-honey-producer can maintain several apiaries, visiting them at regular intervals, with a knowledge that swarms will not issue in his absence, except in those cases in which every rule seems to fail. However, the losses can be made so slight that it does not pay to keep an assistant at each apiary, if the proper measures are adopted. Fortunately for the beekeeper, bees give warning in advance of the probability of the issuing of a swarm by building queen-cells. By examining each colony once in seven to ten days during the swarming season, the beekeeper can subject colonies making these preparations to the chosen manipulation, which may be a preventive or a remedial measure, depending on how far preparations for swarming have progressed. If the manipulations given under the title of Preventive Measures are inadequate, the colony may be handled with another end in view, namely, to satisfy the desire to swarm and to prevent permanent division. It is further possible, especially in apiaries in which increase is desired, so to manipulate every colony before the swarming season arrives that there will be little swarming, even in comb-honey-production, but since increase in the number of colonies during or just before the honey-flow is at the expense of the crop from that honey-flow, beekeepers usually find it advantageous not to attempt to use remedial measures until necessary.

In the literature on swarm control, there are dozens of plans for accomplishing this end, and it is neither desirable nor necessary to give all of them or even all of the successful ones, for to attempt to do so would only be confusing.

Unbalanced condition of swarming colonies

If the conditions found in natural swarming are examined, it will be recalled that, after the swarm issues, it receives no additional young bees for a period of at least twenty-one days (unless they are given by the beekeeper in accordance with some of the plans previously outlined) If, as seems not unlikely, one of the most important factors in the cause of swarming is a preponderance of young bees, this condition is rectified for the swarm and the bees become "satisfied." On the other hand, the parent colony rapidly increases the percentage of young bees (unless, again, they are removed by the beekeeper) and after-swarms are not uncommon, unless the beekeeper manipulates them. It thus appears that the restoration of the balance of the colony is important in bringing it to a condition in which the swarming tendency is lost and in which the storing instinct becomes dominant.

Break in the emergence of brood

Whether this speculation is justified must be determined by future investigations, which are greatly needed. At any rate, and this is the point of importance to the beekeeper, those practical manipulations which are successful in the control of swarming, whether applied before or after queen-cells are built, have for their result a single factor in common—a reduction or temporary cessation in the continuity of the daily emergence of brood. There have been numerous discussions of the principles of swarm control, for this is a problem which has attracted the attention of modern beekeepers to a marked extent, but so far as the author is aware the existence of a single underlying factor in all the methods devised was not shown previous to the discussion of this subject by Demuth. This elimination of the emerging bees, to be successful in its purpose, must occur just before or during the swarming season.

The various manipulations devised by beekeepers which bring about this condition and which have been devised to control swarming come under two headings: (1) the prevention or great restriction of egg-laying; (2) the removal of brood. Even if there were one best manipulation, a beekeeper would probably still prefer the one to which he has become accustomed, but there is so far no one method superior to all the others. As conditions vary from season to season, or even within the season, it becomes desirable that the beekeeper change his manipulations from time to time.

Restriction of egg-laying

The most radical manipulation under this heading is the removal of the queen. She may be removed for a period of perhaps ten days and then returned (after the destruction of all queen-cells), or she may simply be caged and left in the colony, to be released at the end of the period. Another method is to confine the queen to a single comb of brood and several empty combs, or to two or three frames filled with foundation in a hive-body the one containing most of the brood, in which case the queen-cells must be destroyed both before and after the period of separation of the queen and brood.[1] In any event, all queen-cells must be removed before the queen is returned or swarming may occur. These methods are employed only on colonies that have made active preparations to swarm (having advanced larvæ in the queen-cells) and they are successful as a rule, if the swarming period is not prolonged sufficiently to allow time for the swarming tendency to be developed anew. The particular time for making colonies queenless must be determined by the stage in the development of the queen-cells present in the colony preparing to swarm. If only young larvæ are found in the queen-cells, the cells may simply be cut out as a precautionary measure against swarming, but if the queen-cells are advanced, their removal will not prevent swarming and the colony should be dequeened. However, a colony with the queen temporarily removed or even separated from the brood is often not in the best condition for storing, especially when first made queenless, and these methods have sometimes been con-

[1] The removal of the queen has been recommended by Elwood, Quinby, Hetherington and France. Caging the queen was then advised by Doolittle and tried by Miller. The next step was to utilize the queen by keeping her in a nucleus (Miller) and a later development consisted in making the nucleus practically a part of the main colony. This was done by putting a comb or two of brood, without queen-cells, in the lower body and then placing the queen and most of the brood on top of the hive, over a cover. Most of the bees are left with the queenless portion and because of the reduced population in the upper hive, the bees destroy the queen-cells. In about ten days the body containing the queen and brood is put below and the body containing the few combs of brood is removed to be used as needed ("Put-up Plan," C. C. Miller). Another modification which followed this is described above, in which the queen is put below an excluder on one frame of brood and empty combs. Numerous beekeepers have advised requeening in connection with the dequeening, others have modified the plan by making the lower hive into a nucleus for queen-rearing, while in one case it is recommended that a nucelus be established on the side of the hive in which the queen is mated, so arranged that by pulling a slide of perforated zinc, the queen is introduced to the colony after mating. These various systems are mentioned here mainly to show their relation to the fundamental principle of restricting egg-laying and also to suggest the various methods so that the beekeeper may choose the one best suited to his plans.

demned because of this fact. Dequeening is to be preferred in obvious cases of supersedure or in colonies in which the working force is not large, but which still persist in preparing to swarm.

Requeening combined with dequeening

Requeening is desirable whenever a queen is unable to keep up the population of the colony, and many beekeepers find it advantageous systematically to requeen every one or two years. The presence of a young queen was mentioned earlier as a preventive of swarming, but this is not a guarantee that no swarm will issue, under conditions of a prolonged honey-flow. However, requeening combined with queenlessness for about ten days, after swarming preparations have begun, is a much more reliable procedure. The method used in rearing queens, in mating them and in introducing them to the queenless colonies will depend on the equipment and system of the individual beekeeper.

Removal of brood

The removal of a frame or two of brood was mentioned earlier as a swarm-preventive measure in relieving the congestion in the brood-chamber, especially in comb-honey-production. It obviously also has the effect of reducing the number of emerging bees for a period. If a colony persists in its preparations to swarm, a common remedial measure is to carry the removal of brood to the extreme (artificial swarming). In brief, the beekeeper does for the colony in advance of swarming just what the bees would do for themselves if left to their own instincts. The brood-combs are removed from the hive and the bees are shaken or brushed from the combs into a new hive-body. The brood-combs are then comparable to the parent colony, while the bees in the new hive make up the artificial swarm. The treatment of the various parts does not differ from the same procedure under conditions of natural swarming and need not be repeated. Since artificial swarms desert the hive sooner than natural ones, desertion may be prevented by removing only a part of the brood at one time and, in fact, some manipulations do not call for the removal of all the brood.

This manipulation has been modified in a dozen ways by various beekeepers, but the essential principle remains the same. The differences in the directions for the making of artificial swarms are chiefly in the disposal of the two portions of the original colony. It is claimed by some that, to obtain satisfactory results, the bees must be smoked or otherwise manipulated until they fill themselves with honey, just as bees do in natural swarming. This usually occurs during the manipulations without any thought on the part of the beekeeper.

Mechanical appliances

Various mechanical contrivances have been advocated for separating the brood and the adult bees. After the queen has been placed in a new hive, the bees are trapped out and induced to enter the new hive on which have been placed the supers. There is no additional principle involved in these devices and they are serviceable only in changing the work that the beekeeper has to do. They often do not reduce the amount of time and labor needed. Among these devices may be mentioned the Hand bottom board (provided with levers so placed as to force the returning bees into the desired hive) and Dudley tubes for trapping out workers, all of which have been described in bee-journals.

INCREASE

It is assumed in the previous discussion that increase is not desired, and in comb-honey-production in the North, where the swarming problem is most acute, increase during the honey-flow is usually too expensive to be justifiable. If the apiary has been reduced by winter losses or in some other way, or if an apiary is being built up, the beekeeper may prefer to sacrifice honey for bees. In connection with the operation of the various plans for controlling swarming, there will often be brood that can be used for increase. Another method is simply to divide colonies into two or more equal parts, preferably providing each queenless portion with a queen-cell, or better still with a queen, as soon as possible. To obtain increase and to assist in swarm control without decreasing the crop too greatly, combs of brood with some adhering young bees may be removed and made into nuclei to be allowed to build up and to be augmented with frames of brood from other sources as they are available.

In case the main honey-flow is in late summer (*e.g.* buckwheat) it is often possible to make increase in early summer and to have all the colonies up to full strength by the time the honey-flow begins. Increase in such a case may not result in any decrease in the crop and, in fact, it often brings an increase in the harvest.

In the North, in regions where the main honey-flow comes in early summer, it will usually be more profitable to set aside certain colonies from which to make increase, rather than to deplete the colonies throughout the apiary in an attempt to make increase and produce a crop at the same time. It is possible to make increase and to produce the maximum crop of honey in an apiary within a single season, if conditions are favorable, but not simultaneously.

CHAPTER XVI

THE PRODUCTION OF EXTRACTED HONEY

Before the invention of the honey extractor in 1865, honey was removed from the comb either by crushing it and draining off the honey or by melting, allowing the whole to cool, leaving the wax on top. By these methods strained honey is produced, an article greatly inferior to modern extracted honey. In extracting honey, the cappings of the honey-cells of the comb are first removed with a hot knife, the comb is put into an extractor and is then whirled, the honey being removed from the cells by centrifugal force.

The demand for extracted honey is increasing. The estimate for 1909 was that 34.9 per cent of the total honey crop was extracted. By 1914 this had increased 42.1 per cent and for 1922 the estimate was 60.5 per cent. This tendency to produce more and more extracted honey was stimulated by conditions during the War, thus bringing about more rapidly an inevitable condition. These estimated percentages are conservative and among professional beekeepers during this period the rate of increase was doubtless even greater. This change is due only in small part to a demand for honey from bakers and confectioners and a potential influence is the increased confidence of the consuming public that the extracted honey is not adulterated. For this confidence the beekeeper is indebted to the enforcement of the federal and state pure food laws, and this change began definitely with the passage of the Federal Food and Drugs Act, June 30, 1906, the most beneficial law ever passed so far as the effect on beekeeping is concerned. Beekeepers were among the first to demand legal means for stopping food adulterations and have at all times stood firmly against efforts to weaken these laws, such, for example, as the recent effort to permit the use of cheap sugars such as glucose without declaration on labels. The record of beekeepers in such matters is wholly clean and is much to the credit of the industry.

ADVANTAGES OF EXTRACTED HONEY

The fact that the combs may be used repeatedly increases materially the amount of honey produced by a single colony and thereby reduces the cost of production of a pound of extracted honey. There is less secretion of wax and, since the secretion of a pound of beeswax is estimated as costing from six to twenty pounds of honey (and probably considerable bee vitality), this saving is considerable. In light honey-flows, bees often refuse to work in comb-honey sections, whereas they will store the available nectar if extracting combs are on the hive. Under comb-honey conditions the queen is often cramped for room and the population of the colony is thereby reduced, while in extracted-honey conditions she has abundant room, unless otherwise restricted. The larger comb area in extracted-honey-production furnishes the bees plenty of cells in which to store fresh nectar, giving increased evaporating surface and thus hastening the ripening process. The beekeeper can care for more colonies in producing extracted than comb-honey. Swarming is more easily controlled and is much less prevalent because of the abundance of empty comb provided. Furthermore, in comb-honey-production most of the work in the apiary requires skill and experience, while in extracted-honey-production one man can furnish the skill for many colonies and can employ unskilled labor to help during extracting. In selling extracted honey to the consumer there is the marked advantage of blending honeys from different sources, thereby obtaining a mixture which can be duplicated year after year.

DISADVANTAGES OF EXTRACTED HONEY

While more extracted than comb-honey can be obtained from a colony in a season, this is balanced by the fact that the wholesale market value of a pound of extracted honey is less than that of a section of comb-honey, the unit with which a pound of extracted honey must be compared. However, year in and year out the advantage is probably still with the producer of extracted honey, so far as financial return is concerned. In some localities extracted honey does not sell as readily as comb-honey. In extracting honey and in heating later to bottle it, some of the delicate aroma is lost but this usually is not sufficient materially to reduce the value of the honey as a delicacy.

HIVES AND COMBS FOR EXTRACTED HONEY

A hive at least as large as the ten-frame Langstroth should be used, for smaller hives do not provide sufficient room for the activities of a colony headed by a vigorous queen and large colonies are far more profitable than small ones. When a honey-flow begins, the hive should be ready with an extra hive-body containing frames of the same size as the brood-chamber already on top. The extra hive-bodies or supers may be given one after the other as the increase in surplus honey indicates, the empty super being usually put next to the hive containing the brood. If the beekeeper believes the local conditions warrant he may give several hive-bodies at once. It is quite usual to space the frames in the supers farther apart than in the brood-chamber, giving eight frames equally spaced in a ten-frame body. This makes less combs to handle for a given amount of honey, and if the comb is cut deep in uncapping, more wax is obtained. It also make uncapping easier.

Choice of storage-combs

White honey stored in cells in which brood has been reared is sometimes darkened slightly but most beekeepers find it too much work to keep the combs for breeding entirely separate from the storage-combs. Sometimes colonies are also stimulated in the spring by putting a few brood-combs in the upper story to get the bees to go up promptly. This is especially valuable in a swarm prevention. Usually the queen is allowed to go where she will in the hive to deposit eggs.

Use of extracting combs smaller than brood-combs

An exception to the above statements concerning the size of the hive and supers is to be found when deep brood frames are used, when frames of Langstroth depth are often used for extracting combs. Some beekeepers also prefer shallow extracting frames, the length of the Langstroth but 5⅜ inches deep, to obviate the lifting of such heavy supers as those of full Langstroth size. The latter frames are advantageous for bulk comb-honey-production (p. 331).

Number of supers

The character of the honey-flow will determine largely the number of surplus bodies used and the method of taking off the honey. In a slow honey-flow one surplus body is often sufficient and as individual combs are filled and sealed they are removed and the honey extracted. In a heavy honey-flow more bodies should be given at one time so that there will be room for ripening and storing the honey. In the latter case, whole hive-bodies are frequently taken away at one time.

Manipulation of the supers

To confine the queen to the lower hive-body and prevent brood from being scattered throughout the hive, one or two methods may be employed. If a queen-excluder (Fig. 117) is used the queen is kept below, but many honey-producers object to these on the ground of expense and because they believe the workers are somewhat retarded by them. If the new supers are always placed directly above the brood-chamber and under the supers already on, there is little likelihood of the queen going above. Under these circumstances the order of the supers is practically the same as in comb-honey-production (p. 328). Bees probably begin work in new combs more quickly if they are placed near the brood-chamber. In rapid honey-flows, however, bees go readily to the very top of the hive for empty cells without hesitation.

Need of abundance of drawn combs

In any event, plenty of drawn combs should be available and given to the colonies soon enough so that there will always be some empty comb in the hive. If the bees become crowded, the queen may be restricted in egg-laying and there is not room to spread out the nectar for economical ripening. The crowded conditions so common in comb-honey-production should be avoided in the production of extracted honey. The advantage of fully drawn combs is especially evident in poor seasons, for then the bees may refuse to build combs but will store all the honey available if drawn combs are provided.

The giving of frames entirely or partially filled with comb-foundation from which combs must be built, diverts a part of the colony to wax-building and probably reduces the field force, although wax is secreted chiefly by young bees not yet ready for work in the field. Part of the honey is consumed in wax-building. There may be some delay in starting work on the new combs, which in a heavy honey-flow results either in a loss of honey or in the cramping of the queen. The extracted-honey-producer should supply himself with drawn combs in abundance as soon as possible. These may be obtained economically by hiving swarms on full sheets of comb-foundation. Another good method is to put eight frames in a ten-frame hive as an upper story, four on one side being full combs and the other four being frames containing comb-foundation. This is better than to alternate comb and foundation, in which case the combs are usually drawn out abnormally thick and the comb-foundation is drawn out slightly. Better combs are built during a good honey-flow, for the corners are then filled more completely than in a small honey-flow. If desired the nectar obtained at the end of the main honey-flow may be utilized in comb-building.

System in producing extracted honey

The extensive producer of extracted honey may systematize his work so that it is necessary to visit each out-apiary only a few times a year. The number and time of these visits must be determined by the character of honey-flows. Usually the honey from each floral source should be extracted separately and this necessitates a trip after each honey-flow. The apiaries should be of such size that either in one day or two all the extracting can be done, and to help with this work unskilled labor usually may be employed. Since the giving of plenty of drawn combs reduces swarming, it is usually not profitable to keep a helper at each apiary during the swarming season, for the few swarms that would be saved are worth less than the helper would cost. If the apiary can be located near the home of some interested person the swarms may be caught, but frequently it is desirable to put out-apiaries in rather desolate places, some distance from a dwelling. E. D. Townsend of North-star, Michigan, manages a number of out-apiaries in northern Michigan on four trips a year. On the first trip (June) he gives each strong colony two ten-frame supers, each containing eight frames. On the second trip (July) and the third (after the honey-flows) he extracts, two trips being made to keep the clover and basswood honeys separate. In October he sees that the colonies are ready for winter, after which they are not again visited until June.

Removing honey from the bees

Honey should not be removed from the hive for extracting until well ripened. When at least two-thirds of the surface of the comb is capped over the honey will be sufficiently thick, but the humidity should be considered in laying down a rule for this. In dry climates, such as the semi-arid regions of the West, the evaporation of the water in the nectar takes place rapidly and it is not necessary to wait until so much of the honey is capped. Conversely in regions of high humidity it is sometimes difficult to get honey well ripened.

When the time comes to extract, the usual practice is to remove the frames one by one, returning those not ready, and to brush or shake off the adhering bees. Bee-escapes (Fig. 32) may be used in removing bees from extracting supers but this is not usually practiced by extensive producers as it necessitates going to the apiary a day ahead and it is desirable to reduce the trips wherever possible. For the beekeeper with one apiary, these may often be used to advantage. A bee-brush (Fig. 29) may be used for brushing off the bees or a bunch of grass or weeds will answer admirably. The combs practically free of bees are then taken to the house for extracting. For carrying these an ordinary hive-body with a cover answers very well and special handles may be put on it to facilitate carrying, or several bodies may be placed on a wheelbarrow or two-wheeled cart. Some beekeepers have arranged rails through the apiary on which trucks may be run for carrying full bodies in and for returning the empty combs. This is practical for fixed apiary locations but often the professional beekeeper wants to have no apparatus that cannot be moved if desired.

The greatest care should be exercised while honey is being taken from the hives that the bees do not begin robbing. This is especially necessary if extracting is done after the honey-flow has ceased. Should robbing begin, it is often best to stop work for the day, as robbing is not only most annoying to the beekeeper but detrimental to the bees. The feeding of a thin sirup out-of-doors is sometimes practiced to prevent robbing during extracting.

HOUSE AND EQUIPMENT FOR EXTRACTING

The house where the extracting is done need not differ materially from the honey-house described previously (p. 30). If the apiary is on sloping ground, it is preferable to have the colonies above the house, so that the heavy full hives are carried down hill and the empty hives up. To reduce labor, it is desirable that there be an opening for admitting the honey to the house convenient to the uncapping outfit and that the extractor be near at hand. These should be on a high level in the house, if practicable, so that from the time the honey runs from the extractor, its course is down hill to the final container. It is worth the effort to pay considerable attention to this feature, for if the honey must be lifted at any part of its journey a great amount of labor is involved in large apiaries where tons of honey are extracted in a season. If such an arrangement is not feasible, a honey-pump may be used, as is described later.

Portable extracting outfits

In sections where at times it is desirable to move apiaries or where several out-apiaries are under one management, it is occasionally advantageous to have a portable extracting outfit which is virtually an extracting house on wheels. A well-screened truck or wagon is fitted with uncapping cans, extractors (with power if desired) and all the necessary equipment. As the honey is extracted, it can be run into a tank or into barrels or cans. If desired a tank-wagon to carry the honey may accompany the outfit. Some beekeepers have found portable buildings (built in sections) preferable, in which case one is put in each apiary. If these are used, it is better to have a full extracting outfit at each apiary. Because of improved transportation facilities, most extensive beekeepers now do all extracting in a centrally located house well equipped for such work.

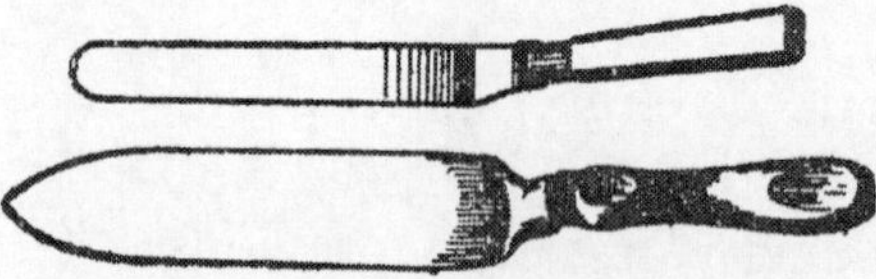

FIG. 118.—Uncapping knives: upper, Novice; lower, Bingham.

Uncapping

When the full combs of honey reach the extracting house, the first manipulation is uncapping. This is done with a specially constructed knife, of which there are several types (Fig. 118). Of these the Bingham knife with heavy wide blade is best. The knife should be kept sharp, clean and hot, and when the usual knives are employed, each operator is provided with two so that one may be kept in hot water, to clean and heat it, while the other is in use. Recently a steam-heated knife (Fig. 119) has been put on the market which is highly recommended. Steam is generated in a small boiler (such as a one-gallon honey-can), passes through a hose into a hollow space in the knife-blade, escaping through a small hole in the tip.

FIG. 119.—Steam-heated uncapping knife.

In uncapping, the lower end of the comb is placed on some support and the comb is slightly tipped so that as the cappings are cut off they fall away from the surface of the comb (Fig. 120). If the knife is first inserted at the lower

FIG. 120.—Capping melter. This also shows the proper method of removing cappings.

end of the comb and brought upward with a sawing motion, the cappings fall away easily and cause no inconvenience or smearing. Some beekeepers prefer to begin cutting at the upper end, thereby utilizing the weight of the knife in cutting the comb. The upward cut is practiced by most extensive beekeepers. Machines for uncapping have been developed for large scale operations and described in catalogues.

Cans for cappings

The uncapping should be done over some sort of receptacle into which the cappings will fall. Hutchinson used a simple, cheap and satisfactory outfit, consisting of a barrel hung with bent wires on the edges of a galvanized iron tub. Across the top of the barrel is nailed a board through which is driven a nail with the point upward. One of the end bars of the frame is placed on this nail point and after one side is uncapped, the frame is turned on the nail. Some beekeepers prefer to bore a one-inch hole in the cross-piece into which the projection on the bar of the frame is inserted. Another cross-piece on which to scrape wax and honey from the knife is an advantage. The cappings drop into the barrel and the honey drains into the tub below through cracks in the barrel. The advantage of this cheap mechanism is that when one barrel is well filled with cappings, the outfit may be set aside to drain and another one substituted. More elaborate tanks (Fig. 121) have been devised for this purpose which have the advantage of durability and permanence. These tanks may be made either of sheet metal or of wood lined with tin. A screen is arranged in the box on which the cappings fall and the honey drains into the lower space.

Capping melters

A later development in uncapping cans is a piece of apparatus in which the cappings are melted at once and the honey and melted wax run out. Honey is then quickly drawn off from the bottom of the receptacle leaving the wax to cool on top of a little of the honey. A small capping melter (Fig. 120) is now marketed, but for extensive operations it is preferable to make a larger tank on this principle. In these melters the honey and wax come in contact only with the inner wall of a water-jacket and do not touch metal which is in direct contact with the flame. The objection has been raised that the heating of the honey in this way discolors it, but if it runs off and is separated from the melted wax quickly this is reduced to a minimum. Apparatus of this type has been adopted by numerous extensive producers. The relief from the care of a great mass of cappings at the end of extracting certainly appeals to the extensive beekeeper.

Types of extractors

After the comb is uncapped on both sides it is ready for the extractor. The development of the extractor from the first simple clumsy machines is of interest and illustrates the progress in beekeeping in recent years. It is impossible to do more than suggest this development. Following the announcement of the discovery of the extractor in Italy, the first type marketed in North America was a revolving can into which combs were placed in pockets. Later the can was made stationary (Fig. 122) and the combs were placed in moving pockets, but in these first types it was necessary to remove the combs to extract from the other side. Later reversible baskets were devised so that the change could be made without withdrawing the combs. The later development consisted in making extractors with a larger number of reversible baskets, in the perfecting of the means of reversing and of the application of power, for it was impossible to use hand-driven machines with six or eight baskets. Different types of attachments of the baskets have been tried, all of these efforts being made for the purpose of strengthening the machines and of facilitating the use of the extractor, all devised for greater and greater speed of operation. By the use of the later machines it is possible to extract tons of honey in a season, a marked contrast to conditions when the first extractors were made.

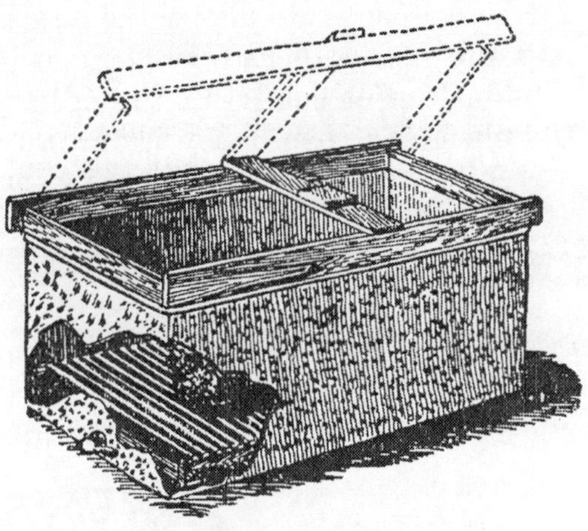

FIG. 121.—Tank to receive cappings.

A later development is to use the radial type of extractor, in which the combs are placed in the extractor in a radial position, the honey being removed from both sides at once so that reversing is unnecessary. Extractors of this type have been tried for many years and several machines on this principle have been made and sold in Europe for some years. The latest American machine of this type (Figs. 123 and 124) holds forty-five frames at once. Nothing better shows the great advance that beekeeping has experienced during the past two decades.

FIG. 122.—Extractor with stationary can.

Extracting

In extracting, care must be exercised not to run the extractor too rapidly as this may break or crush combs, especially new or unwired ones. It is good practice to extract some honey from one side, to reverse and extract the other side clean and then go back to complete the extracting on the first side. With fragile combs, the honey on the inner side may be forced against the midrib of the comb so strongly as to crush it if the comb is revolved too rapidly in extracting the first side. In placing combs in the extractor, those of about the same weight should be put opposite each other to prevent swinging of the extractor, thus making it easier for the operator and less wearing on the machine. The honey is thrown against the side of the extractor can and runs down and out an opening provided at the bottom, usually equipped with a honey-gate (as in Fig. 122) so that it may be quickly and securely closed.

Straining the honey

Since particles of cappings naturally adhere to the comb and since other foreign matter may get into the honey,

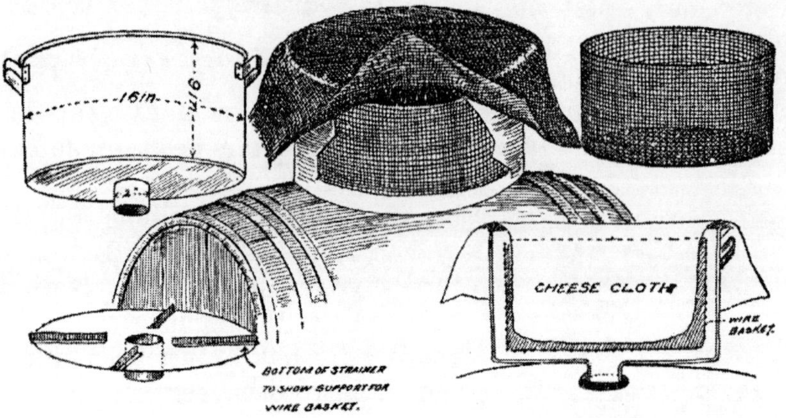

FIG. 125.—Honey-strainer.

including an occasional bee, the honey should be strained as it leaves the extractor. For small operations, it may simply be run through a cheese-cloth bag, greater surface being given by supporting the cheese-cloth on wire netting (Fig. 125). Another type is known as the gravity strainer. In this, the honey runs into a tank with a partition having an opening at the bottom through which the honey can pass to another compartment. No honey flows from the outlet until it fills the strainer to the level of the upper outlet and most of the larger foreign particles rise to the top in the first chamber allowing the honey to pass off relatively free from foreign material. Gravity strainers are widely used and can readily be made to any desired capacity. They are usually combined with a strainer of cheese-cloth to get out more of the impurities.

Storage-tanks

From a strainer of any type it is advantageous to run honey into a tank so that particles that pass the strainer will have an opportunity to rise to the top, the honey always being drawn from the bottom. Many beekeepers, however, run honey directly from the strainer into cans or barrels. The settling in the tank not only removes more small particles of wax, but allows air bubbles to escape and also any surplus water to evaporate in dry weather. Large outdoor tanks of a capacity of several tons are often used by California beekeepers (Fig. 126). If the tank is outside the extracting house, it should be covered tightly to keep out robber bees as well as dirt. Outdoor tanks are not practical except in the dry regions of the West where it does not rain during the honey season. To aid in keeping out bees and dirt, the western honey-tanks have a relatively small opening at the top.

Fig. 126.—Honey storage-tanks.

Reduction of the lifting of honey

If the extracting house can be so arranged that the honey will flow from one piece of equipment to the other, much lifting is avoided. Honey is usually run into tanks through pipes and if desired these may be utilized in carrying the honey from one house to another or to tanks some distance from the extracting house. Care should be taken to keep these pipes clean. If the honey cannot be run by gravity through its entire course, a honey-pump (Fig. 123) may be used and the usual practice is to attach this near the extractor so that it may be driven by the same power that runs the extractor. The whipping of honey in a pump tends to induce granulation so that honey should not be pumped after being heated for bottling (p. 337).

Returning combs to the hives

After the combs are emptied, they may either be returned to the bees to be refilled, if nectar is still coming in, or may be returned to be cleaned of honey and then removed for storage. If the honey-flow is still on, empty combs may be put on a hive as the full ones are removed, but during a light flow of honey or a dearth of nectar this may cause robbing and undue excitement in the apiary. In this event, the combs should be kept in the extracting house until the end of the day. If the combs are returned merely to be cleaned, a half dozen hive-bodies may be put over one colony and the bees will soon clean all of them. After the surplus combs are emptied, they may be left on the colonies to prevent their destruction by wax-moth larvæ or they may be stored in a light well-ventilated room or in hive-bodies where they should be watched and fumigated when necessary.

CHAPTER XVII

THE PRODUCTION OF COMB-HONEY [1]

COMB-HONEY is stored in the comb by the bees, the size and shape of the comb being determined by the small wooden box (section) provided by the beekeeper and the comb being sold with the section still surrounding it. The development of this style of package is readily traced back to a period previous to the invention of the modern hive. Formerly boxes were put on top of the box-hive or skep in which the bees built comb and stored honey. The next step was to make these boxes of a number of units comparable to the modern section and to compel the bees to build one comb in each unit. From this it was a short step to separate sections with partitions (separators) between.

THE MARKET FOR COMB-HONEY

The purchaser of a section of comb-honey may feel sure that he is buying a pure product of the bees, since comb-honey cannot be adulterated with profit. It is impossible to make an artificial comb, fill it with sirup and cap it over so that it even roughly resembles the work of the bees. By the use of modern apiary appliances, comb-honey is produced that is so attractive and uniform in appearance that it is often claimed to be manufactured. An examination will, however, show that no two sections are identical as they would be if machine-made. To show its confidence in the purity of comb-honey, the National Bee Keepers'

NOTE: In the preparation of this chapter, the author is indebted to Geo. S. Demuth for valuable help. Demuth's bulletin, "Commercial Comb-Honey Production" (U. S. Dept. Agr., Farmers' Bull. 1039), should be read and studied by every producer of comb-honey.

Association in 1904 offered $1000 for a single section of manufactured honey which would even approximately resemble the work of bees and a similar offer was made considerably earlier by A. I. Root, Medina, Ohio. Needless to say, no person has been able to claim these prizes.

This calls to mind an episode which at the time caused beekeepers much anxiety. H. W. Wiley stated in "Popular Science Monthly" in 1881, in an article on prevalent practices in food adulteration, that artificial combs of paraffin were being filled with glucose, capped to imitate the work of bees, and sold as comb-honey. In this statement he was entirely wrong and he publicly admitted the error later, there being, however, some basis for his misunderstanding since he had been informed of efforts along this line by a New England inventor. "Popular Science Monthly" did not have a circulation large enough to cause much trouble from such an erroneous statement, but unfortunately it was called to the attention of some prominent beekeepers. They dubbed it the "Wiley lie" and continued to magnify the harm that would come from it and to re-publish the error with denials until the story was spread throughout the country. The last chapter in this incident was the anonymous re-publication of the original statement and a collection of denials in an effort to hinder the passage in Congress of the Food and Drugs Act of June 30, 1906, now so familiar to all consumers of food. It should be stated that this effort was not perpetrated by any organization of beekeepers, although an attempt was made to have it so appear. The only fault that can be found with the beekeepers is that they did not refrain from discussing the matter and thereby probably did the industry far more damage than the original statement, for it appeared that they might be covering their own misdeeds. Occasionally some ignorant or sensational writer even now succeeds in repeating this error in print, but beekeepers promptly demand and usually receive a public correction. There is not the slightest basis for the misrepresentation.

Decrease in comb-honey-production

With the invention of the honey-extractor, some enthusiasts predicted that soon no comb-honey would be produced, but this prophecy has not been fulfilled. Comb-honey has a place in the American trade which cannot be filled by extracted honey. However, a gradual change is taking place and the percentage of the total honey crop that is produced in sections is decreasing annually. Professional beekeepers have found that they can care for more colonies when producing extracted honey, thereby increasing their profits. The spread of the brood diseases is rapidly eliminating the beekeepers with small apiaries for whom comb-honey is more convenient and, while the number of colonies in the United States is increasing, the sale of sections is steadily decreasing. There are other reasons for this change which appear later under the enumeration of the disadvantages in comb-honey-production.

Demand for fancy comb-honey

The American markets are now demanding only fancy comb-honey and the inferior grades and darker comb-honeys find a poor sale. To be successful in competition with extracted honey, comb-honey must be a fancy article, appealing to the fancy trade. For this reason, which is becoming more evident every season, there are still many beekeepers producing comb-honey who should change to extracted, and it is to be hoped that this transition will continue until all the grades of comb-honey which now injure the market are eliminated. On the other hand, there will be increased profits for the best grades of comb-honey, and the beekeepers in favorable localities may find it profitable to increase their production of honey in sections.

Advantages of comb-honey

The advantages in the production of comb-honey are numerous. As stated in the previous chapter, some of the delicate aroma of the finest grades of honey is lost in extracting, but this is retained to the full in comb-honey. In the production of comb-honey by the small beekeeper, less expensive equipment is necessary. The handling of the honey is clean and there is an attractiveness about the product that makes the handling of it a pleasure. The wholesale price of comb-honey is higher than that of extracted, but the amount obtained from each colony is usually less, so that the return is about the same in either case. In a good honey-flow the advantage is with the comb-honey-producer who uses proper methods of manipulation, while in light honey-flows only the producer of extracted honey gets all the crop. The section is a convenient package for retail trade. In this connection it should be noted that in comb-honey-production the beekeeper prepares the honey for the consumer while extracted honey is more often sold in wholesale packages. When the latter is blended and bottled it usually brings as high a retail price as comb-honey, but in this case the beekeeper does not do all the work and the bottler receives a good share of the profits. Comb-honey meets with more ready sale in most markets than does extracted.

Disadvantages of comb-honey

Comb-honey ships poorly and consequently there is often considerable loss from breakage, on which account some wholesale honey dealers refuse to handle it. In colonies run for comb-honey, swarming is a much more serious problem than in the larger hives with plenty of empty comb space used for extracted honey. In light honey-flows, bees work little or not at all in sections, for they are induced to build comb and store honey in small sections with difficulty and there is often a loss before they begin work properly. A serious drawback is that if honey in the comb granulates it is almost a total loss, and usually the only way to save anything is to melt the wax and honey and market them separately. The section of honey is a difficult package for the retail merchant to handle and the careless clerk may often spoil a section by running his thumb into it. For this reason and also for the sake of cleanliness, comb-honey sections in sealed cartons appeal strongly to retailers and consumers.

Restrictions in comb-honey-production

In view of the demands of the market and the tendency toward the production of only the best grades of comb-honey, certain restrictions should apply in its production. When the honey is dark or honeys from various sources are mixed in the combs by honey-flows intermingling, extracted honey should be produced. Honeys which granulate quickly, although they may be of fine color, are undesirable for comb-honey-production. The recent increase in the sale of alfalfa comb-honey has caused many grocers to hesitate to buy, for fear previous unpleasant experiences may be repeated and leave them with unsalable granulated comb-honey on hand. When the honey-flows are slow or intermittent, extracted-honey-production will be more profitable. These general restrictions will, of course, not apply in certain local market conditions. For example, there is demand for buckwheat comb-honey in some limited regions, whereas on the general market it has no sale. It is evident from a survey of the whole field that many beekeepers who now produce comb-honey are doing it to their own detriment while an increase in the production of comb-honey in the more northern clover sections would be beneficial to the markets. The limitations in comb-honey-production will possibly increase the price of the better grades and make it profitable for some northern beekeepers again to produce comb-honey. The restrictions here enumerated obviously require that comb-honey be produced by specialists, for the careless beekeeper and the man who can devote little time to his bees cannot hope to produce the finer grades, except by the accidents of exceptional honey-flows.

EQUIPMENT FOR COMB-HONEY-PRODUCTION

The apparatus for the extensive production of comb-honey is rather complex. The first requirement is a building for storing apparatus, preparing supers and caring for the crop. This building should be rat-proof and is frequently built over the cellar in which the bees are wintered, for commercial comb-honey-production is largely restricted to the North. In managing out-apiaries, it is customary to carry out the empty supers and bring them back completed to the central workshop. The place in which the comb-honey is stored should be the warmest room in the building and should be arranged for artificial heat when necessary. It should be sealed to keep out insects and to allow fumigation.

Hives for comb-honey

The best hive for comb-honey is a matter of dispute. While the Langstroth hive is employed more than any other, the number of frames to be used is much debated. If the locality will permit the building up of the colony to fill ten frames completely, a hive of this capacity is preferable, but in many places this is virtually impossible and an eight-frame hive gives better results. Of course the colony occupies the same hive throughout the year and the need of abundant stores in winter gives the preference to the ten-frame hive but, by care, the disadvantage of the smaller capacity of the eight-frame hive for winter stores may be overcome. Whatever hive is adopted for the production of fine comb-honey, accuracy in the manufacture is far more essential than if it were to be used in extracting. The bee-spaces should be accurate and in self-spacing frames care should be exercised that the deposits of propolis do not force them out of place. Sectional hives, in which the brood occupies two or more shallow hive-bodies, are preferred by some beekeepers, especially among comb-honey-producers. While they have much to commend them, they do not seem to gain in popularity.

Evolution of the section

The early development of the section was suggested in an earlier paragraph. The first ones were made of four pieces of wood and, after the wide adoption of the Langstroth frame, sections 4¼ inches square became in a sense standard, since eight of these sections fit into a Langstroth frame (of special construction, Fig. 136). In 1873, Alexis Fiddes, Centralia, Illinois, made a one-piece section by folding thin strips of wood on a saw-cut at the corner and to him probably belongs the credit of making the first section of this type. In 1876 he described these in a note in "Gleanings in Bee Culture." In 1876, two firms put such sections on the market but it appears that previously other beekeepers had made them on this plan. In 1883, Jas. Forncrook, Watertown, Wisconsin, claimed a basic patent on these sections and brought suit against A. I. Root, Medina, Ohio, for infringement. A decision of the Circuit Court in 1884, upheld by the United States Supreme Court in 1888, declared this patent valueless on the ground that originality was not substantiated. Fiddes is credited with first making such sections. Following this decision, the manufacture of one-piece sections became general and they have entirely replaced the four-piece. They are now made with a V-shaped groove which folds more easily and is stronger than the former method of cutting. Basswood is used exclusively in making these sections.

Types of sections

There is considerable variation in the types of section used and correspondingly in the supers (upper stories) and fixtures made to hold them. The standardization of these appliances is often discussed and is greatly to be desired. There are two styles now in common use which differ in the method of spacing. All are now made of basswood, ⅛ inch thick, as this bends readily at the corners. The bee-way section (Fig. 127) is wide (usually 1⅞ inches, but rarely 1 5/7 or 2 inches) and has passageways cut in two (sometimes three or four) sides to allow bees to enter the sections, comb-building in the individual sections being limited by plain separators placed between them. The plain sections (Fig. 128) are narrow, 1⅜ or 1½ inches, and are separated one from another by "fences" on which are cleats to hold the fence away from the section to allow room for the passage of bees. The bee-way sections are usually made 4¼ inches square, while the plain sections are of the same dimensions, or 4 by 5, 3⅝ by 5, or 4¼ by 4¾. The construction of these sections and the methods of spacing are shown by Figs. 127, 128 and 129. The advantages of the bee-way sections are protection of the honey by the wider wood and extra strength, and some markets prefer them. The plain sections are simpler in construction, cheaper, easily cleaned of propolis and more economical of space in packing. The tall plain sections give the impression of larger size when compared with a square section of equal capacity (Fig. 130).

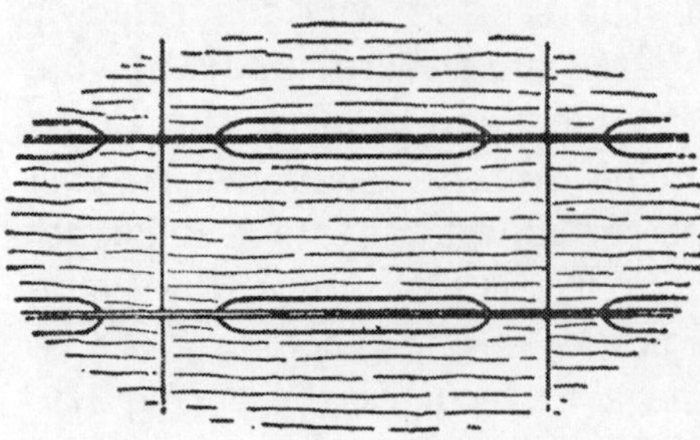

FIG. 127.—Diagram to show method of spacing bee-way sections.

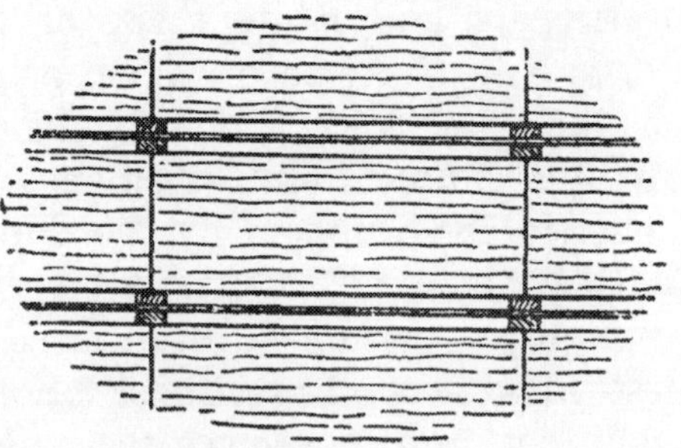

FIG. 128.—Diagram to show method of spacing plain sections.

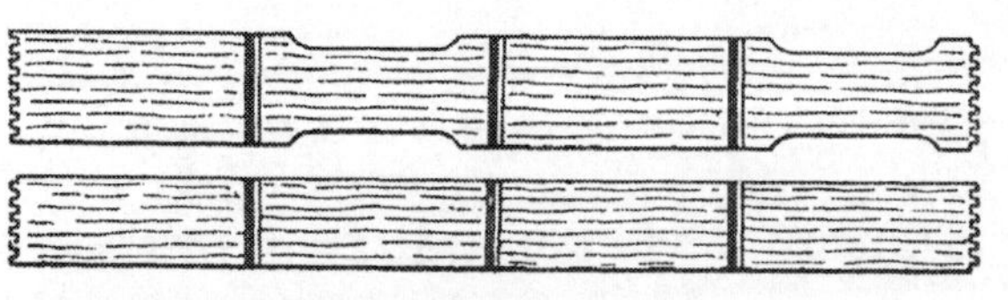

FIG. 129.—Comparison of plain and bee-way sections.

Types of supers

The various supers used to hold these sections differ in the method of support, the protection of the outside of the section and the degree of free communication from section to section. The types in most common use are illustrated (Figs. 131-135) and little needs to be added by way of description. In the T-super (Fig. 131), the sections are supported by strips of tin (shaped like an inverted T in cross-section), no protection being given to the sections on the top or bottom and, when two-bee-way sections are used, as is customary, there is no passage-way horizontally in the super. The super for square bee-way sections with holders (Fig. 132) is used perhaps more generally than any other. The sections are not protected at the top and the communication between sections is the same as in the T-super. For plain sections, the super corresponding to the one just described is shown in Fig. 133 and for tall sections (4 by 5 inches) the corresponding type is represented in Fig. 134. In the two last named, cleated fences are used to provide passage for the bees vertically and there is little opportunity for horizontal passage. To provide protection for the top of the sections a wide frame

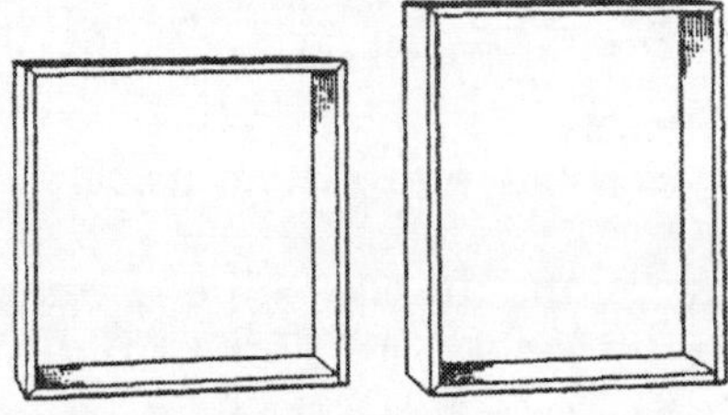

Fig. 130.—Comparison of tall and square sections of equal capacity.

Fig. 131.—T-super.

Fig. 132.—Super for square bee-way sections with section holder.

Fig. 133.—Super for square plain sections with section holders.

is sometimes employed and in Fig. 135 this is shown in combination with shallow extracting combs at the sides devised for the purpose of inducing the bees to begin work in the supers quickly. The modern wide frame is a reversion to the type formerly much used, except that the older types (often for eight sections, Fig. 136) had a tin separator tacked to one side of the frame and bee-way sections were utilized.

Fig. 134.—Super for tall plain sections.

Other equipment

The other apparatus needed in extensive comb-honey-production includes some of the general apiary equipment discussed in Chapter III. A supply of shallow extracting supers may often be used to advantage to induce bees to begin storing in supers, but the combination super (Fig. 135) is generally preferable. If a colony is as strong as it should be at the beginning of the honey-flow, there will be little need for shallow extracting supers. The proper use of bait sections is as good as either of these methods.

Fig. 135.—Super for tall ($4\frac{1}{4}$ by $4\frac{3}{4}$) sections in wide frames. Shallow extracting frames are shown at the sides.

MANIPULATION FOR COMB-HONEY

Preparation of the sections

The folding of the section and the fastening of

the foundation in place are sometimes done in one machine, but in most apiaries these things are accomplished by two operations. To fold the sections (Fig. 137) without excessive breakage, they must be damp to allow the wood to bend. If they are dry they may be moistened by pouring hot water down the V-grooves while still in the crate, the stream, of course, being directed only on the grooves. The whole crate may be wrapped in a wet blanket for a day before the folding.

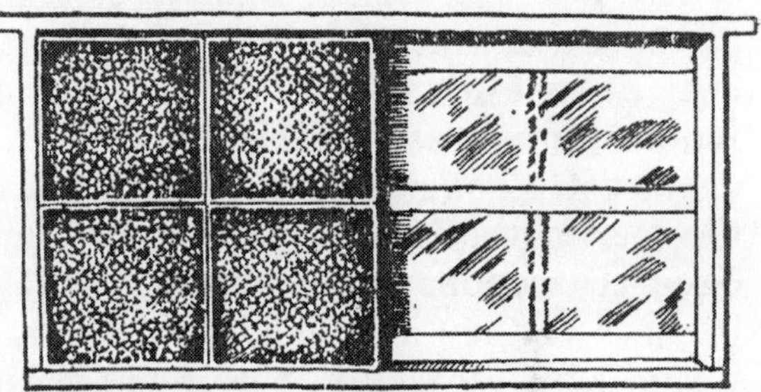

Fig. 136.—Old type of wide frame for holding sections.

Fig. 137.—Section folder.

The use of comb-foundation is necessary to insure straight combs, all of worker-cells, and is essential in the production of fancy comb-honey. The foundation should be as thin as possible without being torn by the bees and usually the grade known in the trade as "thin-super" is preferable. While only narrow strips at the top are sometimes used, it is decidedly preferable to have full sheets to insure uniformity of comb. The sheet is fastened to the top of the section, is slightly narrower than the inside of the section so that it can swing freely and extends to within ¾ to ¼ inch at the bottom. To secure better attachment of the comb to the bottom, it is becoming more common to put a ⅝-inch strip of foundation at the bottom and then make the top piece of foundation long enough to extend within ⅛ to ¼ inch of the bottom starter. The desirability of using the bottom starter is somewhat determined by the character of the honey-flow.

The pieces of comb-foundation are usually fastened in place by a machine in which a heated metal plate is brought near or in contact with the wood at the point where the foundation is to be attached and the foundation is brought against it. The heated plate is then promptly removed and the melted wax fastens the comb-foundation to the wood. Grooved sections which fasten a full sheet of foundation in place as they are folded are sometimes used while some beekeepers (especially in Europe) prefer a section split on top and sides in which the foundation is continuous through a row of sections.

The work of folding the sections, putting in comb-foundation and placing them in supers should be done in advance of the honey-flow and this should usually be the winter employment of the comb-honey-producer. Enough should be prepared to care for the maximum crop, for the beekeeper has no time for this work when the rush is on. Three supers for each colony should be the minimum number. The prepared supers should be carefully protected from dust.

Manipulation of the bees

In the successful production of comb-honey, the skill of the beekeeper is more exercised than in any other branch of beekeeping. From this statement the inference should not be made that the producers of comb-honey are, as a class, better beekeepers than those who extract their honey, for there are many beekeepers who put sections on their colonies and yet fail to get the maximum returns and lose the best of the crop. It is true, however, that much knowledge of the best methods of handling bees has come from the work of the exceptional comb-honey-producers.

It is useless to expect a weak colony to work well in sections and it is, therefore, first of all necessary for the comb-honey-producer to see that each colony has an abundance of workers at the beginning of the honey-flow, as described in an earlier chapter. In the building up of the apiary in preparation for the honey-flow, it is often impossible to get all colonies up to the standard and it is quite common to utilize the weaker colonies for extracted honey-production or to take frames of brood from the weaker colonies to build up those of nearly full strength (p. 273), thereby practically abandoning the weakest colonies for honey-production.

Keeping bees in proper condition

If a colony is of maximum strength when the honey-flow begins, it is ready for the harvest. Every hive should be packed with brood and honey and should have an abundance of young bees. If the colony has previously occupied two stories, as many of them should if properly manipulated, they are reduced to one story and any extra frames of brood are used to build up colonies that need them. This crowding of the brood-nest, so essential to the highest success, is, however, just the condition favorable for swarming, and unless care is exercised the efforts of the beekeeper are rendered less effective. If the colony casts a swarm the working force is reduced and the two parts are not able to do as much as is possible without such a division. On the other hand, the manipulations of the beekeeper may prevent swarming, but still the bees may be put in such a condition that they do not work well. It is necessary not only that the bees be kept from swarming but that the gathering instinct shall overpower all other activities. Increase in the number of colonies during the honey-flow or just before it is, therefore, expensive and should be avoided.

Swarming is a far more serious problem in comb-honey-production than in any other type of beekeeping. The beekeeper, therefore, must exercise all his skill in preventing and controlling this tendency. The manipulations used to prevent swarming are discussed in an earlier chapter. In comb-honey-production the tendency to swarm is so marked that an examination of each colony once in seven to ten days is usually necessary. In case swarms issue in spite of the precautionary measures, various methods are available for handling the swarm and for the disposal of the brood to best advantage, which have been previously discussed (p. 273).

Manipulation of supers

One of the most important factors in success with comb-honey is putting the supers on in the right order and at the right time. This may not only do much toward preventing swarming, but is an important stimulus to storing the maximum amount of honey. No general rule can be laid down for the number of supers that should be put on a colony; they are simply units in the part of the hive devoted to storing which must be given to the colony as needed and not before or after. By proper management supers may be put on slightly before they are needed but they should usually not all be added at once. Many beekeepers make their greatest mistake in this feature and wait until one super is filled and then remove it, substituting an empty one if needed. This not only cramps the colony more than necessary but, when the new super is put on, the bees go into it almost as slowly as they do into a super given at the beginning of a honey-flow. In the meantime the brood-chamber is becoming clogged with honey at the expense of the brood. To give supers as needed necessitates careful observation of the sources of nectar. Supers should be given in time so that there is never a lack of some space for comb-building. Furthermore, space for ripening nectar is needed and comb-building should progress steadily so that the bees will never have honey for which there are no empty cells. If, early in the honey-flow, nectar is coming in rapidly, a new super may be added to strong colonies as soon as work is well begun in the one put on previously. Weaker colonies should of course not be given supers so rapidly. In any event, supers should be added before the bees are in actual need of more storing space.

The position of new supers is determined by the probable future needs of the colony. If the prospects indicate that an additional super will be filled, it should be put below the supers already on, next to the brood-chamber, while if there is a probability that the additional super will not be used it should be placed on top, thus crowding the bees into the earlier supers. In slow honey-flows, supers may also be put on top. In a good honey-flow an empty super should be kept on top at all times so that it is available to the bees if the beekeeper is delayed in reaching the colony to give it more room. The proper order of the supers on the hive is shown in Fig. 138, it being assumed in this case that super 5 is the one which is used near the end of the honey-flow. It will be noticed in the case of supers 1, 2 and 3, that after being placed just above the brood-chamber to be started, they are then put on the top in the next move. This carries up the wax-building bees where they are as far from the brood-chamber as possible and this is perhaps an important factor in swarm prevention.

Fig. 138.—Diagram showing arrangement of the supers.

Removal of supers

Comb-honey intended for market should be removed as soon as possible after it is finished to prevent discoloration of the cappings, known as "travel stain." The extensive beekeeper does not have time to remove the sections individually but should give additional room just rapidly enough to make it possible to complete all the sections in a super about the same time. After the super is removed, often some are not completed and these may be sorted out in the shop and the unfinished ones put in supers and given to colonies. C. C. Miller believed that some colonies are better at this finishing work than others. During the finishing, bees should be crowded to insure completion before the honey-flow ceases.

At the close of the honey-flow, the surplus space should be reduced and all supers in which no work has been done removed. As soon as practical, the surplus space should be reduced to one super but there should always be room for the ripening of new nectar. If desired, extracting combs may be used to receive the honey at the close of the honey-flow.

Caring for the crop

In a heavy honey-flow most of the honey is removed before the flow ceases. In this case the bees are readily removed by smoking and brushing them out. At the close of the honey-flow, all the supers should be removed to prevent honey from being carried down to the brood-chamber and to keep the bees from propolizing the sections excessively. At this time bee-escapes (Fig. 32) greatly increase the ease of taking off supers and, while they are useful at any time, they are specially helpful after the honey-flow ceases. The honey should be taken to the shop and protected carefully from robbing bees.

Preparation of bait sections

Before storing the supers, any unfilled sections should be sorted out and the partially filled ones may be given back to the bees to be emptied. If no disease is present in the apiary or in the neighborhood and if there are a considerable number of such sections, they may simply be exposed where the bees can get the honey from them and they should be left there until a day or two after the bees have ceased to visit them. Bees often leave sealed honey untouched under these circumstances. If there are only a few supers, they may be stacked on colonies and should be left there for a day after the bees have taken out the honey. In this way excitement is reduced to the minimum and general robbing is prevented. The emptied sections should then be saved for bait sections the following season.

Storage in supers

The full supers are so placed in the honey-house as to permit free circulation of air, by laying them crosswise or by putting sticks between the supers. The storage room must be kept dry with the windows open (but screened) during warm weather. During damp cool weather, the windows should be closed and the room may be heated artificially, sudden changes in temperature being avoided. If wax-moths are abundant, the honey may be fumigated with sulfur fumes or carbon bisulfide (p. 439).

Comb-honey should be prepared for market as speedily as practical after its removal from the hive. This is specially true if the honey granulates quickly. If it is necessary to store it until cold weather, the storage room must be kept continuously warm and dry.

Bulk comb-honey

In Texas and in some other parts of the South, honey is frequently sold in the comb, being cut from large combs to any size desired. These pieces are usually put into a can, extracted honey being poured over them to fill the spaces. This is commonly known as "chunk honey," but one German writer on beekeeping, in referring to this American product, inadvertently changed the ch to j. The advantages in producing honey in this form are: (1) it ships well; (2) crowding of the bees is not so necessary since perfect capping is not essential; (3) the bees work more readily in the larger combs; and (4) the beekeeper does not need so much skill in the manipulation of the colonies. The manipulations more nearly approach those incident to the production of extracted honey. Since such honey usually sells readily locally and since beekeepers claim to receive relatively more for it than for extracted honey, no serious objection can be raised to its production, but beekeepers should be warned that the general markets make no demand for honey of this type. Bulk comb-honey is produced in small quantities in all parts of the United States but, except in the regions mentioned, its production is confined to the less skilled beekeepers.

When all the product is for home consumption, it is an excellent plan to have all the honey stored in shallow extracting frames, the length of the regular frames, but only 5⅜ inches deep. Thin super foundation may be used and the frames should not be wired. After being filled, the frames may be stored in supers and a family that consumes honey freely (as all families should) will make short work of the honey in a frame. For serving this honey, a convenient, though perhaps not artistic, method is to put the comb in a tureen. The frames may be refilled with foundation again and again. This is recommended to beekeepers with few colonies as simpler, cheaper and more profitable than comb-honey-production.

CHAPTER XVIII

MARKETING THE HONEY CROP

THE production of honey necessitates skill in the management of bees but the preparation of the crop for market and the selling of the honey are equally important to financial success and are sometimes equally difficult. In the following discussion, the procedure in getting honey into its final package ready for the consumer will be considered first, after which some general principles of honey selling, which apply to all types of honey, will be given briefly.

PREPARATION OF EXTRACTED HONEY

The beekeeping part of the work may be considered as ended when the honey reaches the tank or barrel. Honeys from different sources should, so far as possible, be extracted separately, for they are not of equal money value and the mixing of honeys of two colors or flavors usually reduces the wholesale price of the mixture to that of the least valuable.

Color grading of extracted honey

Honey cannot be graded by flavor but a proper designation of the color is highly important. Many beekeepers object to color grading on the ground that flavor is of first importance, but it must be remembered that color and flavor are closely related and that the lighter honeys from any given source are almost without exception those of better flavor. The wholesale market demands quite properly that honey be graded as to color. Until recently it has been impossible to grade honeys uniformly for all parts of the United States, but the Bureau of Entomology has devised a color grader which should be used as a basis. Information regarding this grading system can be obtained from the Bureau.

Wholesale packages

The usual wholesale package is the five-gallon (60-pound) square tin can, such cans most often being shipped two in a crate (Fig. 139). Most of the foreign honeys that reach the United States markets come in barrels and these are also much used by southern beekeepers. In the West they are rarely employed and are not considered safe. Considerable care must be exercised in their choice and in preparing them to receive the honey. Second-hand alcohol barrels are suitable, provided they have not been charred, but it is better to have them of some wood softer than oak. They must be kept in a dry place and before using must be made as dry as possible, the hoops thoroughly tightened and the barrels tested. The inside may then be coated with paraffin as an extra precaution, but it should be remembered that the barrels must be tight first. If the wood in the barrel is wet, honey will take up this moisture, causing the wood to shrink and the barrel to leak. The usual sizes have a capacity of about thirty gallons, but those holding fifty gallons are frequently used. Unless one is producing a cheap grade of honey for which a cheap package is required, it is better and safter to use the five-gallon tin cans.

Fig. 139.—Crate holding two five-gallon honey-cans.

Retail packages for local markets

In preparing extracted honey for the local trade, it is customary to put it in cans or tin buckets of 2½, 5 or 10 pounds capacity. Fruit-jars and jelly-glasses are also common. These containers can be considered only as articles to hold honey and are entirely unsuitable for a market demanding neat attractive packages. They may often be used in less exacting markets and carry with them the advantage of being useful after the honey is eaten. To the beekeeper, they are desirable on account of their low cost in case his market will not pay a good price for honey. Many beekeepers are, however, guilty of putting fancy honey into these unattractive receptacles, thereby stamping their product as a cheap article.

High-class retail packages

The bottling of honey for the higher class markets requires considerable skill and the beekeeper usually leaves this work to the bottler, who has the necessary equipment and facilities for buying honey from various sources. There can be little question, however, that many beekeepers could well afford to go to the additional trouble and expense of putting honey in attractive artistic packages for the trade that is ready to pay a good price for a high-class product.

An important consideration is the shape of the bottle. If possible this should not be a stock bottle such as is used either by other beekeepers or is obviously employed in the bottling of other commodities. An odd shape or a bottle made for the purpose on an original design will prove a good advertisement The neck of the bottle must of course be wide. A cheap homely label will do much to render a package unattractive. Above all, a label obviously employed by hundreds of beekeepers and with the name of the producer printed in a space left vacant in the making of the original design should not be used. It is possible to make labels in this way which do not tell their history too loudly, but to a bottler who sells honey in considerable quantities the expense of having a distinctive attractive label designed and lithographed will be many times repaid. The beekeeper should note that the extensive bottlers have learned this.

Blending

In a single apiary it is impossible to get honey of the same flavor and color year after year because of differences in the nectar secretion, due to climatic variations. It is rarely desirable to attempt to bottle honey of one source, such as white clover, because of seasonal variations which the consumer does not understand. If, however, honeys from two or more sources are blended, the seasonal differences are hidden and it is possible to give the consumer honey which looks the same and has the same taste year after year. In making up a blend, it is furthermore not desirable to use all water-white honeys, for at some time the supply of such honeys may be limited, and the consumer will not understand why honey of a certain brand has suddenly become darker. It must be remembered that the average consumer is ignorant of the facts that honey varies and that honeys from different sources are unlike in color and flavor and it is useless for one bottler to attempt to educate the entire community on these points in which the consumers have no interest. If he sells pure honey that has a good flavor and if he can duplicate it when desired, no further information is asked by the average consumer. In making a blend it is a good plan to include some sage or tupelo honey as these granulate slowly and granulation injures the salability of bottled honey. An important consideration is the choice of honeys which can be obtained in quantity year after year. To bottle honey for the better markets, it is, therefore, usually necessary to buy some from various sources and the beekeeper who retails honey on a considerable scale should not depend solely on his own apiaries to supply him. In fact, even an extensive series of out-apiaries will not go far toward supplying an energetic salesman.

In the preparation of this chapter the author consulted a

beekeeper of experience and the preceding paragraph was criticized on the ground that the blending of honeys hides the characteristic flavor of honey from each source and, therefore, the flavor of a blend is usually inferior to that of some of the honeys that go to make it. To a connoisseur this is true, but a comparison with another commodity may serve to show that to the average palate this is not the case. The average purchaser of tea buys a certain brand of package tea because he knows it is dependable and uniform. He does not know nor does he care what teas are mixed in this blend, but he may be aware that an individual kind of tea varies and he does not like the variation. On the other hand, there are connoisseurs in tea who, through education and cultivation of taste, are just as particular about the teas they use as the beekeeper is about his honey. The consuming public could become educated in the flavors of honeys but it is not considered worth the effort. Therefore, it is to the interest of the beekeeper to furnish a honey which is the same in color and flavor year after year, so that the variation which comes with honey from one source may be eliminated. It is almost a crime in the eyes of a northern beekeeper to mix any other honey with that from white clover but, as he is not mixing honey for himself, he should give the consuming public what it demands.

Heating honey

In mixing honeys from various sources and in liquefying for bottling those that may be granulated, they must be heated. Direct heat must not be employed and it is a bad practice to run steam-pipes through the honey-tank. Heating must always be done in a double boiler and the temperature of no part of the honey should ever exceed 160° F. A higher temperature darkens it and spoils the flavor. A high temperature not only drives off the volatile substances which give honey its aroma, but a decomposition of a small part of the sugars takes place, which causes darkening. In this decomposition, products are formed which cause honey to respond positively to one of the chemical tests for invert-sugar, which was once a common honey adulterant. The beekeeper who overheats his honey not only injures it but he may find himself unjustly accused of adulteration. The best plan is to bring the honeys to a temperature of about 130° F. and to hold this for two or three hours or until every crystal has dissolved. The temperature is then raised quickly to 160° F., at which point the honey should be put into warm bottles and hermetically sealed while hot. The bottles should be filled as full as possible so that there will not be large air-spaces at the tops. The mixing and heating tank should be deep and the honey should be drawn from the bottom to avoid the scum which rises to the top and to free the honey entirely from air-bubbles which not only detract from the appearance but hasten granulation.

Granulation of honey in bottles spoils the appearance, but by using honeys which granulate slowly (*e.g.* sage and tupelo) in the blend and by treating in the manner just described, granulation may be prevented for a considerable time. Beekeepers often put on their labels the erroneous statement that all honeys granulate and that this is a proof of purity. Artificial invert-sugars which were formerly used in the adulteration of extracted honey frequently granulate quickly. The adding of glucose to prevent granulation, without so indicating on the label, is of course adulteration and is not only dishonest but unlawful.

The granulation of honey after bottling is retarded (1) if the honey is free from air-bubbles, (2) if the bottle is filled to the top, (3) if no scum has been poured into the bottle with the honey, and (4) if not a single honey crystal is unmelted at the time of bottling. If these precautions are taken, even the rapidly granulating honeys will remain liquid for a considerable period.

PREPARATION OF COMB-HONEY FOR MARKET

With comb-honey the beekeeper must do more of the work of preparing his product for the consumer since he is producing honey in retail packages. Recently jobbers have been buying honey and cleaning and grading it themselves, because so many beekeepers fail to do this work carefully, but a better price can be obtained for comb-honey if it is properly graded and cleaned before selling.

Cleaning the sections of propolis

There is usually some propolis on the sections which should be removed. Since the removed propolis adheres to other sections if it comes in contact with them, it is best to have a bench made with a box or tray into which the propolis will fall or to raise the sections an inch or two above the table top on a block while they are being cleaned. These appliances also make it possible to reach the bottom of the section in scraping. Propolis is usually scraped by hand, with a sharp steel case-knife. If the knife does not remove all propolis and stain, sandpaper will complete the work. The scraping of sections requires care to prevent damaging the honey.

Grading

In no other type of honey package is so much care needed to grade properly as in comb-honey. Beekeepers lose thousands of dollars annually by sending ungraded or improperly graded comb-honey to general markets, for all such honey must be regraded before it can be sold, making a useless expense which must ultimately be paid by the producer. If comb-honey is sold locally, less exacting grading may be tolerable, but inaccurate grading is always unwise for it reflects only on the producer and rarely misleads the consumer.

To devise rules for grading comb-honeys from all parts of the country has been exceedingly difficult. The Bureau of Entomology and the Bureau of Agricultural Economics have given much thought to this problem and have recently announced a set of grading rules[1] which are probably the most satisfactory devised. Lithographed illustrations are

[1] Sechrist, E. L. *et al.*, 1927. United States standards for honey. Dept. Circ. 410, U. S. Dept. Agr., 32 pp. See also: United States grades, color standards, and packing requirements for honey. Circ. 24. 1927, 32 pp.

also available from the Department which give a good visual idea of the various grades. The criticism has been made that these grading rules are too complex, but this comes from those whose experience with comb-honey is limited to that obtained in a single region. For any one section, the rules could be simplified materially, and in all probability the various states will shortly establish rules, based on those of the Department, that are locally applicable.

Previous to the establishment of these grading rules, various organizations of beekeepers and some firms dealing in honey had established rules, but with this diversity it was wholly impossible to have the grades on the general market mean anything. This was especially true for the export trade. Without a uniform set of rules which are accepted by the beekeepers in all parts of the United States, it is quite impossible to expect an improvement in the wholesale comb-honey market. Many beekeepers and even some buyers of comb-honey have insisted on grading as their fancy dictates, and when honey thus graded goes to a general market it must be regraded by the purchaser, which means a reduction in price to the seller. It then becomes exceedingly important that producers and dealers try to utilize the standards of the Federal Department, and in case extended experience shows them to be faulty, they can and will beyond doubt be modified suitably.

Grading rules should be followed with the utmost accuracy in preparing comb-honey for market, so that the grade designation will tell the purchaser exactly what he is buying. It is now necessary that each section of comb-honey which enters interstate commerce be marked with the net weight. This is construed to mean the weight exclusive of the wood but including the wax. Similar net weight laws are in force in many states. In the past, sections have frequently been designated "one pound sections," when actually they rarely weigh sixteen ounces. When the net weight is stamped on each section, the purchaser is able to know exactly how much honey he is buying.

In grading comb-honey some beekeepers place each section as graded directly into shipping cases, but since the picture of each grade is mental, it seems preferable to make separate piles of each grade so that all sections can be seen throughout the grading. When enough similar sections are at hand to fill one shipping case, they are then ready to pack, mark and prepare for shipment. Each section must be indicative of every other section in the case. It is often desirable, especially for the benefit of the retailer, to make several subgrades so that the sections in any one case shall be uniform. A failure to grade properly and honestly is doubtless today the most serious handicap to the development of a better market for comb-honey.

Fig. 140.—Shipping cases for comb-honey.

Shipping cases

The commonest case for shipping comb-honey holds twenty-four sections in one tier (Fig. 140), but a two-tier case is preferred by many western beekeepers. Other types are used for certain local markets. It is customary also to make the shipping cases with glass fronts so that the case may be used for displaying the honey. A shipping case of corrugated paper without glass is gaining in popularity.

Glazed sections

Formerly it was not unusual for pieces of glass to be fastened to each side of sections by means of tacks or tin triangles or by strips of paper before being offered for sale, thus protecting the honey from dust and insects. This is extensively practiced in some European countries. Formerly it was not uncommon to sell the package by weight, in which event the glass was sold at a considerable profit. The amendment to the Food and Drugs Act requiring that each package of food be marked with its net weight has almost destroyed the market for glazed sections.

Use of cartons

The modern retail market deals chiefly in package goods and the purchaser usually sees only a carton or case and not the food that he buys. Similarly comb-honey is now frequently put in a carton and this plan commends itself because of the security from dust and insects. The cheap cartons that slip over sections are not so efficient, neither are they so attractive as those that may be completely sealed. Most cartons are now made of thin cardboard but a sealed corrugated paper carton would be more serviceable in the delivery of the honey from the retailer. The comments on labels for extracted honey may well apply to the printing on the comb-honey carton. Individuality and attractiveness are essential in making an appeal to the fancy trade and the carton will appeal to the consumer as a more sanitary package than an exposed section. When cartons are used, the corrugated paper shipping case is preferable since there is no advantage in a glass front.

Shipping comb-honey

The fragile comb in a section of honey carries considerable weight as compared with the heavier reinforced combs in the brood-chamber of the hive. In cool weather, when the wax becomes brittle, it is less capable of withstanding jars and at any time comb-honey is not capable of withstanding much hard usage. Naturally a small package like a single shipping case is easily thrown about by careless expressmen and consequently it is safer to ship in larger packages. For this reason and also to protect the wooden shipping cases from dirt and to prevent the breakage of the glass, several shipping cases (usually eight) are packed together in a crate. Comb-honey should be shipped to its final destination before cold weather. For carload shipments it is safe to pack in a car without crates since the shipping cases are not handled individually en route.

PREPARATION OF GRANULATED HONEY FOR MARKET

As has been shown previously, some honeys granulate quickly to a semi-solid condition and some beekeepers have developed a market for it in this form. Alfalfa honey is exceptionally fine for this purpose. The honey may be poured while in a liquid condition into special paper bags or oyster pails and allowed to granulate before being sold, though such packages are somewhat crude. A better method is to allow it to granulate in larger vessels (such as five-gallon square cans) after which it is removed and cut into bricks as butter is cut. It is then wrapped in waxed paper and put in a neat carton. Since this is a comparatively unknown article of food to the average consumer, its source and nature should be stated on the package. Granulated honey in paper containers should not be allowed to remain on store shelves until warm weather, for the crystals may dissolve, causing considerable loss and inconvenience. Granulated honey which has been stirred or rolled is an excellent article with a flavor somewhat different which is now sometimes sold in tin containers. The market for such honey is not well developed but it is worthy of considerable attention since many persons prefer it to liquid honey.

WORDING OF LABELS

Beekeepers are often at a loss to know just what should be put on labels in order to conform with the various provisions of federal and state food laws. In the case of the net-weight amendment of the Federal Food and Drugs Act, the requirement is definite, that the net weight or volume shall be indicated. Since bottles vary somewhat, it is best to test a number to find the minimum and then have on the label, "Net weight not less than —— oz." or "Minimum weight —— oz." Aside from this there is no difficulty. If the label tells the truth about the contents, the beekeeper will not get into trouble. He should not label his honey "pure clover honey" if it is partly sage honey, nor should he attempt to deceive the customer by labeling it "clover brand honey" if it is not as nearly all clover honey as it is possible to get. Some beekeepers have worried over the fact that even in the purest honey there is possibly a little nectar from some other source. If this causes worry it may be entirely avoided by stating the exact facts. Furthermore, it must be remembered that the officials who enforce these laws are sensible men and a slight discrepancy on the label would probably not be considered a violation of the law, provided there is evidently no intent of misrepresentation. The various pure food laws are designed to protect the purchaser against fraud and the honest producer against dishonest competition. It may perhaps be considered as ingratitude, therefore, if a beekeeper complains at the necessity of telling the exact truth on his label. Beekeepers are unanimously opposed to the adulteration of honey and should do everything possible to aid in the enforcement of these laws.

DEVELOPMENT OF THE MARKET

During the period of the World War there was no difficulty in selling all the honey that one could produce at good prices. The increase in prices was due to a serious shortage of sugar in this and the allied countries, and much of the honey which entered wholesale markets was shipped abroad. With the close of the War and the financial collapse of some of the European countries, the export trade largely disappeared, but recent data indicate that it is again being developed.

Within recent years the American market has been flooded

with inferior sirups and cheap materials which may take the place of honey in the diet. Because of the exceedingly low production cost of many of these products, it becomes possible for the manufacturers to advertise them extensively, thus forcing them on the consumer who does not discriminate carefully in his food materials. Most of these materials are not in themselves injurious, but, lacking the sweetness of cane-sugar and honey, there is a marked tendency to overeat on carbohydrates, so that this development promises to become serious to the public health.

The movement of so large a proportion of the inhabitants to cities and large towns has also hurt the honey market, for persons in cities seem to accept advertisements on their face value more than do those of rural districts. One who has not been brought up on or near the farm often knows little or nothing about the virtues of honey as a food, and it is exceedingly difficult to educate city dwellers to the advantages of honey in place of cheap substitutes which are often sold at exorbitant prices in its stead. This combination of circumstances tends to make the market a serious problem to the extensive producer of honey. There seems to be nothing in this situation to indicate that the honey market will be destroyed or that means cannot be found to develop a suitable and permanent trade in this excellent product, but because of these factors honey marketing is now undergoing changes which are a serious cause of worry to many.

Know honey

The person producing and selling honey should know more of the nature and virtues of his product than is now the case. An attempt has been made in earlier pages to show the composition of honey. Special attention should be given to the presence of mineral materials, enzymes and possibly of vitamins in honey, for the substitutes which so flood the markets are deficient in these respects.

Beekeepers know to a considerable extent the flavors of honeys from the various flowers of their own regions, but frequently have little opportunity to know honeys of other sections which compete on the market with their own, which is especially regrettable since it is quite impossible to describe in words anything pertaining to flavor. An ability to talk intelligently about honeys is a first requisite of a good honey salesman.

The home market

The data presented in Fig. 100 indicates that for the twenty-two chief beekeeping states and for the period covered, the beekeepers reporting sold 67 per cent of their honey away from wholesale markets. These figures were prepared in 1923 and are the latest attempt to analyze this situation, but of more recent years beekeepers have found the wholesale markets still more unsatisfactory, so that it is a safe assumption that this represents approximately the situation today. The separation of these data into eastern and western states shows clearly that the West is more dependent on wholesale markets than the East, although the leading wholesale markets are eastern cities. On the other hand, within recent years a large number of eastern beekeepers have so increased their production that they find it necessary to place dependence on wholesale markets, and if beekeeping continues to develop on a commercial scale, this will increase. It must also be recalled that those who reported to the Bureau of Agricultural Economics and whose reports were used as a basis for the data presented included many commercial beekeepers. Those who own a smaller number of colonies may be assumed to sell even a larger percentage of their honey at home. The economic waste of shipping honey to wholesale markets only to have it shipped back again to one's own town by the jobbers need not be pointed out. The wholesale markets are at present scarcely to be considered as highly satisfactory, and for this reason alone many beekeepers prefer to do the best that they can in selling nearer the point of production.

Many beekeepers not only sell their own crops but do or could buy considerable quantities from other producers. When honey is sold locally the retail price should be considerably more than the wholesale, and if the beekeeper cannot sell his honey at retail at a price which will bring him a good return for his labor in producing as well as a return for his efforts and expense in packing and selling, he may well turn his attention to some other activity. The "price cutter" who sells locally and who takes too little account of the costs of packing and selling has for some years been a distinct menace to a proper development of local honey markets. It is the experience of beekeepers who have counted costs that the retail price must be at least twice the wholesale cost unless the beekeeper is to lose money, for packages and labor are expensive.

If the producer is so situated that he has time available in the parts of the year when the bees need no attention, and unless he has some other work which brings him a better return for his time, he may well consider the development of local market for his own honey and for that of other beekeepers from whom he can purchase a grade of honey suitable to his market. He will perhaps find that his home town consumes little honey until he undertakes to advertise his products, but the experience of those who have tried it is that the per capita consumption of honey is easily increased to many times what it was formerly. Selling honey in a limited way is much more difficult in cities than in rural districts, towns and villages. Individual cases of success in the building of a good local market might be multiplied. Those who have made a success of such efforts usually have a facility for attracting attention to their work and to their product by means somewhat other than those of the usual channels of advertising, and there are abundant opportunities for such persons to talk about bees and honey to schools, clubs and societies. By the use of window displays of an attractive and educational character, it is often simple to get an entire town talking about bees, which results in a great increase in honey sales. The consumers naturally have greater confidence in the honey purchased locally, even though at present honey adulteration does not occur. A beekeeper who develops such a local market not only builds for himself a paying business but to some extent he discourages the use of cheap jams and sirups which are now being pushed on the consuming public by heavy advertising.

To stimulate trade and to create public comment, no better advertisement can be obtained than an observatory hive filled with bees. When such a hive is placed in a store window, the sidewalk is often soon blocked with the curious, and in some cases beekeepers have been asked to remove such exhibits because the crowds too greatly obstruct traffic. Interest may also be increased by giving exhibits of handling bees or of extracting honey. The ingenious beekeeper will think of a dozen ways to use his bees or his commodity as advertising matter, and he will probably be surprised at the ignorance but also at the interest of the public concerning anything pertaining to bees.

While for local markets the less expensive containers for honey may be used, many beekeepers make a serious mistake in trying to sell too cheap a package. Honey in tin often sells well on local markets, but even for such markets there will be a sale for attractive packages in glass. Above all, attractive and artistic labels should be used, avoiding cheap color schemes and bad arrangement of the printed material on the label.

Wholesale markets

In a book of this character, it is impossible to give a suitable discussion of the best way of selling honey at wholesale, especially since it does not lie within the power of the beekeeper to influence this market greatly. Before selling honey, a careful study should be made of prices.

The beekeeper should by all means obtain regularly the crop reports issued by the Bureau of Agricultural Economics, Washington, D. C., which are sent without charge twice a month on request. The bee-journals either re-use these reports or furnish additional information which will be helpful.

The bonding of commission merchants has put a stop to the frauds formerly practiced sometimes in giving false reports of prices obtained, so that the shipper of honey is now in a safer position than formerly. It would be unsafe to give advice as to which cities honey should be shipped or what firms should be selected, for this is a risk which the beekeeper himself must assume. It cannot be emphasized too strongly that accurate and truthful grading is an absolute essential on wholesale markets, and the beekeeper must remember that the wholesale dealers are usually far better informed about the various grades of honey than is the producer whose experience is limited to a single region.

Cooperative selling

The beekeepers of various states or regions have within recent years organized themselves into societies for cooperative selling of their products. In some cases this has been highly beneficial and profitable, while in other instances it has resulted in financial loss to the beekeeper. The safest advice that may be given is for the beekeeper to take no part in such organizations until he is assured that the plan of organization and of operation has been carefully studied by some persons thoroughly informed about such societies. Most of the failures have been due to ill-advised following of inexpert advice rather than to defects in the organization plans. Beekeepers who have similar honey and who are so situated as to be unable to develop home markets may well consider the feasibility of such an organization, but so far almost every effort to form such societies among beekeepers who are widely scattered or who have honeys of different types has resulted in failure. Experience in such societies so far suggests that the greatest essential is a competent manager, and such a man cannot be secured without the payment of a high salary. Unless the cooperative society forms a short cut to the consumer, it is scarcely to be advised, for some of the organizations of this character have in reality constituted only one more link in the chain of dealers between producer and consumer.

CHAPTER XIX

THE PRODUCTION AND CARE OF BEESWAX

Beeswax was formerly an important part of the products of the beekeeper for, at the close of the season, certain colonies were chosen to be killed after which the honey and wax were removed. With the introduction of modern methods, honey-production increased, but there was less beeswax since the combs are not destroyed, except as they are accidentally broken. In spite of this entire change of policy on the part of the beekeeper, beeswax is a part of the product of the apiary which should not be neglected. Cappings from extracting, pieces of comb built in parts of the hive where frames have accidentally not been supplied, burr and brace combs and combs accidentally broken in extracting may be mentioned as sources which in the aggregate furnish the beekeeper with a considerable amount of wax, while occasionally the combs of diseased colonies still further increase the supply. The preparation of this wax for market often involves considerable labor and the beekeeper too often neglects it on that account. However, if pieces of comb are carefully preserved from wax-moth larvæ, they may be kept until there is an accumulation sufficient to justify the necessary expenditure of time, or combs may now be sent to central stations or dealers for rendering.

RENDERING THE WAX

Beeswax is ordinarily removed from the combs by heat. Cappings from extracting and new combs may be melted up and the wax allowed to harden in a cake since these contain little or no foreign matter. If any dirt is present, it will settle at the bottom in cooling and may be cut from the cake. A common method for melting combs and pieces of wax is by the use of the solar wax-extractor, the combs being put in a box covered with glass and the heat of the sun, being confined by the glass, melts the wax, which runs into a lower compartment where it hardens. In Hawaii, the beekeepers have unusually large solar extractors to melt their cappings as well as other pieces of comb. A more rapid method is to place the combs in a double boiler (Fig. 141), the combs being either hung on cross supports or thrown on a screen (like that in an uncapping tank) and as the wax melts it runs out a gate provided for the purpose. A less efficient method is to boil combs in water and skim off the wax. Miller found a dripping pan in the oven of the kitchen stove a good substitute for a solar extractor in the winter.

Fig. 141.—Double boiler for melting combs.

Wax-presses

These methods are satisfactory for clean combs, free from pollen, cocoons and other substances, but in the case of old combs much of the wax adheres to the cocoons and is not liberated. To render old combs they should (if the weather is cold) be broken up and then soaked in water after which they should be put into a sack, heated and pressed under strong pressure while hot. In this way most of the wax is removed from the cocoons. There are three types of press in common use. In the steam-heated press the mass of comb is kept hot by steam generated below during the process of pressing out the wax, which drops down and is drained off. In the hot-water process (Fig. 142), the whole process takes place under hot water, the liberated wax rising to the top where it is removed. A method in common use is to melt up the combs in a boiler and dip off the melted mass into a burlap bag which is then subjected to pressure, no additional heat being supplied. Small presses of these types may be purchased from dealers in supplies but if there is much wax to be rendered larger machines of the hot-water type should be made to which more pressure may be applied. In any type it is desirable to press the bag of comb thoroughly and then loosen it to allow the combs to be filled with water before pressing again. This may be repeated several times until no more wax is liberated. It is advised that soft water be used in rendering combs.

Fig. v42.—Hot-water (Hershiser) wax-press.

The residue after the removal of the wax is commonly known among beekeepers as "slumgum" and since beekeepers seem to have a vocabulary of their own and since there is no other name for this substance it must be accepted. In most cases, slumgum contains a considerable amount of beeswax, some samples supposed to be practically free being found on analysis to contain 40 per cent beeswax. Cocoons entirely free from beeswax are brownish-gray and cannot be pressed into a hard cake. If then the slumgum after removal from the press forms a black hard mass, the beekeeper may rest assured that it still contains wax.

This may be shown quickly by putting some in the fire, where it burns briskly. It is almost permissible to believe that every man who makes a wax-press thinks that no other could ever equal it and some of the most powerful and elaborate ones that have been demonstrated to the author were the least efficient.

Removing wax by dissolving

In Europe, the wax in slumgum is sometimes dissolved out with turpentine or some other light oil and the solvent is then regained by distillation, but there is no record of this being done on a commercial scale in America. By no other means can all the wax be removed, but it is claimed that this "extracted wax" differs slightly both physically and chemically from wax removed by melting. If a solvent is used carbon tetrachloride would probably be the most satisfactory.

CLEANING AND PREPARING WAX

After the wax is extracted, it usually contains many foreign particles. While still in a liquid condition the wax should be placed over an inch or more of water in a vessel which will conserve the heat so that the wax can remain liquid for a considerable time. If a heavy wooden box is available this is good, but even better results may be accomplished by packing a thinner vessel in a box filled with sawdust. If it can remain liquid for twenty-four hours or more the results are best. Just before hardening (when the temperature is just above the melting point of wax) it should be carefully dipped off from the top into vessels to cool. These vessels should either have the top wider than the bottom or have smooth straight sides which are covered with a thin layer of honey just before the cooling wax is poured in. Every beekeeper should know that wax and honey never mix. The particles of dirt will have settled to the bottom and when the wax appears discolored the remainder may be left to harden in the insulated vessel.

The dirt may then be scraped away from this cake, and if there is much wax still in the dirt it may be kept to put in the next melting and the dirt will gradually be eliminated.

Extensive dealers in wax use a little sulfuric acid to assist in cleaning. Manufacturers of comb-foundation usually advise against this practice because beekeepers often use too much acid. A proportion of not more than one pint to forty gallons of water should be used, this water being sufficient for the melting of 750 pounds of wax.

Granulation of wax

In rendering, wax may be formed into an emulsion due to the presence of gums in the honey which adheres to the combs and on hardening resembles a thick paste of corn-meal. Many beekeepers believe that this is pollen from the combs and throw it away. It is, however, almost solid wax. In melting up combs which had contained honey-dew on one occasion the author found the whole mass of wax in this condition after cooling. Such granulated wax (as it is usually called) should be melted slowly by dry heat (not in water) and with care the wax may be saved. It is claimed that this emulsion is less common when sulfuric acid is used in clearing and Dadant believes it is increased by excessive heat. The important fact for the beekeeper is that this is not pollen and should be saved.

Bleaching wax

The bleaching of wax is rarely done by the beekeeper and requires little mention in a book on beekeeping. It is interesting to note, however, that waxes from various regions vary greatly in bleaching, some of the darker waxes being easily bleached while some lighter waxes do not respond to this treatment. Presumably this is due to the kind of honey and pollen available to the bees when the wax was secreted. Dealers claim that wax from some of the southern states is the best obtainable in the United States for bleaching. Usually wax is cut into thin ribbons and exposed to sunlight, but chemicals are sometimes used in bleaching. White (bleached) wax differs physically and chemically from yellow wax.

Adulteration of wax

Fortunately this also is a subject in which beekeepers take no interest, but nevertheless beeswax is frequently adulterated by the addition of mineral waxes, wax from other insects or tallow or by cruder methods, such as the addition of gypsum, starch or flour. The detection of these adulterations (except the cruder ones) must usually be left to the chemist, but beekeepers rely on what is known as the "break test." If a cake of pure wax is cracked it presents a granular surface which is not seen in wax with even a small percentage of paraffin. The determination of the specific gravity is also useful to the beekeeper in confirming his suspicions of a lot of wax.

Preparation of wax for market

Usually the beekeeper ships his cakes of wax in bags or barrels to the dealer and most commonly to the manufacturer of comb-foundation. To see a great pile of these cakes as they come in is sufficient to convince one that beekeepers are not as a rule sufficiently careful in cleaning their wax. One large company of beekeepers puts up wax in cakes just large enough to go into a shipping case such as is used in shipping two five-gallon square cans of extracted honey. Each cake is wrapped in paper and there is not a particle of dirt on the bottom of the cake. This firm receives an equivalent of about two cents a pound more than beekeepers similarly located and in fact has received over five cents a pound more than beekeepers through whose territory the wax passes on its way to market. The fact that they produce several thousand pounds of wax a year makes this a considerable item and it may not be so well worth while for a beekeeper with only a little wax to ship at one time.

SPECIAL PRODUCTION OF WAX

In the previous discussion it is assumed that beeswax is always a by-product of the apiary, but the manipulation of bees for the production of wax is a phase of beekeeping which might well be tried in some tropical or sub-tropical regions. If the honey is of low grade and the cost of transportation is excessive, this should be attempted. In Hawaii the author advised [1] that by special manipulations the honey-dew honey be converted into wax and this has been tried. While the manipulation is reported not materially to have reduced the output of honey-dew honey it did increase the wax considerably. In Porto Rico and in other tropical countries there are good locations from which the transportation of honey is almost impossible and the author advised [2] that this be tested out in Porto Rico. There are records in bee-journals of this being done with success in such localities but details are lacking so that to the present the subject is one chiefly of speculation. It is usually believed that from seven to twenty pounds of honey are consumed in the building of one pound of comb and in the literature the preference is given to the higher estimates. However, bees appear to build comb much more quickly than usual under some conditions, and this suggests that because of some physiological condition the building of comb is more economical. Careful work as to the cost of wax in terms of honey is greatly needed, as well as tests as to the possibility of producing wax where honey is worth only about three cents a pound at the apiary.

USES OF BEESWAX

The only way in which the beekeeper utilizes beeswax to any extent in his work is in the form of comb-foundation. This is made of thin sheets of pure beeswax embossed with the bases of cells of the comb. It is supposed that Mehring

[1] Phillips, E. F., 1909. A brief survey of Hawaiian beekeeping. U. S. Dept. Agr., Bur. Ent., Bull. 75, Pt. V.

[2] Phillips, E. F., 1914. Porto Rican beekeeping. P. R. Agr. Exp. Sta., Bull. 15.

in 1857 made the first comb-foundation and during the next twenty years some progress was reported, but not until Root (1876) invented a machine by means of which foundation is made between rollers was there much advance. Repeated and continuous efforts to improve the product have led to great advance in the reliability of the manufactured foundation and comb-foundation is now used by all progressive beekeepers. Better results are obtained if the wax is sheeted and then put between the rollers under considerable pressure, and as a result the home-made article is less dependable than that manufactured in well-equipped factories. Over 500,000 pounds of beeswax is annually made into comb-foundation in the United States. The Rietsche press is used in Europe but rarely in America. Two concrete or plaster of paris molds are made so that if hot wax is poured on one and the other applied the wax is molded to foundation. This foundation is soft, breaks easily and is more wasteful of wax than that manufactured on rolls.

As was stated earlier, comb-foundation is made of pure wax. It is reported that in Europe it is sometimes adulterated by adding paraffin or cerasin, but it is claimed that when this is done the foundation is not easily accepted by the bees and sags badly after the comb is built. It may be stated that the manufacturers of comb-foundation in America do not practice this deception and the author has personal knowledge of several cases in which these manufacturers have rejected shipments of adulterated wax even when offered at a very low price. This should give the American beekeeper confidence in the marketed product.

In addition to the utilization of beeswax in beekeeping it has many uses in the arts, sciences and industries. It is extensively employed in making candles, which are not molded as are tallow candles but are made by pouring, drawing or dipping. Beeswax candles are used chiefly in church ceremonies. It is also used for making furniture and leather polishes, sealing and grafting waxes and certain varnishes. It is also employed in electrical work as an insulation and to wax threads, especially in sewing leathers. Numerous salves and cosmetics in which beeswax is an ingredient are recommended in books on beekeeping, but it is surely safer to take the advice of a physician on these matters.

In view of the fact that American beekeepers produce relatively little beeswax in proportion to the extent of the industry, it is necessary to import a considerable amount from other countries to supply the heavy demands. This now amounts to between four and five million pounds annually, a great increase during the past few years.

CHAPTER XX

THE CARE OF BEES IN WINTER

FOR honeybees to survive the winter season in cold climates it is necessary that they be able to generate considerable heat. They cannot hibernate as do solitary insects and they cannot migrate to warmer climates. The only method open to them is, therefore, the storage of food and the production of heat when the outer temperature falls below the critical temperature, 57° F. The behavior of the cluster during the winter season has been discussed in an earlier chapter (p. 97).

THE PROBLEM OF WINTERING

That the winter problem warrants considerable investigation and study is shown by the fact that American beekeepers annually experience a tremendous loss in the number of colonies. Fig. 143 gives the average winter losses by states and a careful study of this map shows some of the facts about wintering that most beekeepers overlook. The value of the colonies which actually die out annually amounts to millions of dollars and the weakening of those colonies which still survive constitutes a far greater loss to the beekeeping industry in reducing the income from the honey crop in the following year. The death of entire colonies alone far surpasses all losses from disease and is equalled only by the losses incident to a shortage of food in spring. The weakening of colonies by poor wintering is the greatest drawback to a proper development of beekeeping in the United States. While it is easily possible to recount instances of excessive winter losses in certain regions, it is far more significant that such excessive average losses occur throughout the entire country.

While the accompanying map deserves considerable study, only one feature will now be emphasized, namely that winter losses are by no means confined to cold climates. The losses in the middle latitudes equal or exceed those of the coldest states, indicating that cold weather alone is not

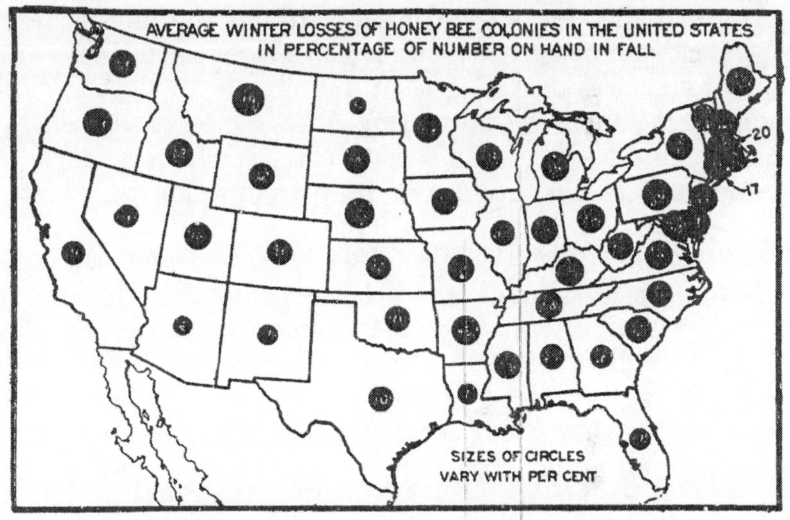

Fig. 143.—Map of the United States showing the average winter losses by states over a period of years.

the cause of the heaviest winter losses. This in turn indicates that something other than protection against cold is the most important consideration in preparing bees for winter. In the middle latitudes, the honeys for winter use are more frequently higher in indigestible materials than are the honeys used for wintering in the North, and when a period comes when flights are not possible, there results an enormous loss from dysentery. This indicates that the winter food is the most important consideration. The losses in the southernmost states indicate that better winter protection is badly needed.

Object of winter protection

In providing extra protection to the colonies outdoors or in placing them in special cellars, the object of the beekeeper is to reduce the expenditure of energy on the part of the bees. As was shown earlier (p. 136), a worker-bee may for all practical considerations be considered as capable of only a certain amount of work and when this is performed the bee dies. Consequently if too much energy is expended during the winter the entire colony may die, or if some bees still live they are unable to do the work required of them in the spring. To conserve the energy to the fullest extent, numerous external factors must be considered by the beekeeper in planning for the winter.

Requirements for successful wintering

Before discussing the methods advocated for the care of bees in winter, it will be well to name the factors essential to the activities of bees during the season. First of all, to winter well, a colony must be large enough to generate heat and to conserve it economically. It should also contain a great number of young bees, full of vitality and capable of prolonged heat production should this become necessary. To accomplish these requirements breeding should be prolonged in the fall. The colony should also have a good queen capable of keeping up egg-laying rather late and then able to permit the colony to build up rapidly to full strength the following spring.

Winter stores

The colony should be provided with an abundance of food of good quality. No food better than good honey has ever been found for bees and the safest plan is to leave enough in the hives to supply the bees without feeding. Not all honeys are equally good and in general it is safe to consider the lighter honeys preferable. The fall honeys are not as good as those obtained earlier. There are exceptions to these statements, however, since buckwheat honey is satisfactory. Most honeys from tree sources are not so good as those from smaller plants because of the higher gum-content. Honey-dew honey should not be left in the hives for winter stores, but if some is present the danger may be reduced by feeding ten pounds or more of sugar sirup after brood-rearing ceases. In case the colony is short of stores a sirup made of granulated sugar may be

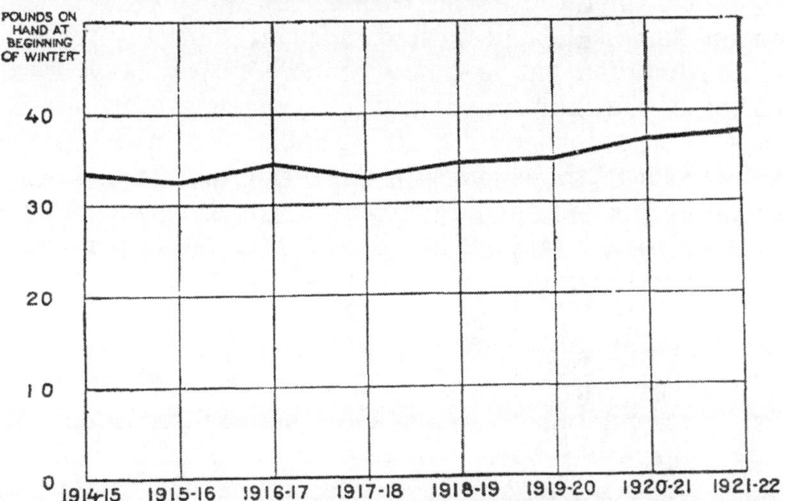

Fig. 144.—Average winter honey supply reported by a large number of beekeepers for the years 1914 to 1921 inclusive.

fed. If the feeding is done early, one part of sugar to one part of water (by measure) is a proper proportion, but for later feeding one part of water to two and one-half parts of sugar is preferable. To the latter sirup, one teaspoonful of tartaric acid should be added to fifteen or twenty pounds of sugar while it is being heated to change the cane-sugar to invert-sugar. Heating should be continued until every crystal is dissolved. Late feeding should be done rapidly. The use of candy for colonies which exhaust their stores in winter should be considered as an emergency treatment and nothing but granulated sugar should be used in making the candy.

Before cold weather arrives each colony which is considered fit to winter out-of-doors should have in the combs thirty pounds of honey, and preferably considerably more. Fig. 144 gives data furnished from 1914 to 1921 by a large number of beekeepers, indicating that the amount of stores left for the bees has been somewhat increased. The amount left in the fall must be adequate not only for winter consumption but to supply stores for the heavy brood-rearing of the following spring in so far as nectar does not come to the colonies from the field. To insure proper building up of the colonies in the spring, nothing less than forty-five pounds should be considered as a safe amount to leave in the fall. Many of the best beekeepers leave still larger amounts.

Causes and effects of humidity in the hive

In winter, especially in a cold or poorly ventilated cellar, the atmosphere in the hive may become so laden with water-vapor that water will condense on the cover, combs and sides of the hive, drop to the bottom board and even run out the entrance. The source of this moisture is, of course, the food of the bees. Honey is a carbohydrate, and when consumed ultimately becomes carbon dioxide and water, one gallon of honey producing approximately one gallon of water. Unless the moisture is carried off in the form of vapor by convection currents in the atmosphere, it will be condensed in the hive, for bees do not ventilate the hive by fanning when clustered.

The condensation of water may be prevented by raising the temperature, by abundant ventilation or by artificial drying, as by the use of unslaked lime. These methods may be applied in the bee-cellar. It should be recalled that an increase in the temperature of the atmosphere increases the capacity of the atmosphere for water-vapor and thereby decreases the relative humidity.[1]

Bees need water in winter but they get enough in their food provided the temperature does not go so high that the relative humidity of the outer air is too low. The optimum relative humidity has not been determined and, in fact, virtually no observations have been made on the relative humidity of the atmosphere of the hive or bee-cellar. Probably the great diversity of opinion as to the best temperature for the bee-cellar is due to the unrecorded differences in the relative humidity of the various cellars observed.

Effects of ventilation

Ventilation of the hive and of the bee-cellar depends on the currents of air caused by the differences in temperature in two points, since bees do not mechanically ventilate the hive in winter. The movements of air serve not only to remove carbon dioxide and bring in oxygen but, probably more important, they carry out the surplus water-vapor. Abundant ventilation is beneficial and becomes harmful only if the temperature is too greatly reduced thereby. It has been determined that bees survive in an atmosphere which contains an unusually high percentage of carbon dioxide but it is not wise to err on that side.

Source of heat and effects of changes of temperature

It has been determined by Demuth and the author[2] that bees generate heat in winter by muscular activity and that undisturbed broodless bees generate virtually no heat between 57° and 69° F. (Fig. 145). When the temperature of the air about the bees falls below 57°, the bees form

[1] The beekeeper interested in cellar wintering will do well to consult Marvin, 1912, Psychrometric tables, Weather Bureau Publication 235 and other works dealing with the relation of relative humidity to temperature.

[2] Phillips and Demuth, 1914. The temperature of the honey bee cluster in winter. U. S. Dept. Agr., Bull. 93.

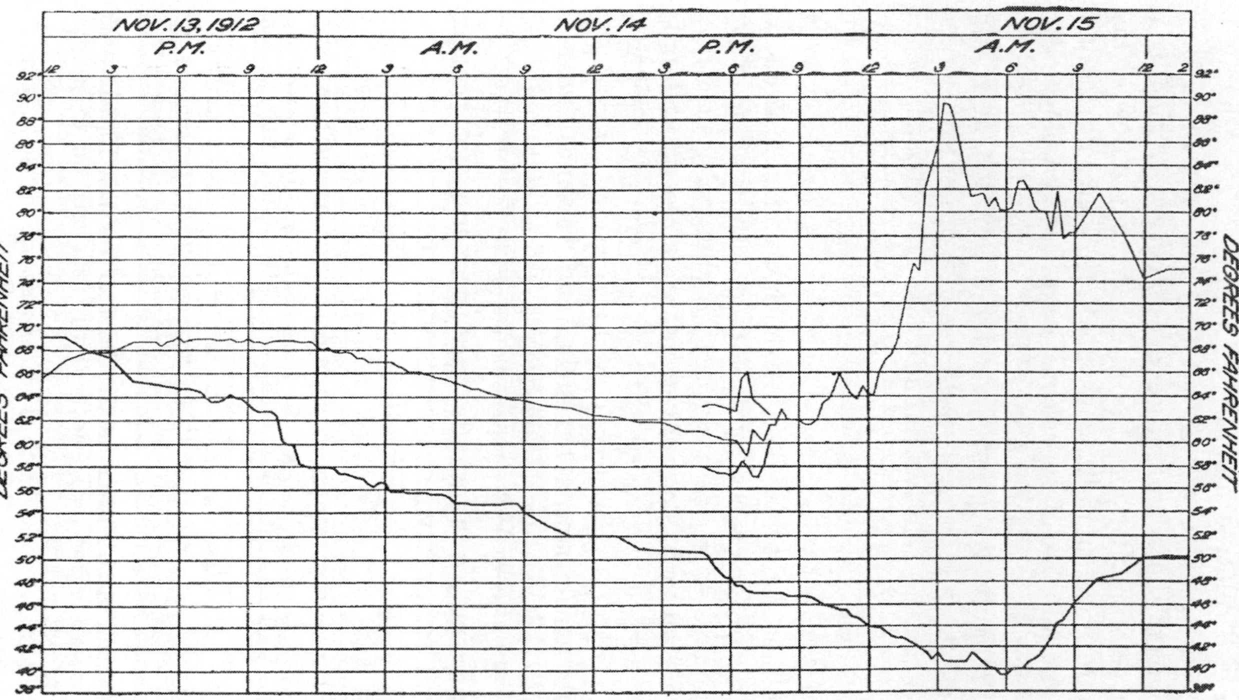

FIG. 145.—Diagram showing the response of a colony of bees to changes in outside temperature-record of Nov. 13-15, 1912. The heavy line represents the outer temperature and the lighter line that within the cluster. The two short lines represent temperatures on the edge of the cluster where activity was first observed.

a cluster and raise the temperature, often almost to blood heat. It follows that when the temperature of the bees is above 57° and below 69° F. they do less work than at other temperatures and their energies are thereby conserved. However, to raise the outer temperature to 57° F. often so reduces the relative humidity of the surrounding air as to create excitement in the cluster and thereby to destroy the desirable condition. Other factors not yet worked out probably have a bearing on this problem. Most beekeepers consider 40° to 45° F. as the best cellar temperature, but it is clear that the temperature can usually be raised still more with beneficial results. Humidity and ventilation are so intimately connected with temperature that one cannot be investigated separate from the other.

Disturbance

Any factor which induces undue activity in the winter must be considered as a disturbing factor. For example, low temperature, improper humidity, poor food or insufficient ventilation, create an undue excitement which should be avoided. Disturbance is usually considered, however, as applying to manipulation of the colony or to jarring while the colony is clustered. Any such circumstance causes the colony to raise the temperature, which may not again become normal for many hours. All manipulation or handling is to be avoided, therefore, especially in cold weather or in the cellar. Colonies sometimes begin brood-rearing in winter, usually induced by some improper outside condition. The care of the brood then causes a high temperature and corresponding excessive activity which decimates the colony. Brood-rearing should, so far as possible, be avoided until the bees can fly freely.

In this connection it will be recalled that breeding often begins in colonies wintered out-of-doors during the coldest weather. The previously mentioned results on colony temperatures lend support to the theory that excessive outside cold causes the raising of the temperature of the cluster to the point where egg-laying is possible and that the beginning of breeding is a response to the stimulus of external cold. Similarly, colonies wintering in the cellar may have their temperature raised by reason of an undue accumulation of feces and breeding may be begun. If these theories are tenable, winter breeding is to be considered as indicative of poor wintering and there is abundant evidence that the best results are obtained where no breeding takes place until the bees fly freely.

METHODS OF WINTERING BEES

There are two main ways of wintering bees and it is often difficult for the beekeeper to decide which he should

Fig. 146.—The winter packing case used in the Bureau of Entomology Apiary. In the specifications given in this bulletin, provision is made for a third hive-body in the spring. (*a*) Detail of tunnel to hives.

adopt. They may be left on their summer stands with suitable protection (Figs 146, 147) or they may be placed in a cellar or special repository (Figs. 148, 149) as a protection against extremes of temperature, in which event they normally have no opportunity to fly and void their feces until again placed in their summer locations. The beekeeper cannot decide which method is preferable with-

Fig. 147.—An apiary packed in cases each to hold four colonies.

out taking into consideration the temperatures to which bees are exposed outside. Fig. 150 shows the average January temperatures of 15° and 25° F. When the average January temperature is below 25° and above 15°, the beekeeper may consider cellar wintering possible, but when it is below 15°, cellar wintering becomes almost obligatory. Detailed weather records for any given locality may usually be obtained from the United States Weather Bureau, but it must be remembered that temperatures differ in places not many miles apart, due to differences in prevailing winds and altitude. There seems to be a tendency

Fig. 148.—Interior of bee-cellar with hives in piles of four. Insulation above the ceiling is not shown.

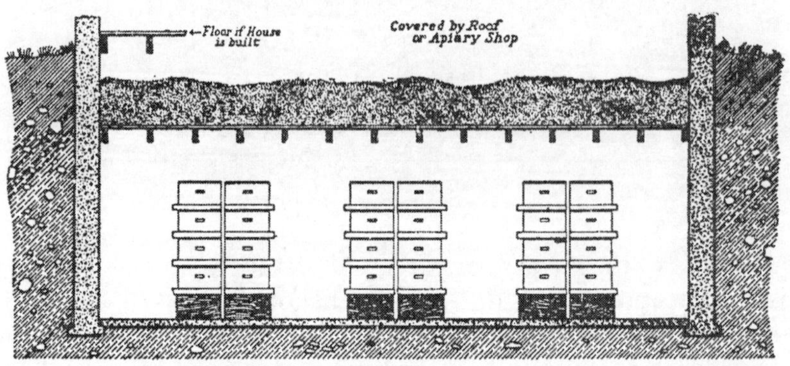

Fig. 149.—Diagram of bee-cellar. Clearance 6½ feet, ceiling below, ground level, packed with about 1½ feet of sawdust.

on the part of beekeepers to prefer outdoor wintering, and this becomes possible when better methods are practiced, especially with regard to winter food and suitable protection.

Outdoor wintering [1]

In warm situations, bees may be left outside all winter with no added protection, for they are able to withstand considerable hardship and may even live through zero

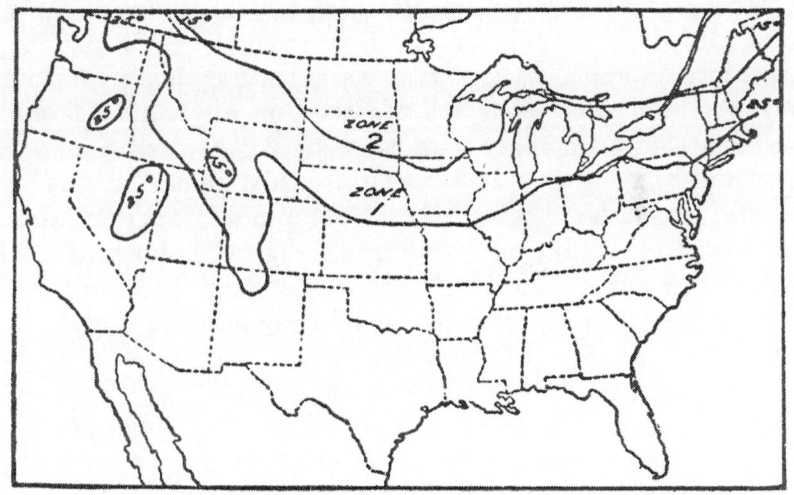

FIG. 150.—Map of the United States showing regions where cellar wintering is practicable, based on the average temperature of January.

weather in a single-walled hive. However, if their energy is to be conserved for the heavy work of the spring, there should be no such waste of vitality. Beekeepers are rapidly coming to realize that heavy insulation is most important. The packing placed about the hive or hives serves to prevent the loss of heat generated by the bees and thereby greatly reduces the muscular activity necessary to heat production. Just as it is practically impossible to

[1] For greater detail regarding this method of wintering, the reader is referred to the following bulletins which may be obtained without charge from the Department of Agriculture, Washington, D. C.: Phillips, E. F., and Demuth, Geo. S., 1915. Outdoor wintering of bees, Farmers' Bull. 695, U. S. Dept. Agr., 12 pp.; and Phillips, E. F., and Demuth, Geo. S., 1918. The preparation of bees for outdoor wintering, Farmers' Bull. 1012, 20 pp.

leave too much honey on the hive in winter, so also it is quite impossible to pack a colony too heavily. Bees, as has been shown (p. 67), are cold-blooded animals and do not generate heat constantly as do mammals. It then follows that they do not get too warm when heavily insulated.

A plan of outdoor wintering which has much to commend it is to place four colonies close together in a packing case, two facing east and two west, leaving room for four to eight inches of insulating material on all four sides and perhaps a foot on top. The construction of such a case is shown in Fig. 148 (see also Fig. 103), the dimensions varying according to the degree of cold commonly experienced in any locality. Bottom packing is highly important and provision is made for this in the case figured. The space left for insulation may be filled with planer shavings, sawdust, chaff or dry leaves, there being slight differences in the insulating values of these common materials. Sawdust holds moisture if it becomes wet while dry leaves do not. Tunnels through the packing (Fig. 146, *A*), provide entrances to the hives and the roof must be water-tight to prevent the packing from being wet from rain or snow. This method of packing is used with excellent results in all parts of the North and in Canada. Packing may be provided equally well for two colonies side by side or, if desired, for individual colonies or to hives in rows to suit the convenience of the beekeeper, and there is no virtue to the quadruple case except economy of cost and materials.

To secure the best results, each colony should be given two hive-bodies, the upper one being filled with honey. If bees are wintered in single hive-bodies, it becomes necessary to give additional room and stores before the proper time for removing the packing. While wintering in two hive-bodies demands heavier packing, this is more than compensated by the lack of necessity for unpacking early. If two hive-bodies are given each colony with plenty of stores, if the stores which will be used by the bees during winter are of good quality and if the bees are then heavily insulated, this combination of conditions will give the best possible results in outdoor wintering. The beekeeper may be assured that the labor involved in proper packing and in furnishing proper stores will be repaid many fold. A packing case usually pays for itself each year.

Colonies wintered outdoors should be provided with packing early. While the temperatures of autumn nights are not so low as to endanger the bees, still the heat which must be generated in an unpacked hive is an unnecessary drain on the vitality and stores of the colony and for the average northern apiary it is desirable that the colonies be packed early in October. Similarly, the packing should not be removed too early. When frequent examinations of the colony become necessary the temporary packing around the hives becomes bothersome, but it is best to leave it on so long as it does not interfere with the work of the apiary. Where heavy outside packing is needed, the packing may usually be kept on until some time in May.

To reduce convection currents a tall hive is preferred in winter. For summer manipulations most American beekeepers prefer a hive not deeper than the Langstroth, which is rather shallow for best results in winter. This may be overcome by giving each strong colony two hive-bodies, the top one being well filled with stores. If such a hive is well packed it is highly satisfactory.

Hives of various types are made in which insulation is provided permanently, and were it not for the difficulty of moving such hives they would probably be more in favor among commercial beekeepers. Top packing is the most beneficial and may be retained profitably throughout the summer if practical.

Insulation for the conservation of heat is of the greatest importance, but even a well insulated hive or group of hives may not offer adequate protection unless sheltered from strong winds. The enormous loss of heat due to wind is usually not appreciated. A high fence or a heavy evergreen hedge is the means of a great saving of bee vitality.

The weakest place in the protection of the colony is the entrance. It is not safe to contract the entrance too much for it may then become entirely closed by dead bees. Neither is it safe to close the entrance entirely and provide indirect ventilation, for the bees become restless when confined. The entrance should be closed as much as possible and yet provide room for dead bees. An entrance 3/8 by 4 inches is perhaps the largest ever needed in wintering outside and this is usually too large, especially for relatively weak colonies.

The wrapping of hives in black tar paper or other material and leaving unprotected the fronts of the hives which face south are often advocated on the theory that the heat of the sun will warm up the hive more rapidly on bright days. Since the sun shines on the hive only a small fraction of the time in the average apiary in the winter season, the benefits of heat from the sun should not be overestimated. Any arrangement for absorbing heat from without is equally effective in dissipating heat from within and consequently a heavy packing on all sides is advisable. If possible it is best to have the packing cases painted white to reduce loss of heat.

To summarize: for outside wintering, leave abundant stores, pack early and heavily, protect from wind and unpack late.

Cellar wintering [1]

It is more difficult to give brief directions for cellar wintering of bees than for outdoor wintering. If the cellar is constructed so as to give proper insulation to the bees inside, if the food is of correct amount and quality and

[1] For greater detail and explanations of the recommendations, the reader is referred to: Phillips, E. F., and Demuth, Geo. S., 1918. Wintering bees in cellars, Farmers' Bull. 1014, U. S. Dept. Agr., 21 pp. This bulletin may be obtained without charge from the Department.

if the temperature and ventilation of the cellar are well regulated, excellent results may be obtained from cellar wintering and a considerable saving made in the honey consumed, although saving of stores is a minor consideration in wintering. The construction of the cellar is shown in Fig. 149, and little need be added in the way of explanation. The necessity of getting the ceiling of the cellar below frost line should be mentioned, for without this provision it becomes impossible to maintain a uniform temperature high enough to protect the bees properly. The arrangement of colonies in the cellar is shown in Figs. 148 and 149. The capacity of the cellar should be such as to provide approximately fifteen cubic feet of space to each colony, and if too much space is provided the bees have great difficulty in maintaining a proper cellar temperature.

A temperature of 40° to 45° F. is usually considered best for the bee-cellar, but it is obvious from what has been said about the responses of bees to outer temperatures that at such cellar temperatures the bees are required to generate considerable heat. It would be advantageous to raise the temperature to 50° F. or higher, except for the fact that at higher temperatures the relative humidity of the cellar is usually too low, causing excitement and activity on the part of the bees. Sufficient ventilation must be provided to prevent condensation of water when the cellar temperature is 45° F., and if this is done, the beekeeper may be sure that the ventilation is adequate to provide the necessary oxygen and to eliminate the carbon dioxide generated by the bees. Light should be excluded and the colonies left absolutely undisturbed for the entire period that they are in the cellar. Many cellars are over-ventilated and give better results when this is reduced, often until all ventilation comes through walls and ceiling.

Many beekeepers use the cellars under their residences, but as a rule better results come from specially constructed cellars or repositories. These may be built in a hillside with relatively little expense and will give good results only in case they are heavily protected on all sides. A good entrance is perhaps the most difficult part of the construction, for it must be as heavily insulated as any other part. Double doors with insulating materials well packed between is usually the best method for protecting the cellar at this weak point. Drainage should be provided if necessary.

Colonies should not be placed in the cellar until all brood has emerged and until all young bees have had opportunity for flight to void their feces. There is a growing tendency to place bees in cellars earlier than formerly, and it is usually good practice, wherever cellar wintering is feasible, to put the bees in after a good flight shortly before the middle of November. To wait until later is usually dangerous. After a good flight and when the bees have again clustered, the hives should be carried in with as little disturbance as possible. They may be piled as high as convenient (Fig. 149) and the tiers should be separated only enough to provide convenient passage.

During the winter, dead bees should be removed from the floor as well as from bottom boards (with the minimum disturbance) and a careful watch should be kept that the bees do not become disturbed by too high or too low a temperature. A reliable thermometer is practically necessary for good wintering and the use of a sling psychrometer to determine the relative humidity in the cellar is recommended. One of the difficulties of cellar wintering is the fact that the bees must be watched to prevent the introduction of some disastrous condition.

Bees may be left in the cellar until incoming nectar and pollen is available in small quantities in the field if they are wintering well. If dysentery develops, an earlier removal is necessary to prevent serious damage. The usual time of removal is late in March or in early April. It is obviously impossible to give exact dates for putting bees in cellars or for removing them. These dates must be determined by the beekeeper each year. If he happens to have access to a station of the Weather Bureau, he can often get warning of a coming cold period in the fall which will show the necessity of putting the bees in their winter quarters. It is extremely dangerous to leave bees out late in the hope of still one more flight which may not come, and if bees are subjected to extreme cold they may be seriously depleted, even though they may gain one flight by the delay.

After the bees are removed, it is usually desirable to give them some protection against cold in the form of insulation, even though it is scant. The elaborate packing for outdoor wintering is scarcely possible for spring, but it must be remembered that the cluster temperature in spring is higher than during the broodless period, so that the need of protection is sometimes as great then as in the dead of winter. Protection from cold winds is highly important for cellar-wintered colonies after removal from the cellar. If stores are not in the hive for the spring development of the colony, these should be given at the first opportunity after they are on their summer stands.

Effects of confinement

Bees normally do not eject their feces in the hive, and if confined there for a time, either outdoors or in the bee-cellar, feces may so accumulate (Fig. 78) that the bees are unable to hold them. The hive and combs are then spotted and this condition the beekeeper knows as dysentery. The feces are composed of the parts of the food which cannot be digested and assimilated and of the excreted products. Therefore, a food which contains an unusual amount of indigestible material is ill suited for a period of confinement. Honey-dew honey is specially bad, since it contains a relatively large percentage of gums, and sugar sirup is ideal in so far as the prevention of dysentery is concerned.

It has been shown in the paper previously mentioned that the accumulation of feces causes the bees to become more active, and this in turn causes an increase in the temperature of the cluster (Fig. 151). The temperature may finally reach a point where brood-rearing may begin, and this with the increased activity causes excessive feeding and still greater accumulation of feces. It is, therefore, quite

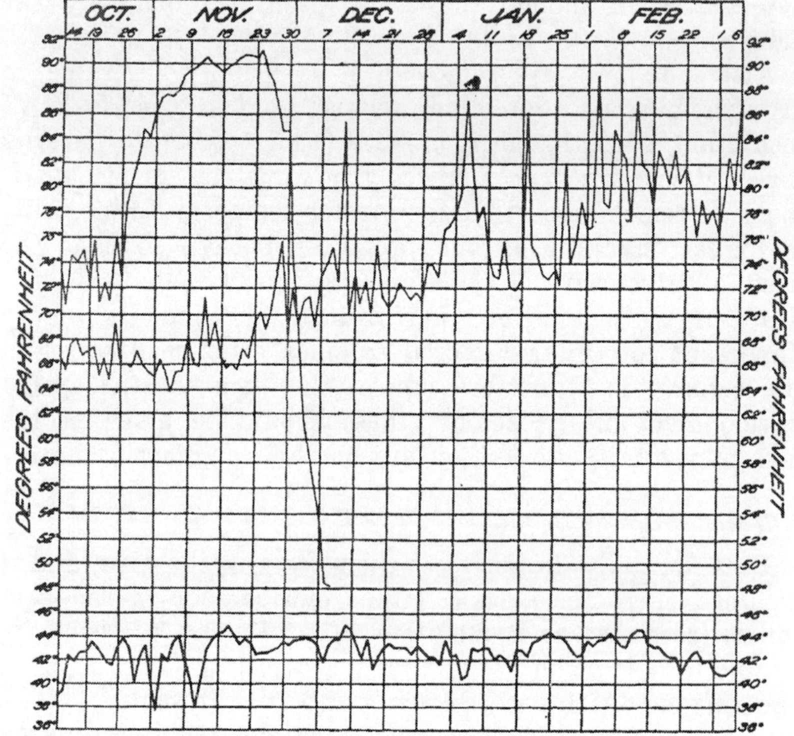

Fig. 151.—Diagram showing the effects of an accumulation of feces. The heavy line represents the temperature of the cellar, lighter ones those inside the clusters. The colony which died in December was on honey-dew stores and the one which lived through the winter was on honey stores. Brood-rearing occurred in the honey-dew colony during November and it also suffered from dysentery.

plain that a good food free from gums is of primary importance in successful wintering. If the bees are free to fly at frequent intervals the inferior food will do less harm and bees may even winter on honey-dew honey if there are no long periods of confinement. It is, however, doubtful whether they are as vigorous later on if the food is inferior.

Years ago it was asserted that the presence of pollen in the hive where the bees could eat it is responsible for dysentery, but later work and the experience of beekeepers do not warrant this conclusion. A suggestion made by Holterman is worthy of consideration in this connection. He advocated giving each colony ten pounds of sugar in the form of sirup late in the fall to be sure they have enough food. This serves another purpose perhaps not fully appreciated. The sirup will be stored next to the cluster, the bees will then use it first and, since it contains no gums, the accumulation of feces cannot occur until the sirup is exhausted.

Spring dwindling

If the colony goes into winter quarters with few young bees or if by excessive activity during the winter because of poor care they age rapidly, the adult bees are often unable to do the work required of them when brood-rearing begins. Then they may die more rapidly than they are replaced by the emerging bees. To this condition the name spring dwindling is applied. Obviously the proper course is to prevent the condition. The prolonging of brood-rearing in the fall and especially the giving of proper care in winter, including good food and protection from cold, will prevent this condition. If it should occur, it may be reduced somewhat by abundant protection from cold and wind in the spring.

Within the past few years great advance has been made in knowledge of the proper care of bees in winter. Many beekeepers have profited by this advance and have vastly reduced their winter losses, while many others have made no change and are still suffering heavily from this cause. There have arisen many points of dispute, most of them based on inaccurate knowledge of bee activity, such for example as the teaching that it is possible to insulate bees too heavily for their welfare. The beekeeper may rest assured that the more insulation he gives his bees, either outdoors or in the cellar, the better will they repay him for his care in the honey crop of the following year. Winter losses are by no means necessary and beekeepers make a serious mistake who look on these losses as fatalists. There can be no wholesome development of beekeeping until the enormous winter losses are reduced.

CHAPTER XXI

THE SOURCES OF NECTAR AND POLLEN

To the beekeeper who studies his locality properly, one of the most difficult and important problems is to determine the sources from which his bees gather important amounts of nectar and pollen and to schedule the usual blooming dates of these plant species. The books and journals devoted to beekeeping give considerable information regarding honey-plants, but to determine which ones are of greatest importance in any given place and properly to identify those on which bees work is sometimes difficult for one who is not a botanist. In localities where only one or two species yield surplus, this problem is relatively easy. For example, in part of the irrigated regions of the West, alfalfa and sweet clover are almost the only plants which the beekeeper need consider, while in the northeastern part of the United States there are localities where white and alsike clovers are virtually the only surplus-yielding species which need influence the apiary management. Two important books [1] now available to the American beekeeper will be most useful; since this subject is now so well treated, only a general discussion can be attempted here.

Since the beekeeper does not cultivate anything especially for his bees, it may not be evident why he should study the honey-plants. While it is true to a large extent that the beekeeper must take whatever the plants in the region

[1] Lovell, John H., 1926. Honey plants of North America (North of Mexico) Medina, Ohio: The A. I. Root Co., 408 pp., ill.

Pellett, Frank C., 1923. American honey plants, Hamilton, Ill., American Bee Journal, 392 pp., ill.

furnish, he must, to be successful, know when the dependable species will bloom so that he may have his colonies strong and ready to gather the harvest. In the establishment of out-apiaries he should also study the country to decide on the best locations, those nearest to the most valuable and abundant sources.

It frequently happens that a beekeeper maintains his apiary for years in one locality, sometimes experiencing a total failure of his crop, when within a few miles of him there are nectar resources on which he might draw, but of which he is in ignorance. Many beekeepers have come to see this only after they have established out-apiaries. A beekeeper who is depending on bees for a considerable amount of his income should make a study of the regions about him, perhaps for a distance of several miles, and when he finds a locality which looks promising, but concerning which he can get no definite information, it will pay to place one or two colonies there and to inspect them at intervals during the season. In this way, it is possible at times to find locations favorable for migratory beekeeping. Any swamps within moving distance should be investigated, as these regions are more dependable than drier locations. In view of the fact that many beekeepers by staying at home are losing nectar that is abundant only a few miles away, it is evident that scouting should be more generally practiced. The increasing use of automobile trucks by beekeepers will probably lead to more migratory beekeeping than has existed in the past.

NECTAR

Nectar is a secretion found at the bases of the flowers of many species which the bees gather, carry to the hive and modify into honey. A similar sweet material is secreted from other parts of certain plants, and when these appear the bees often gather them just as they do floral nectar. Nectar usually consists of a solution containing sucrose (cane-sugar), levulose and dextrose, with small amounts of other materials including coloring matter and those ingredients which give to honeys their characteristic flavors. The water-content is usually considerably higher than that of fully ripened honey, this excess water being evaporated by the bees during the ripening process. The honeybee is the only insect which gathers nectar and stores it in such form that honey may be obtained for human use.

Function of nectar

The nectar secreted in the flowers of numerous species is not a mere by-product of plant activity but serves a definite function in the life cycle. Numerous adaptations of plant structure and physiology serve to bring about cross-fertilization, by which the ovule of one flower is fertilized by pollen from another flower, often from another plant of the same species. Pollen of certain species is carried from flower to flower by the wind but one of the most common methods is through the agency of insects. The insects which perform this mission are usually attracted by the nectar which the flowers secrete and, in going from flower to flower to get this nectar for food, they act as unconscious agents of cross-fertilization by carrying pollen from the stamen of one flower to the pistil of another. The nectar is, therefore, the attractive object in this process.

Many insects do this work; some flowers are visited most frequently by flies, others by small wild bees, but a honeybee not only goes for nectar for its own food but also carries it to the hive for food for the brood and for the adults in adverse seasons. It, therefore, makes many visits. The honeybee is unique in many ways, not the least wonderful of which is its hoarding instinct. That the honeybees gather at times more than they need makes it profitable for the beekeeper to care for them so that he may take this surplus.

In the adaptations of Nature, nectar is first of all to attract insects, then when honeybees gather it, they do so to feed themselves and their brood. The surplus honey is, therefore, simply a by-product, an over-production due to the prodigality of Nature, by which the beekeeper profits. Unless gathered by the bees and appropriated in part by the beekeeper, much of this nectar would dry up, consequently honey-production is the conservation of a natural resource, which if not taken immediately is lost.

Variations in nectar

Nectar varies with each species. Since plants vary in the color of flowers, shape of leaves and in innumerable other characters, it should not be a matter of surprise that they also show marked differences in color, water-content and flavor of nectar. Not only do flowers of different species secrete nectar of various types but nectar of any one species may differ according to soil, climatic conditions and other environmental factors influencing the growth of the plant, just as may the leaves and other parts. For example, in Colorado alfalfa honey is a beautiful white product but farther south it is more amber in color. This may sometimes be due to an admixture of other nectars.

Variation in secretion

Nectar secretion may, in a sense, be taken as an indication as to the most favorable conditions for growth and most species which furnish nectar are highly susceptible in this respect to outside influences. Within the limits of the geographical distribution of a nectar-secreting species there may be a more restricted area in which the flowers secrete nectar. The species may be rather prevalent outside its usual nectar-secreting boundaries, but there is probbly some factor in the environment not best suited to the plant if it fails to produce nectar. For example, alfalfa is now grown in all sections of the United States but the Mississippi River may be taken roughly as the eastern boundary of its secreting area. White clover produces in the northern part of the United States a superb honey, often in exceedingly heavy honey-flows, but farther south, it becomes a honey-plant of secondary importance.

Effects of climatic conditions on secretion

Any species of nectar-secreting plant is often rendered non-productive by unfavorable weather conditions. Smaller plants usually cease nectar secretion at once in dry weather, while tree sources are less quickly affected. Basswood seems to be an exception to this statement. Hot sultry weather with rains at night during the blooming period of white clover usually brings a heavy honey-flow. The sages of southern California secrete nectar in abundance only if there is adequate rainfall while the plants are growing, whereas rain during the blooming period may stop all secretion. Because of this condition, the beekeepers of that region watch the records of rainfall during the winter to judge as to their prospects for a heavy honey-flow in the following summer.

The factors influencing nectar secretion have been a subject for much speculation among beekeepers and a small amount of investigation has been done in this field. The physiology of nectar secretion is so little understood, by beekeepers at any rate, that the relative importance of temperature, humidity, barometric pressure and other environmental factors in bringing about abundant secretion are not known. It appears to be a rather general rule that a large range of daily temperatures is highly advantageous. These factors have been studied by Hambleton[1] with regard to the influence on gathering by the bees. If these influences were better studied, the beekeeper could more accurately forecast his crop and could plan his work day by day with better results during the season. Unfortunately

[1] Hambleton, Jas. I., 1925. The effect of weather upon the change in weight of a colony of bees during the honey flow. U. S. Dept. Agr., Bull. 1339, 52 pp., 12 figs.

a considerable amount of speculation on this subject has been published which has tended to confuse rather than to help the beekeeper.

Advantages of swamp sources

Since plants which grow in swamps are less subject to changes in available moisture and usually get an abundance, the swamp honey-plants are usually more dependable than those growing in dry soils. In swamp lands, also, the honey-plants are less liable to destruction through agricultural operations and conditions are more likely to remain the same year after year. These facts should be more generally recognized by beekeepers seeking new locations for the establishment of apiaries. The tree sources are usually more dependable than smaller plants.

Cultivation of plants for nectar

It was stated earlier in this chapter that the beekeeper does not cultivate anything especially for his bees. This has been tried several times without profit. However, plants which are nectar-producers and also have a value in some other respect may often be cultivated with profit to the beekeeper. Alsike clover is an excellent honey-plant and many beekeepers have materially improved their ranges, either by planting this clover as a forage or by encouraging neighboring farmers to do so. Buckwheat, alfalfa and cotton may also be mentioned among the cultivated plants of value to the beekeeper. In seeking to improve a range by changing the flora, it is often profitable to scatter seed of some plant which will occupy waste land. Although the appreciation of the value of sweet clover as a forage and soil renovator is increasing among farmers, it is still valuable to the beekeeper chiefly as occupying waste land, crowding out less valuable plants. The scattering of sweet clover seed along embankments and over waste land has proved so profitable to beekeepers that the seed is now offered for sale annually in the bee-journals.

Value of the minor sources

Those plants which, because of scarcity or limited secretion of nectar, fail to give the beekeeper a surplus are, nevertheless, of marked value and are worthy of more consideration than they usually receive. The amount of honey consumed by an average colony of bees in a year has been variously estimated as 200 to 600 pounds.[1] This will, of course, vary according to the locality, strength of colony and other factors. Accepting even the lowest figure, it is evident that a moderate-sized apiary obtains tons of sugar from the flowers in the surrounding territory. While nectar comes in abundantly enough at times to produce a surplus, the beekeeper does not leave in the hives at the close of a surplus honey-flow enough to feed the bees until another major honey-flow, except possibly at the close of the season. The bees are almost constantly gathering nectar from the minor sources during the summer and the aggregate from these plants is enormous. If, for example, nectar were obtained in the North from white clover only, at the close of the honey-flow the beekeeper would be compelled to leave about 200 pounds for the bees, and there is rarely enough honey from white clover to permit this. This indicates that the beekeeper is debtor to the minor sources for much more than he is accustomed to believe.

POLLEN AND CROSS-POLLINATION

The bees gather enormous quantities of pollen from many species of plants which they carry to the hives and use chiefly in the elaboration of food for the rapidly growing larvæ. A careful study of the uses of pollen by bees has been made by Parker[2] who not only gives many

[1] A recent estimate is one made by Hommell (1913, [Consumption of a hive of bees during the year] La Vie Agricole et Rurale, II, No. 22, pp. 653-655) in which it is concluded that an average of 480 pounds is needed, divided as follows: maintenance of bees, 400 pounds; feeding of brood, 70 pounds; wax production, 10 pounds.

[2] Parker, R. L., 1926. The collection and utilization of pollen by the honeybee. Cornell Univ., Agr. Exp. Sta. Mem. 98, 55 pp, 16 figs.

important facts but also an excellent summary of the literature. He finds among other things that no satisfactory substitute for pollen has been found. So far as the prosperity of the colony is concerned, available supplies of pollen are fully as important as adequate amounts of nectar, for without pollen no brood can be reared.

Gathering of pollen

The amount of pollen consumed by a colony annually is also considerable. Estimates of the averages in this phase of bee-feeding are not available, but there is, nevertheless, some basis for judging the consumption. If during the active season a colony becomes queenless and has no brood to feed, the stores of pollen increase rapidly and several combs are often filled in a short time. It can scarcely be claimed that queenless bees gather more pollen than normal ones and, in fact, it is sometimes stated that the gathering is then reduced, so that it is safe to conclude that had brood been present these extra stores of pollen would have been consumed almost as fast as gathered. It must be true, therefore, that a colony uses many frames of pollen in a season, so that pollen sources are important to the beekeeper. In gathering pollen a bee is less uniformly beneficial to plants than when collecting nectar. They may cross-pollinate the flowers when so engaged but they are, at the same time, appropriating a part of the pollen on which fertilization depends. In some species of plants, an abundance of pollen seems to serve as an attractive agent, just as does nectar in those species provided with nectaries.

Value of bees in cross-pollination

In discussing the plants from which bees gather nectar, further mention should be made of the beneficial results which arise from the visits of bees to the flowers of certain fruits. As was explained earlier in this chapter, nectar is serviceable to the plant in acting as an attraction to insect visitors, which act as agents in cross-pollination. Because of the mutual adaptations of the insects and plants, they often become mutually indispensable. Some varieties of fruit-trees are incapable of self-fertilization, in other cases fertilization is more abundant with cross-pollination and in no case is cross-pollination detrimental. It is, therefore, evident that successful fruit-growing is dependent on insect visitation. Of all the insects which serve the fruit-grower, none is more efficient than the honeybee. Furthermore, in one important respect the honeybee becomes the most dependable of all. At the season when the fruit-trees blossom, insects of the wild species may be scarce, having been decimated by severe winter conditions. While honeybees also suffer, sometimes severely, from the winter, it is relatively easy not only to build up the colonies in the early spring but to bring in additional colonies as agents of fertilization. It, therefore, is simple for the fruit-grower to provide insects to fertilize his blossoms, if the weather is suitable for flights during the blooming period. Progressive fruit-growers in all parts of the country are coming more and more to realize this and many of them now keep bees solely for the benefits to the fruit crops.

Unfortunately it sometimes happens that ignorant or incorrectly informed fruit-growers do considerable injury to colonies of bees in their neighborhood by spraying or dusting their trees with poisonous chemicals while in full bloom. It may be well to examine the facts to determine who receives the greatest benefits from the presence of bees in the average farming community. If one examines a fruit-tree in full bloom, many species of insects will be found at work on the blossoms, gathering or eating nectar and pollen. These numerous species vary greatly in their efficiency in bringing about cross-pollination, and none is better fitted by structure or behavior for this work than the honeybee. Furthermore, if colonies of bees are found near by, as there generally are, there are usually as many honeybees on the trees as insects of all other species combined. Insects of many of the visiting species stay only long enough to get sufficient to eat to satisfy their own immediate needs, but the honeybees hurry back and forth from the hive, making repeated visits and cross-fertilizing innumerable blossoms, in their efforts to increase the colony stores. The honey obtained from fruit blossoms is usually small in quantity and serves only to stimulate brood-rearing, but in getting it the bees benefit the fruit-grower to an extent which can scarcely be over-estimated. One peculiarity of behavior is worthy of special mention in this connection. Honeybees rarely go from one species of flower (p. 128) to another (unless the flowers are virtually identical) while on one trip from the hive. There is also evidence worthy of belief that an individual honeybee confines its visits to one species of plant, sometimes for several days. For example, a bee will not be seen flying from an apple blossom to a dandelion flower growing beneath the tree and then perhaps back to an apple blossom. Consequently, on visiting an apple blossom it does not present dandelion pollen or, in fact, any pollen other than that from the apple and, by virtue of this constancy, the benefits of the visits of honeybees are increased many fold.

In view of these facts, it is not difficult to believe that in many orchards over half of the fruit set is attributed to the visits of the honeybees. Were this estimate reduced to ten per cent, which even an avowed enemy of the bee would consider too low, it appears that the fruit-growers receive more actual financial benefit from the presence of bees in the average farming community than do the beekeepers who own them. It, therefore, seems quite obvious that it is to the interest of fruit-growers to encourage beekeeping in every way in their immediate localities.

RELATION OF BEES AND FRUIT-GROWING

Damaging effects of incorrect spraying

Since the spraying of fruit-trees while in bloom is highly injurious, not only to honeybees but to all of the insect visitors, it is evident that such spraying is to that extent detrimental to the interests of the fruit-grower himself. Since spraying in full bloom is not necessary to control the codlin-moth and is not advised by entomologists and since it is injurious to bees, several states, at the instigation of the beekeepers, have enacted laws prohibiting such spraying. However, it is difficult to enforce such a law and, through ignorance, carelessness or neglect, serious damage is done to beekeepers at times. It may also be added that spraying in full bloom not only is unnecessary and detrimental to bees but it directly injures the fruit blossoms.[1] It is, therefore, evident that in the light of present knowledge, spraying fruit-trees while in full bloom is unwarranted and unwise.

The control of insect pests and plant diseases by means of applications of dust has recently increased considerably in parts of the United States. When materials poisonous to honeybees are thus applied, it becomes virtually impossible to confine the application to the trees that need it, and the poisonous materials often drift for a half mile or more. It frequently happens, therefore, that this poisonous material falls on open flowers on adjacent trees or on low-growing plants, from which honeybees gather it. Dusting has been the cause of enormous losses to beekeepers in many parts of the country, with the result that in some sections the beekeepers have found it necessary to remove their bees from regions where dusting is practiced. Large scale applications of dust have also been made by airplane in the control of certain insect pests, with equally disastrous results to honeybees. Since the fruit-grower is the one who most largely benefits from the presence of bees in his neighborhood, it need scarcely be pointed out that promiscuous dusting of the countryside works more to his disadvantage than to that of the beekeeper. Fortunately bees do not collect this dust in such a way as to have any of it

[1] *Cf.* Beach, S. A., and Bailey, L. H., 1900. N. Y. Agr. Exp. Sta., Geneva, Bull. 196.

reach the honey which they are producing, so that the bees alone are killed by the application.

Bees do not puncture ripe fruit

In discussing the relationship existing between beekeeping and fruit-growing, there still remains one source of misunderstanding between men engaged in these branches of agriculture which should be mentioned. Fruit-growers often make the statement that honeybees puncture ripe fruit to suck the juices, thereby causing considerable financial loss, as well as hindering the picking of the fruit. This claim has been the cause of ill-feeling in certain localities. It has, however, been abundantly demonstrated that honeybees do not puncture the skin of any fruit. To show this, if a colony of bees is confined in a hive without honey and is given specimens of sound fruit, they will die of starvation without puncturing a single fruit. On the other hand, if an apple, plum or grape is punctured, even slightly, and given to bees in this way they will suck all the juice. If it is maintained that confined bees may act differently from those free to fly, it may be replied that no one has ever seen honeybees puncture fruit either by stinging or biting. Furthermore, if any nectar is available, honeybees will always take that in preference to the juice of injured fruits. If then a fruit-grower sees honeybees sucking his fruit, he may be sure that the fruit was first damaged by some bird, by some other insects (*e.g.* hornet), by a bruise or by some form of decay and he may further be certain that the bees are sucking the juices of only damaged unmarketable fruit. It may also be added that fruit juices are most undesirable stores for bees and, if used exclusively in winter, the colony will probably die. The beekeeper is, therefore, often being injured as much as the fruit-grower when the bees suck overripe or injured fruits.

Beekeepers naturally appear biased in seeking to prove the bee a harmless and solely beneficial insect. They even minimize the annoyance of the stings in their loyalty to the bee. In pointing out the benefits of bees and denying injuries so often laid at their door, the present writer may also be accused of this bias. The investigations that have been made, however, uniformly support the contentions of the bee-enthusiasts and the supposedly harmed fruit-grower should be led to suspect that his judgment is in error. The ranks of the bee advocates are year by year being materially augmented by fruit-growers who have become convinced of the correctness of the attitude that the beekeeper maintains toward his bees.

Transmission of fire-blight

Honeybees are frequently accused of carrying fire- or pear-blight from tree to tree. By a very unscientific experiment, it was shown that the mouth-parts of honeybees may at times carry the organisms causing this plant disease, from which it was erroneously concluded that they are the main carriers. It is scarcely to be questioned that at times honeybees may carry this disease, but on the other hand there is excellent evidence that other insects are far more important carriers. Honeybees do not visit nursery stock which frequently is attacked to a serious extent. The fruit-grower is scarcely justified in asking that all bees be removed from his region in order to prevent this disease, for he cannot remove by legislation the real culprits and if he has the bees removed, he alone will suffer the greatest loss through lack of proper pollination.

SUPPOSEDLY POISONOUS HONEYS

Frequent mention is made in the literature on bees of supposedly poisonous honeys. It is of course true that the juices of many plants are poisonous to man and this may be the foundation for the belief that nectar of such species also contains the poisonous principles. Among the plants sometimes reported to produce poisonous nectar from which poisonous honeys are made by the bees, are mountain laurel (*Kalmia latifolia*), tobacco (*Nicotiana Tabacum*), yellow jessamine (*Gelsemium sempervirens*), sweet pepper-bush (*Clethra alnifolia*) and rhododendrons (one species of which is supposed to be the source of honey reported by Xenophon as having poisoned his soldiers). It would be unsafe to deny that the nectar of any plant produces a poisonous honey, but it is certain that not all of the plants named above yield such honey. Mountain laurel, yellow jessamine and rhododendrons are abundant in the lower Appalachian Mountains and there are more bees to the square mile in this section than anywhere else in the United States. Assuredly much nectar is gathered by bees from these plants, and if all the honey from these sources were poisonous there would be an epidemic of poisoning annually in this region. Clethra is the source of much honey, eaten widely with immunity. If any plant is ever the source of poisonous honey, this fact should be determined and made known, but the vague rumors now current are valueless. It should be remembered in this connection that certain individuals have idiosyncrasies toward certain foods and this may account for some of the recorded cases of honey-poisoning. In some rare individuals the eating of honey from any source or thick sugar sirup causes violent pains in the stomach. Until physiologists agree as to the cause of this phenomenon it is unsafe to speculate, but assuredly honeys should not be ranked as poisonous because they cause distress in eccentric individuals.

HONEY-DEW

By all odds, the main source of the sugars that bees get is nectar from flowers. Other sources which should be mentioned, however, occur more frequently than is recognized by beekeepers. In the absence of floral nectar, bees gather sugars from any available source, giving preference to those which have attractive odors. Many species of plants are provided with glands which secrete sweet liquids and which are located outside the flowers (extra-floral nectaries). Examples of this are found on the leaves of cotton (*Gossypium hirsutum*) and Hawaiian hau (*Hibiscus* or *Paritium tiliaceum*, on outside of flower-bracts also). Various acacias have glands on the stems. Other examples are found on castor-beans (Ricinus) and partridge-pea (*Chamœcrista fasciculata*) and other cases are mentioned in the list of honey-plants at the close of this chapter. To the product which the bee makes from sugar from these sources the name plant honey-dew honey is given.

The main source of honey-dew is, however, not plant but insect excretion. Certain plant-sucking insects, belonging to the order Hemiptera, such as plant-lice (Aphidæ), scale insects (Coccidæ), leaf-hoppers (Jassidæ), white-flies (Aleyrodidæ) and tree-hoppers (Membracidæ), all belonging to the Homoptera, suck the juices of the various plants on which they are specifically parasitic and the portion of the sap not utilized by the sucking insect is ejected, falling on the leaves and stems of the plant and even running off to the ground below. Many of these juices are sweet and are gathered by bees exactly as they gather nectar, except that if nectar is available honey-dew is abandoned. This is carried to the hive, ripened and sealed, making what is known as honey-dew honey. This substance is high in its content of gums and is a poor food for bees in winter. It was formerly believed that the honey-dew of some aphids was secreted from the tubular processes on the dorsal side of the abdomen but it is now established that it is an intestinal excretion, just as in the other families. Honey-dew is gathered by ants more than by bees.

The sugars in honey-dew honey are the same as those in honey and the chief chemical difference is in the higher percentage of gums. The flavor is usually poor, and most honey-dew honeys are dark in color and granulate quickly, often before sealing. An exception is that from the sugar-cane leaf-hopper (*Perkinsiella saccharicida*) of Hawaii which rarely granulates. Honey-dew honey is probably much more common than is appreciated by beekeepers, for the excreting insects are present in millions every summer and probably many honeys contain small amounts of this substance. It is not unlikely that the variation in gum-content of honeys and the variation in color from a supposedly uniform floral source may in part be due to varying mixtures of honey-dew.

In the summer of 1909, honey-dew honey was exceptionally abundant throughout the eastern United States. This was due not only to the shortage of nectar but to an exceptionally large number of aphids. The prevalence of these insects is determined largely by immediate climatic conditions and they are destroyed by millions by heavy rains. Dry seasons may, therefore, dry up the nectaries and at the same time allow plant-lice to propagate excessively, giving honey-dew seasons.

ANNOTATED LIST OF HONEY-PLANTS

In the following list an effort is made to give the plants of value to the beekeeper, as sources of nectar and pollen, with brief notes which will be helpful in determining the relative importance of the various species. While this list is chiefly for plants in the United States, mention is made of some important species of tropical America, especially of Hawaii and Porto Rico. The list will also apply to Canada.

The arrangement in alphabetical order is adopted as placing the notes where they will first be sought by most readers, under the common name of the species. The following of the natural order, by families and genera, would show relationships which can only be suggested here by naming under each family the species that are mentioned in the notes.

This list is unavoidably incomplete because so little systematic work has been done on honey-plants. There are hundreds of valuable notes on these plants in the bee-journals but they are hard to find and often it is impossible to tell what species is being discussed, since the scientific name is not given or is incorrect and since the same common name is sometimes applied to two or more species in various parts of the United States.

Acacias, wattles, Acacia spp. Shrubs or trees, flowers small, in heads. Catclaw, *A. Greggii*, May and July. Honey white, fine flavor. Catclaw, *A. Greggii* and *A. Wrightii*, semi-arid regions of Texas and Arizona. Catclaw and the closely related huajilla, *Havardia* (*Xygia*) *brevifolia*, are of first rank among honey-plants. The various wattles are listed as important honey sources in Australia, Africa and tropical America. Black wattle, *A. decurrens mollis*, and other species are of value in California and in Hawaii. Huisache, *A.* (*Vachellia*) *Farnesiana*, is also present along the Rio Grande. *A. constricta*, June, Arizona. Various species in subtropical regions, probably all valuable.

Aceraceæ; see Maple family.

Æsculaceæ; see Buckeye family.

Ailanthus, tree of heaven, *Ailanthus glandulosa*. Native of China, reported in eastern United States and as valuable in California. Honey ill-tasting. Extra-floral nectaries present.

Ailanthus family, Simarubaceæ; see Ailanthus and Manchineel.

Alder, Alnus spp. Pollen.

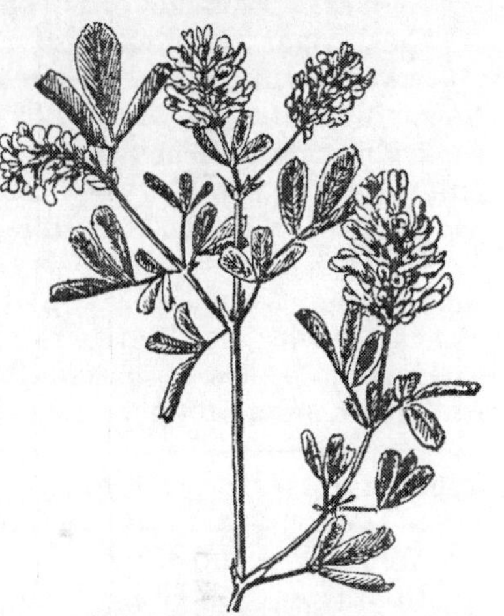

Fig. 152.—Alfalfa.

Alfalfa, *Medicago sativa* (Fig. 152). Perennial, 12–18 inches, excessively branched after cutting, short raceme of blue or violet flowers. Blooms several times during summer, depending on number of cuttings. Honey light in color, granulates quickly, especially after extraction, flavor excellent. Grown throughout United States but valuable as a honey-plant only west of Mississippi River (except in rare cases). Native of old world. The main source of honey in the irrigated regions of Colorado, Utah and other western states. The honey from this source is reported as amber from more southern localities, but this may be due to an admixture of other honeys. Alfalfa honey is produced extensively as comb-honey, but in this form it suffers in comparison with that of the clovers because of rapid granulation. The flavor is described as mint-like. Also called Spanish trefoil, lucerne and purple medic. An excellent forage plant yielding several crops a season. Frequently cut before or during blooming period. *M. denticulata* and *M. lupulina* reported from California.

Alfileria, pin clover, *Erodium cicutarium*. Annual, April–September, throughout United States, especially California. Native of old world; honey of good quality, pollen abundant. *E. moschatum*, good in California.

Algaroba; see Mesquite and also Saman.

Alsike clover, *Trifolium hybridum.* Perennial, erect, 1–2 feet, quite similar to white clover except in size. Cultivated extensively (usually with timothy) for hay. Flowers white tipped with pink, to pink. May–October, but especially June–July. Honey only slightly darker than that from white clover. This clover is rapidly increasing in importance to the beekeeper. Called also Swedish clover. Not a hybrid between white and red clovers as name indicates.

Amaryllidaceæ; see Amaryllis family.

Amaryllis family, Amaryllidaceæ; see Century Plant and Lophiola.

Ambrosiaceæ; see Ragweed family.

American bee balm; see Horsemint.

American holly; see Gallberry.

Ampelopsis, Ampelopsis spp. Nectar, pollen.

Anacardiaceæ; see Sumac family.

Anemone, *Anemone quinquefolia.* Pollen.

Antigonon (Corculum). Listed by Root, 1910, Florida, California, tropics.

Apple, *Pyrus Malus* (Fig. 2). Honey light amber, superb; pollen.

Apple family, Malaceæ (a subfamily of Rosaceæ); see Pear, Apple, Juneberry and Haws.

Aquifoliaceæ; see Holly family.

Asclepiadaceæ; see Milkweed family.

Ash, Fraxinus spp. Pollen.

Asparagus, *Asparagus officinalis.* Honey amber, pollen.

Asters, Aster spp. Perennial (rarely annual), 1–4 feet or more, ray flowers white or purple, sometimes pink or blue, July to frost. Honey amber in color, flavor often pronounced. Throughout the United States, especially in North, different species being adapted to differences in soils and moisture. *A. ericoides* and *A. novæ-angliæ* are said to be the most valuable to the beekeeper. The goldenrods which bloom at the same time and which are more conspicuous get much of the credit for nectar-secretion which belongs rightly to the asters. Valuable especially in providing winter stores, although the so-called fall honeys are not so good for this purpose as the purer types of honey (see Wintering). Britton and Brown mention 142 species of this genus in the United States and 250 species in all. Plants of related genera are also sometimes known as asters. The species blooming early are rarely valuable as honey-plants.

Azalea, wild honeysuckle, Azalea spp. Some nectar, pollen.

Ball or button sage; see Sage.

Banana, Musa spp. Cultivated in Florida and extensively in tropical America. Pollen.

Banana family, Musaceæ; see Banana.

Barberry, *Berberis vulgaris*. Pollen, nectar.

Barberry family, Berberidaceæ; see Barberry, *Berberis pinnata* and *B. trifoliolata*.

Basswood, linden, whitewood, *Tilia americana* (Fig. 153). In forests and in moist soils, tree to 125 feet, leaves oblique, flowers borne on bracts 2–4 inches, June–July (usually at end of white clover honey-flow). Honey light amber to white, flavor when unmixed is pronounced (especially if extracted when unripe) and not especially pleasant, but when mixed with white clover honey is exceptionally fine. In rich woods in northeastern United States and in mountains south to Georgia, west to Nebraska. Formerly much more abundant. The cultivated species, *T. europæa*, is equally valuable when present. The wood is used in making the one-piece sections used almost universally for comb-honey. Nectar secretion quickly affected by adverse weather conditions. A heavy yielder when weather preceding the honey-flow is favorable. The heavy cutting of these trees has greatly decreased the importance of this tree to the beekeeper. The name linn (or lin) or lime tree is given to the European species, *T. europæa*. *T. heterophylla* is also common (called bee-tree). *T. pubescens* has a more southern distribution. The other species of Tiliaceæ are mainly tropical.

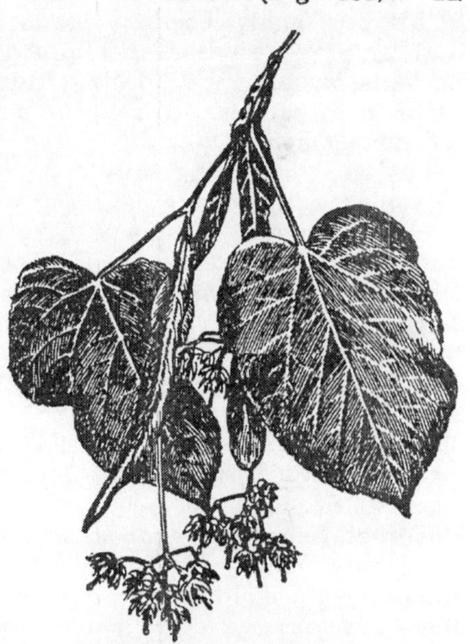

Fig. 153.—Basswood.

Bayberry; see Sweet-Gale.

Bayberry family, Myricaceae; see Sweet-Gale.

Bearberry; see Manzanita.

Bee balm, *Melissa officinalis*. Nectar.
Beech, Fagus spp. Pollen.
Beech family, Fagaceæ; see Beech, Chinquapin, Chestnut and Oak.
Bee-tree; see Basswood.
Beggar's tick; see Spanish Needle.
Bell-flower, campanula, campanilla, Ipomœa spp. Of primary importance in Cuba, honey white of finest flavor. Other species in this family furnish nectar.
Bell-flower family, Campanulaceæ; see Bell-flower.
Berberidaceæ; see Barberry family.
Berberis pinnata. California. Honey amber.
Berberis trifoliolata. Texas, January–February, nectar and abundant pollen.
Betulaceæ; see Birch family.
Bignoniaceæ; see Trumpet-creeper family.
Birch, Betula spp. Pollen.
Birch family, Betulaceæ; see Hornbeam, Hazelnut, Birch and Alder.
Blackberry; see Raspberry.
Black mangrove, *Avicennia nitida*. Perhaps the most abundant source of nectar ever observed. Killed by frost in Florida in 1894 and is returning abundantly. Found in Porto Rico.
Black sage; see Sage.
Black ti-ti; see Ti-ti.
Black walnut, *Juglans nigra*. Pollen.
Black wattle; see Acacia.
Bloodroot, *Sanguinaria canadensis*. Pollen.
Bloodwort family. Hæmodoraceæ; see Morong.
Blueberry, Vaccinium spp. Nectar, pollen.
Blue-curls, *Trichostema lanceolatum*. Honey white, granulates quickly, August–November.
Blue gum; see Eucalyptus.
Blue-thistle; see Viper's Bugloss.
Blueweed; see Viper's Bugloss.
Bokhara clover; see Sweet Clover.
Boneset, thoroughwort, *Eupatorium perfoliatum*. Nectar. Autumn.
Borage family, Boraginaceæ; see Viper's Bugloss.
Boraginaceæ; see Borage family.
Buckeye, *Æsculus glabra*. Pollen, nectar.
Buckeye family, Æsculaceæ; see Horsechestnut, Buckeye and California Buckeye.
Buckthorn, coffee berry, *Rhamnus cathartica*.
Buckthorn family, Rhamnaceæ; see Buckthorn, Cascara Sagrada, Coffee Berry, White Lilac and Rattan Vine.
Buckwheat, *Fagopyrum esculentum* (Fig. 154). Annual, 1–3 feet,

blooms June–September, depending on time of planting. Honey dark purple in color, flavor strong and rank, of use mainly in baking, body usually heavy although in rapid flows it may be thin. In New York, Pennsylvania, Michigan, especially, but found in almost all parts of northern United States. Native of old world. Sometimes escapes from cultivation. Reliable as a nectar plant especially in more northern localities. Nectar secreted most abundantly in the morning.

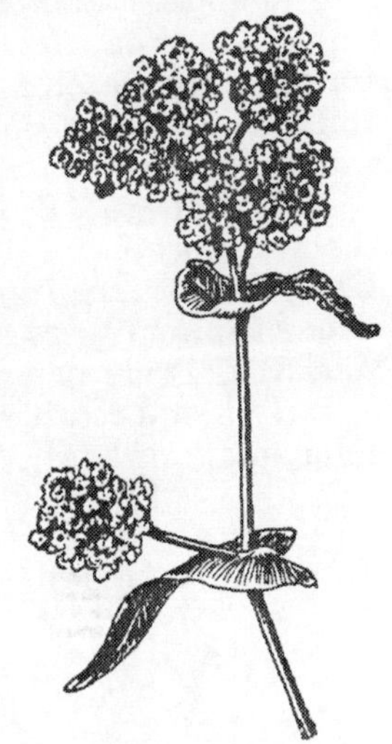
Fig. 154.—Buckwheat.

Buckwheat family, Polygonaceæ; see Wild Buckwheat, Antigonon, Buckwheat, Heartsease and *Polygonum lapathifolium.*

Bur-marigold; see Spanish Needle.

Bush clovers, Lespedeza spp.

Butterfly-weed; see Milkweed.

Button-bush, honey-balls, *Cephalanthus occidentalis.* In swamps, honey mild, light color.

Cabbage palmetto, *Sabal palmetto.* To 30 feet, July–August, honey white, mild, Florida.

Cabbage tree; see Moca.

Cactaceæ; see Cactus family.

Cactus, prickly pear, Opuntia spp. Locally in deserts and semiarid regions, honey heavy of poor flavor.

Cactus family, Cactaceæ; see Cactus.

Cæsalpinaceæ; see Senna family.

California buckeye, *Æsculus californica.* Considerable nectar. Reported that the honey poisons the bees (California); more than doubtful.

California laurel, *Umbellularia californica.* December–March.

California poppy, *Eschscholtzia californica.* March–July, pollen, some nectar, California.

Campanilla; see Bell-flower.

Campanula; see Bell-flower.

Campanulaceæ; see Bell-flower family.

Canada thistle, *Carduus arvensis.* Honey of good quality.

Caper family, Capparidaceæ; see Cleome and Jackass Clover.

Capparidaceæ; see Caper family.

Caprifoliaceæ; see Honeysuckle family.

Carpet-grass, *Lippia nodiflora.* Of value in California.

Carrot family, Umbelliferæ. Various species are of minor importance as sources of nectar and pollen.

Cascara Sagrada, *Rhamnus Purshiana.* Honey dark, does not granulate. California.

Catalpa, catawba, *Catalpa speciosa.* Of little value.

Catawba; see Catalpa.

Catnip, *Nepeta Cataria.* Nectar. Unimportant.

Century plant, *Agave americana.* Heavy yielder in semi-arid tropical localities, July–August. Also other species of Agave.

Chestnut, *Castanea dentata.* Some nectar, pollen.

Chicory, *Cichorium Intybus.* July–October, eastern United States

Chicory subfamily; see Chicory, Dandelion and Sow Thistle.

China-tree, Pride of India, *Melia azedarach.* Spring, of value in early brood-rearing, Texas.

Chinquapin, *Castanea pumila.* Honey dark amber of most unpleasant flavor, Georgia and other southern States.

Fig. 155.—Spider-flower (Cleome).

Cichoriaceæ; see Chicory.

Cistaceæ; see Rock-rose family.

Citrus fruits, lime, orange, grape fruit, lemon, Citrus spp. Cultivated, Florida, California, Texas, some species wild in Florida. Trees. Honey white, heavy body, delicious flavor. The value of these trees to the beekeeper is probably overestimated and honey from other sources is probably sold as "orange honey," under which name the citrus honeys are usually all sold.

Clematis, Clematis sp. Superb honey when sufficiently abundant, New England. Pollen.

Clematis ligusticifolia. In hills of California, June–July. Pollen abundant.

Cleome, spider-flower, *Cleome serrulata* and *C. spinosa* (Fig. 155). Herbs 2–3 feet, erect, flowers pink or white in *C. serrulata*, purple in *C. spinosa*. *C. serrulata* in prairies Illinois west to Rocky Mountains; *C. spinosa*, from tropical America, sometimes cultivated, Illinois to Louisiana. *C. serrulata* is called Rocky Mountain Bee-plant by Colorado beekeepers. Under favorable conditions both species are heavy yielders, but they are, nevertheless, not of primary importance.

Clethraceæ; see White Alder family.

Clover; see Sweet Clover, White Clover, Alsike Clover, Crimson Clover, Bush Clovers and Alfileria.

Cocklebur, *Xanthium pennsylvanicum.* Pollen in Autumn

Cocoanut palm, *Cocos nucifera.* Honey amber, of secondary importance, West Indies.

Coffee berry, *Rhamnus californica.* Honey amber, April–May. Foothills of Sierra Nevada Mountains.

Coffee berry; see also Buckthorn.

Compositæ; see Thistle family.

Coral-berry; see Indian Currant.

Corculum; see *Antigonon leptopus.*

Coreopsis; see Spanish Needle.

Corn, *Zea mays.* Pollen. Reported as sometimes yielding nectar from the tassels.

Cornaceæ; see Dogwood family.

Cotton, *Gossypium hirsutum* (Fig. 156). Cultivated, southern States. June–August. Increasing in importance. Extra-floral nectaries on leaves and bracts.

Fig. 156.—Cotton.

Cowpea, *Vigna sinensis.* Honey light, of poor flavor. Bees get nectar from extra-floral nectaries.

Creeping thyme, *Thymus Serpyllum.* Perennial herb, branched, creeping, forming dense mats, flowers in clusters. Honey probably amber, flavor not as good as that of many other honeys. In thickets and waste places south to Pennsylvania. June–September. Native of Europe. From a plant of this genus the celebrated honey of the ancient Greeks was produced, especially on Mount Hymettus.

Crimson clover, *Trifolium incarnatum.* Annual erect, 6–30 inches, flowers crimson in long heads. Honey quite like that of white clover. Cultivated for hay and in waste places. Native of Europe. Blooms somewhat earlier than the other clovers.

Crowfoot family. Ranunculaceæ; see Anemone, Liverwort, Clematis and Meadow-rue.
Cruciferæ; see Mustard family.
Cucumber; see Gourd family.
Cucumber tree; see Tulip Poplar.
Cucurbitaceæ; see Gourd family.
Currant, Ribes spp. Pollen, nectar.
Cyperaceæ; see Sedge family.
Cyrilla family, Cyrillaceæ; see Ti-ti.
Cyrillaceæ; see Cyrilla family.

Dandelion, *Taraxacum officinale*, or *Leontodon Taraxacum* (Fig. 157). Perennial herb growing close to ground. Flowers yellow, blooms throughout year but most abundantly in early spring (with or following fruit bloom in North). Honey amber. In waste places and a weed in lawns and fields throughout the United States. Not valuable as a source of surplus honey, but especially helpful in building up colonies in early spring.

FIG. 157.—Dandelion.

Date palm, *Phœnix dactylifera*. Abundant nectar, California, Arizona.
Desert willow, *Chilopsis linearis*. New Mexico.
Dogwood family, Cornaceæ; see Tupelo.
Dutch clover; see White Clover.

Ebenaceæ; see Ebony family.
Ebony family, Ebenaceæ; see Persimmon.
Elder, Sambucus spp. Pollen, nectar.
Elm, Ulmus spp. Pollen.
Elm family, Ulmaceæ; see Elm, Granjeno and Hackberry.
English walnut, *Juglans regia*. Nectar, pollen.
Ericaceæ; see Heath family.
Eucalyptus, Eucalyptus spp. Numerous species of value introduced into California. The species vary greatly in nectar

secretion. Honey-scented gum, *E. melliodora*, swamp mahogany gum, *E. robusta*, white iron wood, *E. leucoxylon*, and blue gum, *E. globulus*, are those most valued. Primary honey plants in Australia. Honey sometimes strong flavored.

Eucalyptus family, Myrtaceæ; see Eucalyptus and Rose Apple.

Evening primrose family, Onagraceæ; see Willow-herb.

Eysenhardtia, rock brush, *Viborquia orthocarpa*. Important in southwest Texas.

Fagaceæ; see Beech family.

Figwort family, Scrophulariaceæ; see Mullen and Simpson's Honey Plant.

Fireweed, *Erechtites hieracifolia*. Eastern United States, July–September.

Fireweed; see also Willow-herb.

Frostweed; see Rockrose.

Gallberry, inkberry, *Ilex glabra*. Shrub, 2–6 feet, leaves evergreen, few teeth at apex or entire. May–July. Honey light color and of fine quality. Sandy soils, Massachusetts to Florida, west to Louisiana, mainly along coast, abundant in North Carolina, South Carolina, Georgia and Alabama, especially in cut-over forest lands. An important and increasingly valuable source of nectar in the southern States where considerable honey is produced (chiefly for local consumption). A reliable yielder. Other species of holly are also valuable, as American holly, *I. opaca*, April–June.

Geraniaceæ; see Geranium family.

Geranium family, Geraniaceæ; see Alfileria.

Goldenrod, Solidago spp. Perennial herbs, 1–5 feet, flowers generally yellow in panicles or heads, August to frost. Honey golden yellow, not of finest flavor, heavy body. Various species are adapted to all types of soil, but those growing in moist soils are the only ones of value to the beekeeper. The value of the goldenrods is probably exaggerated. In many places they are the most conspicuous flowers in the fall and get credit for honey which probably comes mainly from the asters. Eighty-five species, mostly in North America. The species which bloom early are usually valueless. The odor of the fall honeys is so pronounced that it can be detected some distance from the hive when freshly gathered.

Gooseberry, Grossularia spp. Pollen, nectar.

Gooseberry family, Grossulariaceæ; see Gooseberry and Currant.

Gourd family, Cucurbitaceæ. Various species furnish pollen and nectar, especially the genera Cucurbita, Cucumis and Citrullus, pumpkin, squash, cucumber and watermelon.

Gramineæ; see Grass family.

Granjeno, *Celtis pallida*. Southwest Texas, of value.

Grape family, Vitaceæ; see Grapes, Ampelopsis and Virginia Creeper.

Grape fruit; see Citrus Fruit.

Grapes, Vitis spp. Pollen, some nectar.

Grass family, Gramineæ; see Sorghum and Corn. Wind pollinated, some species visited for pollen.

Greasewood, *Adenostema fasciculatum*. April–July. California.

Grossulariaceæ; see Gooseberry family.

Guamá; see Guava.

Guava, *Inga vera*, and **guamá**, *I. laurina*. Of primary importance in Porto Rico, found elsewhere in West Indies and Central America.

Gum; see Eucalyptus.

Fig. 158.—Heartsease.

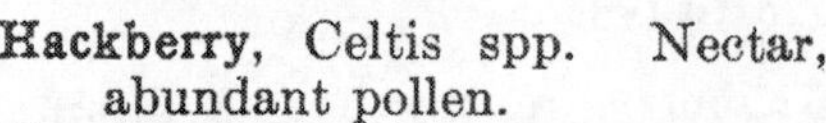

Hackberry, Celtis spp. Nectar, abundant pollen.

Hæmodoraceæ; see Bloodwort family.

Hamamelidaceæ; see Witch-hazel family.

Haws, Cratægus spp. Nectar, pollen.

Hazelnut, Corylus spp. Pollen.

Heartsease, lady's thumb, smartweed, *Persicaria persicaria* (Fig. 158). Annual herb, 6–24 inches or more (especially in middle west). Flowers in dense racemes, pink and purple, June–October, especially August–October. Honey light amber to dark, flavor good but easily lost by heating, granulates. On waste land throughout the United States, often abundant. An important source in middle west. Native to old world. The common name heartsease is given to this plant by most beekeepers. There are about 200 species of this genus, 71 occurring in North America, probably most of them contributing nectar.

Heath family, Ericaceæ; see Azalea, Rhododendron, Mountain Laurel, Sourwood and Manzanita. The heather, *Calluna vulgaris*, of Europe is a member of this family.

Heather; see Heath family.
Hemp, *Cannabis sativa.* Pollen, eastern United States.
Hickory, Carya sp. Pollen.
Hog plum, jobo, *Spondias lutea.* Valuable in Porto Rico.
Holly; see Gallberry.
Holly family, Aquifoliaceæ; see Gallberry.
Honey-balls; see Button-bush.
Honey-locust, *Gleditsia triacanthos.* Nectar. Much less important than black locust.
Honey-scented gum; see Eucalyptus.
Honeysuckle; see Tartarian Honeysuckle.
Honeysuckle, wild; see Azalea.
Honeysuckle family, Caprifoliaceæ; see Elder, Indian Currant and Tartarian Honeysuckle.
Hop, *Humulus lupulus.* Pollen, general in the United States.
Horehound, *Marrubium vulgare.* Common throughout most of United States, native of old world. Honey dark amber, strong flavor, surplus locally in California.
Hornbeam, *Carpinus caroliniana.* Tree to 40 feet, pollen, eastern United States.
Horsechestnut, *Æsculus Hippocastanum.* Some pollen and nectar.
Horsemint, *Monarda punctata* (Fig. 159). Perennial herb, 2–3 feet, flowers in whorls on stem and terminal, April–June in Texas, later farther north. Honey amber, flavor somewhat strong. Southern New York to Florida, west to Wisconsin and Texas, especially valuable in eastern Texas where it is of major importance. In the genus Monarda there are ten species, probably all valuable to the beekeeper. Wild bergamot, *M. fistulosa*, and American bee balm, *M. didyma*, should be especially mentioned. *M. clinopodioides* is also listed for Texas as important.

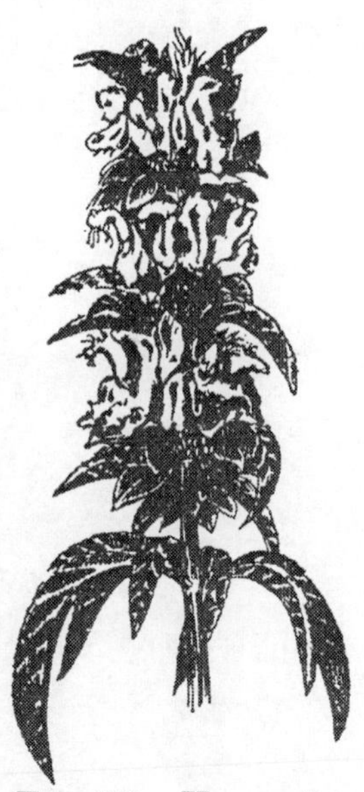

Fig. 159.—Horsemint.

Huajilla; see Acacias.
Huckleberry, Gaylussacia spp. New England, of importance along coast.
Huckleberry family, Vacciniaceæ; see Huckleberry and Blueberry.
Huisache; see Acacia.
Hydrophyllaceæ; see Water-leaf family.
Hypericaceæ; see St. John's-wort family.

Indian currant, coral-berry, *Symphoricarpos racemosus*. Nectar, July.
Inkberry; see Gallberry.
Iron-weed, Vernonia spp. Nectar, late summer.
Iron-wood; see Ti-ti.

Jackass clover, *Wislizenia refracta*. August–October. Honey white. San Joaquin valley, California, increasing.
Jerusalem artichoke; see Sunflower.
Jobo; see Hog plum.
Judas tree, red bud, *Cercis canadensis*. Nectar, pollen.
Juglandaceæ; see Walnut family.
Juneberry, service berry, *Amelanchier canadensis*. March–May, tree to 60 feet.

Keawe; see Mesquite.

Lady's thumb; see Heartsease.
Lantana, Lantana sp. Valuable in Hawaii.
Lauraceæ; see Laurel family.
Laurel family, Lauraceæ; see Red Bay and California Laurel.
Leatherwood; see Ti-ti.
Leguminosæ; see Pea family.
Lemon; see Citrus Fruits.
Lilac; see White Lilac.
Liliaceæ; see Lily family.
Lilies, Lilium spp. Pollen.
Lily family, Liliaceæ; see Onion, Lilies, Asparagus and Yucca.
Lima bean, Phaseolus sp. Important locally in California, where grown extensively.

Fig. 160.—Locust.

Lime; see Citrus Fruits.
Lime tree; see Basswood.
Lin; see Basswood.

Linden; see Basswood.
Linden family, Tiliaceæ; see Basswood.
Linn; see Basswood.
Liverwort, *Hepatica triloba.* Pollen.
Locust, *Robinia Pseudacacia* (Fig. 160). Tree to 80 feet, flowers white, fragrant, in drooping racemes. May–June. Honey white, fine flavor, heavy body. Pennsylvania south to Georgia and west to Iowa. There are six species of Robinia native to America, of special value as honey-plants where white clover is not dependable, usually furnishes nectar for about ten days only.
Locust; see also Honey Locust.
Logwood, *Hæmatoxylum campechianum.* In Jamaica this produces a honey of superb quality and color. Native of tropical America and West Indies.
Loosestrife, *Lysimachia vulgaris.* Pollen.
Lophiola, *Lophiola americana.* Pine barren bogs, eastern United States, June–August.
Loranthaceæ; see Mistletoe family.
Lucern; see Alfalfa.
Lupine, Lupinus spp. Nectarless, visited for pollen.
Lupinus affinis. Reported from California as a nectar plant.

Madder family, Rubiaceæ; see Button-bush.
Magnolia, Magnolia spp. Not important.
Magnolia family, Magnoliaceæ; see Magnolia and Tulip Poplar.
Magnoliaceæ; see Magnolia family.
Malaceæ; see Apple family.
Mallow, Malva spp. Some nectar, pollen.
Mallow family, Malvaceæ; see Marshmallow, Mallow, Cotton and Sida spp.
Malvaceæ; see Mallow family.
Manazanillo; see Manchineel.
Manchineel, manazanillo, *Hippomane Mancinella.* Important in southern Florida.
Manzanita, bearberry, Arctostaphylos sp. Shrub or small tree, November–February. Foothills of western slope (2000–9000 feet), California. Honey amber (or white) of excellent flavor.
Maple family, Aceraceæ; see Maples.
Maples, Acer spp. Nectar, especially pollen.
Marshmallow, Althæa spp. Nectar, unimportant.
Meadow-rue, Thalictrum spp. Pollen.
Meadow sweet, *Spiræa latifolia.* Some nectar.
Melia family, Meliaceæ; see China-tree.
Meliaceæ; see Melia family.

Menthaceæ; see Mint family.

Mesquite, *Prosopis glandulosa.* Shrub and tree, flowers in dense spikes, seed in constricted pods. April and June–July. Honey light amber, of good flavor. Fifteen species in tropical regions. *P. glandulosa* is of value as a honey-plant in the semi-arid regions of Texas, New Mexico and Arizona, extending into Mexico. *P. juliflora*, introduced from Mexico, is the chief floral nectar source in Hawaii (called algaroba, keawe), honey white, granulates quickly. This species is also found in Peru and has recently been introduced to Porto Rico. *P. velutina* and *P. pubescens*, April–July reported from Arizona.

Milkweed, Asclepias spp. Various species of value, especially those in swamps. Pollen masses adhere to bees, sometimes making them incapable of flight. Butterfly weed, pleurisy-root, *A. tuberosa*, especially valuable.

Milkweed family. Asclepiadaceæ; see Milkweed.

Mimosa spp. Tropical and subtropical. Probably of value.

Mimosa family, Mimosaceæ; see Acacia, Mesquite, Guava, Saman and Mimosa spp.

Mimosaceæ; see Mimosa family.

Mint, Mentha spp. Honey amber, of value locally.

Mint family, Menthaceæ; see Blue-curls, Horehound, Catnip, Sages, Horsemint, Pennyroyal, Bee Balm, Creeping Thyme and Mint. An important family.

Mistletoe, Phoradendron spp. Parasitic, December–January, Texas, California, earliest source of nectar in Texas.

Mistletoe family, Loranthaceae; see Mistletoe.

Moca, cabbage tree, *Geoffræa jamaicensis.* Of marked value, West Indies, tropical America.

Moraceæ; see Mulberry family.

Morong, red-root, *Gyrotheca capitata.* Pine barrens.

Mountain laurel, Kalmia spp. Valuable locally, Allegheny Mountains.

Mulberry, Morus spp. Pollen.

Mulberry family, Moraceæ; see Mulberry, Hop and Hemp.

Mullen, Verbascum spp. Pollen, nectar in some species.

Musaceæ; see Banana family.

Mustard; see Rape.

Mustard family, Cruciferæ; see Rape and Radish. Numerous species of this family are valuable but are not of primary importance.

Myricaceæ; see Bayberry family.

Myrtaceæ; see Eucalyptus family.

Oak, Quercus spp. Pollen, some nectar.

Oleaceæ; see Olive family.
Olive, *Olea europæa*. April–May, California, value doubtful.
Olive family, Oleaceæ; see Ash, Privet and Olive.
Onagraceæ; see Evening Primrose family.
Onion, *Allium Cepa*. Nectar. Valuable where abundant.
Orange; see Citrus Fruits.
Orchid family, Orchidaceæ. Usually adapted to larger insects. Some pollen.
Orchidaceæ; see Orchid family.

Palm family, Palmaceæ; see Cabbage Palmetto, Saw Palmetto, Date Palm, Royal Palm and Cocoanut Palm.
Palmaceæ; see Palm family.
Paloverde, *Cercidium torreyanum*. Reported as valuable in Arizona, May.
Papaveraceæ; see Poppy family.
Partridge pea, *Chamæcrista fasciculata* (Fig. 161). Annual herb, 1–2½ feet, leaves sensitive, flowers yellow, solitary or in small clusters. Nectaries on petioles. July–September. Honey light amber, body thin, flavor not good, of value only for baking. Maine to Florida, west to Kansas and Texas, but valuable as a producer of surplus only in Georgia and Florida. The species of this genus are not nectar yielders, except such as have extra-floral nectaries, from which nectar is quickly washed out in rainy weather.

Fig. 161.—Partridge pea.

Pea family, Leguminosæ. This family contains many species of the highest importance to beekeepers. The honeys are usually white. See Lupines, *Lupinus affinis*, Alfalfa, Sweet Clover, White Clover, Alsike Clover, Crimson Clover, Wild Alfalfa, Locust, Moca, Bush Clover, Vetches, Lima Bean and Cowpea.
Peach, *Prunus persica*. Nectar, pollen.
Pear, Pyrus spp. Nectar, pollen.
Pecan, Carya sp. Pollen.
Pennyroyal, *Hedeoma pulegioides*. Annual, eastern United States, July–September. Four species in Florida of value locally, January–February.

Pepper tree, *Schinus Molle.* Southern California, introduced. Regular producer of nectar. Honey amber, strong flavor.

Persimmon, *Diospyros virginiana.* Tree to 100 feet, May–June, eastern United States.

Phacelia hispida and P. tanacetifolia. Of value in California. Honey of *P. hispida* granulates quickly. Species of *Phacelia* valued by beekeepers in Europe.

Plantaginaceæ; see Plantain family.

Plantain, Plantago spp. Pollen.

Plantain family, Plantaginaceæ; see Plantain.

Pleurisy-root; see Milkweed.

Plums, Prunus spp. Cultivated and various wild species. Spring.

Polygonaceæ; see Buckwheat family.

Polygonum lapathifolium and P. punctatum are of value in California.

Poma rosa; see Rose Apple.

Poplar; see Tulip Poplar.

Poplars, Populus spp. Pollen.

Poppy, Papaver spp. Pollen.

Poppy family, Papaveraceæ; see Poppy, Prickly Poppy, Bloodroot and California Poppy.

Potato family, Solanaceæ; see Tobacco.

Prickly pear; see Cactus.

Prickly poppy, *Argemone platyceras.* Texas, pollen, May–July.

Pride of India; see China-tree.

Primrose family, Primulaceæ; see Loosestrife.

Primulaceæ; see Primrose family.

Privet, Ligustrum spp. Not important.

Pumpkin; see Gourd family.

Purple medic; see Alfalfa.

Purple sage; see Sage.

Radish, *Raphanus sativus.* Pollen, nectar.

Ragweed, *Ambrosia elatior.* Annual herb, 1–6 feet, July to frost, flowers in racemes, green. Throughout United States, a troublesome weed. An important source of pollen, yields no nectar.

Ragweed family, Ambrosiaceæ; see Ragweed and Cocklebur.

Ranunculaceæ; see Crowfoot family.

Rape, mustard, Brassica spp. Pollen and nectar. Especially valuable in California (*B. nigra*). Honey granulates rapidly.

Raspberry, blackberry, Rubus spp. Various species of value.

Raspberry; see also Wild Raspberry.

Rattan vine, *Berchemia scandens.* Some surplus. Honey dark amber, April, Texas.

Red bay, *Persea borbonia.* **Southeastern United States, April–June.**

Redbud; see Judas Tree.

Red clover; see White Clover.

Red-root; see Morong.

Rhamnaceæ; see Buckthorn family.

Rhododendron, Rhododendron spp. Valuable locally, Allegheny Mountains.

Rock brush; see Eysenhardtia.

Rockrose, frostweed, Helianthemum spp. Pollen.

Rockrose family, Cistaceæ; see Rockrose.

Rocky Mountain bee-plant; see Cleome.

Rosaceæ; see Rose family.

Rose apple, poma rosa, *Caryophyllus jambos.* Tropical, of value.

Rose family, Rosaceæ; see Meadow Sweet, Raspberry, Blackberry, Wild Raspberry, Greasewood, Strawberry, Roses, Plum and Peach.

Roses, Rosa spp. Pollen only.

Royal palm, Roystonea spp. Honey amber, West Indies. Secretes heavily.

Rubiaceæ; see Madder family.

Rue family, Rutaceæ; see Citrus Fruits.

Rutaceæ; see Rue family.

Sage brush, *Artemisia californica.* Valuable for pollen, southern California.

Sages, Ramona spp. (Also classified as Audibertia spp. and Salvia spp.) Plants of California species vary in size up to 10 feet. April–July. Honey "water-white," granulating least quickly of any American honeys, flavor mild and delicious. The semi-arid regions of southern California in cañons to 5000 feet (Richter). The black, ball or button sage; *R. stachyoides* (Fig. 162), is perhaps the most important, although white sage, *R. polystachya* (Fig. 163), and purple sage, *R. nivea,* are valuable. These plants require about twenty inches of rainfall in late winter followed by warm spring, free from fogs, to produce

Fig. 162.—Button sage.

best results. When at their best these plants equal any other species in nectar secretion, but failures in crop are common. The sage worm (*Platyptilia marmarodactyla*) does considerable damage to the button sage, destroying the nectaries, especially in cloudy weather. Britton and Brown list seven species of Salvia for the eastern United States and state that there are twenty-five other species in the United States. Richter lists seven other species as California honey-plants.

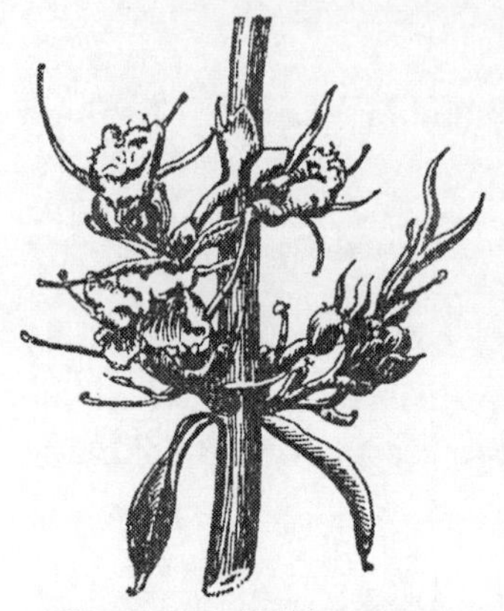

Fig. 163.—White sage.

St. John's-wort, Hypericum spp. Pollen.

St. John's-wort family, Hypericaceæ; see St. John's-wort.

Salicaceæ; see Willow family.

Saman, algaroba, *Pithecolobium Saman.* West Indies, Central and South America.

Saw palmetto, *Sabal megacarpa.* To 7 feet, May, honey amber, thick. Florida.

Scrophulariaceæ; see Figwort family.

Sedge family, Cyperaceæ; see Tule.

Senna family, Cæsalpinaceæ; see Judas Tree, Partridge Pea, Honey Locust, Eysenhardtia, Paloverde and Logwood.

Service berry; see Juneberry.

Sida spp. Tropical, listed for Hawaii.

Simarubaceæ; see Ailanthus family.

Simpson's honey-plant, *Scrophularia vernalis.* This common name is used only among American beekeepers. The species is native of southern Europe and was formerly cultivated for bees in parts of the United States, but without profit. Nectar abundant. Other species of Scrophularia are good honey-plants.

Smartweed; see Heartsease.

Solanaceæ; see Potato family.

Sorghum, *Holcus halepensis.* Pollen.

Sorrel-tree; see Sourwood.

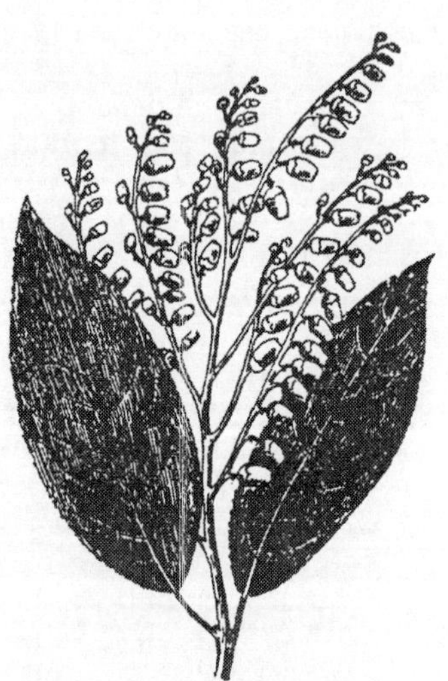

Fig. 164.—Sourwood.

Sour clover; see White Clover.
Sour gum; see Tupelo.
Sourwood, sorrel-tree, *Oxydendrum arboreum* (Fig. 164). Tree to 60 feet, flowers white in numerous racemes, June–July. Honey light in color, granulates slowly. In dry woods, Pennsylvania to Florida, especially in Piedmont region and lower mountains. An exceptionally heavy yielder, little affected by changes in climatic conditions, nor is nectar washed out by rains.
Sow thistle, *Sonchus oleraceus*. Some nectar.
Spanish needle, Bidens spp., Coreopsis spp. The numerous species of these genera are variously adapted to all conditions of soil and moisture, but the swamp species are most important to the beekeeper. Annual or perennial herbs to several feet, ray flowers yellow. Autumn. Honey amber, body heavy, flavor somewhat pronounced, granulates slowly. *Bidens involucrata*, native of middle west, is abundant (introduced) in the Delaware River bottoms south of Philadelphia, where it yields excessively. *B. aristosa* is the species reported as so valuable in the Illinois and Mississippi River bottoms. The Kankakee Swamps (northern Indiana and Illinois) contain Spanish needle in abundance. There seems to be considerable confusion as to the identification of the various species, and a careful study should be made of these valuable fall flowers.

The common name Spanish needle is the one usually adopted by beekeepers. Tickseed, sunflower, beggar's tick and bur-marigold are also applied to various species.

Spanish trefoil; see Alfalfa.
Spider-flower; see Cleome.
Spikeweed, *Centromadia pungens*. Central California, formerly a leading source of honey, now being superseded by other plants.
Squash; see Gourd family.
Strawberry, Fragaria sp. Nectar in some localities.
Sumac, *Rhus glabra*. Shrub to 20 feet, flowers yellowish green in dense conical panicles. June–August. Honey amber of fine flavor when well ripened. Distributed widely in moist regions of United States, yielding a surplus in New England. There are several species of Rhus of value to the beekeeper. Poison ivy, *R. radicans*, yields nectar.
Sumac family, Anacardiaceæ; see Sumac, Pepper Tree and Hog Plum.
Sunflower, Helianthus spp. Nectar often abundant. Jerusalem artichoke, *H. tuberosus*, cultivated for edible tubers is of value in moist soil. *H. annuus*, common in West.
Sunflower; see also Spanish Needle.
Swamp mahogany gum; see Eucalyptus.

Swedish clover; see Alsike Clover.

Sweet clover, *Melilotus alba* (Fig. 165), *M. officinalis*, *M. indica* Biennial herbs (*M. indica*, annual), 3–10 feet. Flowers white in *M. alba* and yellow in other two species, in slender racemes. June–September, or even later, usually in July. Honey slightly green in color, flavor described as like cinnamon. Throughout United States, usually in waste places but becoming more common as a forage plant. Secretes nectar wherever grown. Native of old world. In some sections (Kentucky, Utah) this plant is valued as a soil renovator (see Farmers' Bulletin No. 485, U. S. Department of Agriculture). White sweet clover, *M. alba* (Fig. 165), is the most common species. Seed is now offered for sale annually in the bee journals. It has been sown extensively by beekeepers in waste places and along embankments. Called also Bokhara clover and has numerous other common names. Twenty species, all native of old world. *M. indica* more abundant in far west.

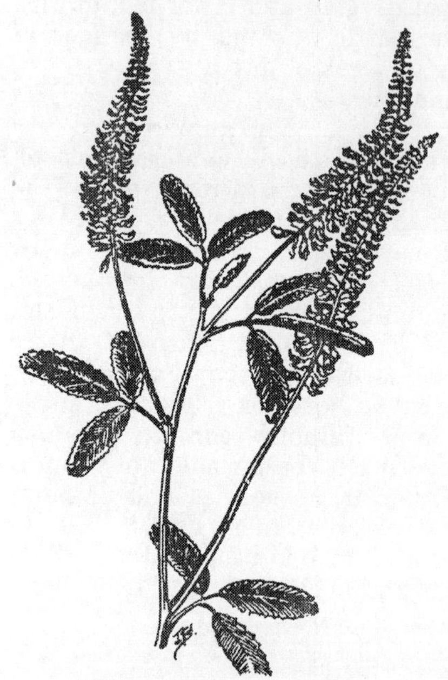

Fig. 165.—Sweet clover.

Sweet-gale, bayberry, Myrica spp. Wind pollinated, some pollen.

Sweet gum, *Liquidambar Styraciflua*. A source of abundant propolis.

Sweet pepper bush, *Clethra alnifolia*. Shrub, 3–10 feet. Honey light amber, good body. In swampy woods, Maine to Florida, especially near coast, July–August. Of special value in New England and New Jersey.

Tartarian honeysuckle, *Lonicera tatarica*. Nectar, important locally, other species valuable in which flowers are not too long for bees to reach. Bumble-bees sometimes pierce tubes of the honeysuckle, *L. Periclymenum*, to obtain nectar, after which honeybees work on the pierced flowers.

Thistle, Carduus spp. Considerable nectar.

Thistle family, Compositæ; see Iron-weed, Boneset, Goldenrod,

Asters, Sunflower, Spanish Needle, Sage Brush, Fireweed, Thistle, Canada Thistle and Spikeweed. This is a most important family from the standpoint of the beekeeper.

Thoroughwort; see Boneset.

Tickseed; see Spanish Needle.

Tiliaceæ; see Linden family.

Ti-ti, leatherwood, iron-wood, *Cyrilla racemiflora*. Evergreen shrub to 35 feet, flowers small, white in narrow racemes. May–July, February–March in Florida. Honey red, flavor strong, good only for baking. Virginia to Florida to Texas, of value chiefly in Georgia and Florida. Not a reliable source, as the nectar is washed out by rains, which are frequent during blooming period in Florida. Precedes tupelo in Appalachicola region. Black ti-ti, Cliftonia sp., blooms later and is more reliable.

Tobacco, *Nicotina Tabacum*. Nectar locally, especially in Connecticut, honey fair.

Tree of heaven; see Ailanthus.

Trumpet-creeper family, Bignoniaceæ; see Catalpa and Desert Willow.

Tule, Scirpus sp. Reported as a honey-plant from interior valleys of California; probably incorrect.

Fig. 166.—Tulip poplar.

Tulip or yellow poplar, poplar, white wood, cucumber tree, tulip tree, *Liriodendron Tulipifera* (Fig. 166). Tree to 175 feet, flowers 2 inches wide, resembling tulips, greenish yellow, orange inside. May–June. Honey dark amber, of pronounced flavor. In woods, eastern half of United States. Especially abundant in Ohio Valley and southern Appalachian mountains. An unusually heavy and reliable yielder.

Tulip tree; see Tulip Poplar.

Tupelo, sour gum, Nyssa spp. Trees to 100 feet, leaves oval or acute or slightly toothed (*N. aquatica*). April–June. Honey of fine quality, light amber, rarely granulating, flavor mild but characteristic. Swamps of eastern United States, west to Missouri and Texas, especially abundant in Florida, Alabama and Georgia. The honey from tupelos is of especial value in blending extracted-honeys for table trade because of its slowness in granulating. There are four species of Nyssa of value to the beekeeper. Tupelo, *N. aquatica*, is found abundantly in southern swamps, especially along the Appalachicola River. Secretes so abundantly that it will support thousands of colonies. Sour gum, *N. sylvatica*, is found farther north and with *N. biflora* furnishes abundant nectar. In abundance of nectar these trees equal the basswood.

Ulmaceæ; see Elm family.
Umbelliferæ; see Carrot family.

Vacciniaceæ; see Huckleberry family.
Verbenaceæ; see Vervain family.
Vervain family, Verbenaceæ; see Carpet Grass, Lantana and Black Mangrove.

Vetches, Vicia spp. Nectar, pollen.

Viper's bugloss, blueweed, blue-thistle, *Echium vulgare*. Biennial herbs, 1–2½ feet, stem erect bearing numerous blue to purple flowers, stem hairy, July–September and later. In fields and waste land, native of Europe, especially abundant in Virginia, Maryland and Pennsylvania. The common name blue-thistle is the one by which beekeepers usually know this plant. An important source in the Shenandoah Valley.

Fig. 167.—White clover.

Virginia creeper, *Parthenocissus quinquefolia*. Nectar, pollen.
Vitaceæ; see Grape family.

Walnut family, Juglandaceæ; see Black Walnut, English Walnut, Hickory and Pecan.

Water-leaf family, Hydrophyllaceæ; see Phacelia.

Watermelon; see Gourd family.

Wattles; see Acacias.

White alder family, Clethraceæ; see Sweet Pepper Bush.

White clover, *Trifolium repens* (Fig. 167). Perennial, creeping branches often taking root at nodes. Blooms from May on, but especially in June–July, when it is especially valuable. Honey light in color, granulates slowly, flavor superb. In pasture lands and waste places in moist regions of United States and Canada. Valuable as honey source chiefly in North and East. Not cultivated, thrives in limestone regions. Native of Europe and introduced into United States. One of the most important sources. May be considered as a "standard" for comb-honey, being equaled by no other source for this type of honey. Nectar-secretion quickly affected by adverse weather conditions. Honey often mixed with basswood in Michigan, Wisconsin and adjoining States. Also called Dutch clover, under which name seed is often sold. Other species of *Trifolium* are also valuable, *e.g.* sour clover, *T. fucatum*, California. Red clover, *T. pratense*, usually has a corolla tube too long for the honeybee to reach the nectar. At times bees get considerable nectar from this source. See also Crimson Clover and Alsike Clover.

FIG. 168.—Willow-herb.

White ironwood; see Eucalyptus.

White lilac and others, Ceanothus spp. California, February–May. Nectar and abundant pollen.

White sage; see Sage.

Whitewood; see Basswood and also Tulip Poplar.

Wild alfalfa, *Lotus glaber*. June–September, California.

Wild bergamot; see Horsemint.

Wild buckwheat, *Eriogonum fasciculatum*. Honey light amber, granulates quickly. April–November, southern California.

Wild honeysuckle; see Azalea.

Wild raspberry, *Rubus strigosus*. Shrubs, 3–6 feet, stems with small prickles. May–July or later. Honey white, flavor unsurpassed by that of any other honey. In dry lands, Canada south in mountains to North Carolina and in west to New Mexico, to 5500 feet in North Carolina. Especially valuable in cut or burned over lands in northern Michigan and noted in parts of New York. This is said to be the original of the Cuthbert red raspberry so widely cultivated. Reliable where abundant.

Willow family, Salicaceæ; see Poplars and Willows.

Willow-herb, fireweed, *Chamænerion angustifolium* (Fig. 168). Perennial herbs, 2–8 feet, flowers pink to purple (rarely white), in spike-like racemes. Honey white, flavor excellent, not pronounced. In dry soil, especially in burned-over forest lands. Labrador south to North Carolina, Kansas and California, but especially in Michigan, Wisconsin, Minnesota, Canada and Washington. This species continues in bloom from July to frost, the flowers maturing in series upward on the stem. A heavy reliable yielder.

Willows, Salix spp. Extraordinary value for pollen, some nectar Early spring.

Witchhazel family, Hamamelidaceæ; see Sweet Gum.

Yellow poplar; see Tulip Poplar.

Yucca, *Hesperoyucca Whipplei*. Semi-desert, California.

CHAPTER XXII

BEE DISEASES AND ENEMIES

THE honeybee is subject to several diseases which are at times serious handicaps to the industry. Within recent years knowledge of these diseases has greatly increased, so that it is now possible for the beekeeper to control all of the diseases known to occur in America. There is still a disease of adult bees in Europe, the so-called Isle of Wight or acarine disease, for which no satisfactory control methods have been devised, but this is apparently absent from the American continent.

These diseases may be divided into two classes, those affecting the brood and those to which adult bees are subject. In America the brood diseases are the more destructive and far more is known regarding their causes, distribution, symptoms and treatment. One of the first steps in the education of the beekeeper regarding these diseases is proper diagnosis, for to apply the wrong treatment to a disease through misdiagnosis usually makes matters worse rather than better.

BROOD DISEASES

There are three recognized diseases of the brood, known as American foulbrood, European foulbrood and sacbrood or pickled brood. These diseases weaken colonies by reducing the number of emerging bees needed to replace the adults which die from natural causes. The adult bees are not known to be affected. The larvæ dead of these diseases show certain differences in appearance which are useful in determining which disease is present. These diseases are entirely distinct, as shown by differences in appearance, in response to treatment, in the age of the larvæ affected and by bacteriological examination. There is no evidence that chilled or starved brood develops into an infectious disease or that dead brood favors the development of an infectious disease.

American foulbrood

This disease[1] (Fig. 169) is frequently called simply "foulbrood." It usually shows itself in the larvæ just about the time that they fill the cells and after they have ceased feeding and have begun pupation. At this time the larva is sealed over in the comb (Fig. 169, *a, b, f*). The first outward indication of the infection is a slight brownish discoloration and the loss of the well-rounded appearance of the normal larva (Fig. 169, *l*). The larva gradually sinks down in the cell and becomes darker in color (Fig. 169, *h, m*) and the posterior end lies against the bottom of the cell. Frequently the segmentation of the larva is clearly marked. By the time it has partially dried down and has become quite dark brown (coffee-colored) the most typical charac-

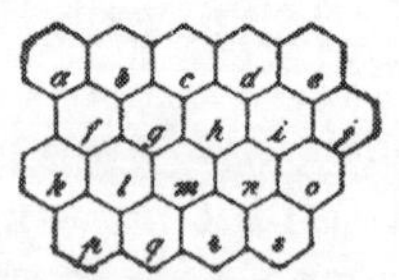

FIG. 169.—American foulbrood: *a, b, f,* normal sealed cells; *c, j,* sunken cappings, showing perforation; *g,* sunken capping not perforated; *h, l, m, n, q, r,* larvæ affected by disease; *e, i, p, s,* scales formed from dried-down larvæ; *d, o,* pupæ affected by disease. Twice natural size.

[1] Phillips, E. F., 1920. Control of American foulbrood. Farmers' Bull. 1084, U. S. Dept. Agr., 15 pp., 5 figs.

teristic of this disease manifests itself. If a match stick or tooth-pick is inserted into the decaying mass and withdrawn, the larval remains adhere to it and are drawn out in a thread (Fig. 170), which sometimes extends for several inches before breaking. This ropiness is the chief characteristic used by the beekeeper in diagnosing this disease. The larva continues to dry down and gradually loses its ropiness until it finally becomes merely a scale on the lower side wall and base of the cell (Fig. 169, *e, p, s*). The scale formed by the dried-down larva adheres tightly to the cell and can be removed with difficulty from the cell-wall. The scales can best be observed when the comb is held with the top inclined toward the observer so that a bright light strikes the lower side wall (Fig. 171). A characteristic and usually penetrating odor is often noticeable in the decaying larvæ. This can best be likened to the odor of heated glue.

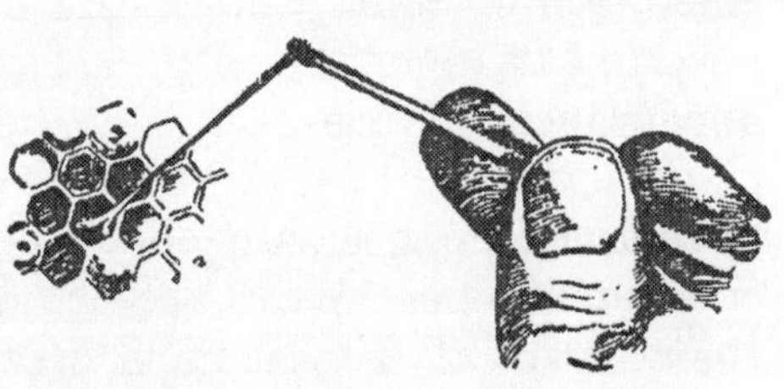

Fig. 170.—The ropiness of American foulbrood.

Fig. 171.—American foulbrood comb showing irregular patches of sunken cappings and scales. The position of the comb indicates the best way to view the scales.

The larger part of the larvæ which die of this disease

are attacked after being sealed in the cells. The cappings are often entirely removed by the bees, but when they are left they usually become sunken (Fig. 169, *g*, *c*, *j*) and frequently perforated (Fig. 169, *c*, *j*). As the healthy brood emerges the comb shows the scattered sunken cappings covering dead larvæ (Fig. 171), giving it a characteristic appearance. Pupæ also may die of this disease, in which case they also dry down (Fig. 169, *o*, *d*), become ropy and have the characteristic odor and color. The tongue frequently adheres to the upper side wall and often remains there even after the pupa has dried down to a scale. Younger unsealed larvæ are sometimes affected. Usually the disease attacks only worker brood, but occasionally queen and drone brood are diseased. It is not certain that race of bees, season, or climate have any effect on the virulence of this disease, except that in warmer climates, where the breeding season is prolonged, the rapidity of devastation is more marked. The cause of American foulbrood is *Bacillus larvæ*.

European foulbrood

This disease[1] (Fig. 172) was formerly called "black brood." It usually attacks the larva at an earlier stage of its development than American foulbrood and while it is still curled up at the base of the cell (Fig. 172, *r*). A small percentage of larvæ dies after capping, but sometimes quite young larvæ are attacked (Fig. 172, *e*, *m*). Sunken and perforated cappings are sometimes observed just as in American foulbrood (Fig. 169, *c*, *g*, *j*). The earliest indication of the disease is a slight yellow or gray discoloration and uneasy movement of the larva in the cell. The larva loses its well-rounded opaque appearance and becomes slightly translucent, so that the tracheæ may become prominent (Fig. 172, *b*), giving the larvæ a clearly segmented appearance. The larva is usually flattened against the base

[1] Phillips, E. F., 1918. The control of European foulbrood. Farmers' Bull. 975, U. S. Dept. Agr., 16 pp., 1 fig.

of the cell but may turn so that the ends are to the rear of the cell (Fig. 172, *p*) or may fall away from the base (Fig. 172, *e, g, l*). Later the color changes to a decided yellow or gray and the translucency is lost (Fig. 172, *q, h.*) The yellow color may be taken as the chief characteristic of this disease. The dead larva appears as a moist somewhat collapsed mass, giving the appearance of being melted. When the remains have become almost dry (Fig. 172, *c*) the tracheæ sometimes become conspicuous again, this time by retaining their shape, while the remainder of the body content dries around them. Finally all that is left of the larva is a grayish-brown scale against the base of the cell (Fig. 172, *f, h*) or a shapeless mass on the lower side wall if the larva did not retain its normal position (Fig. 172, *n, o*). Very few scales are black. The scales are not adhesive but are easily removed and the bees carry out a great many in their efforts to clean house.

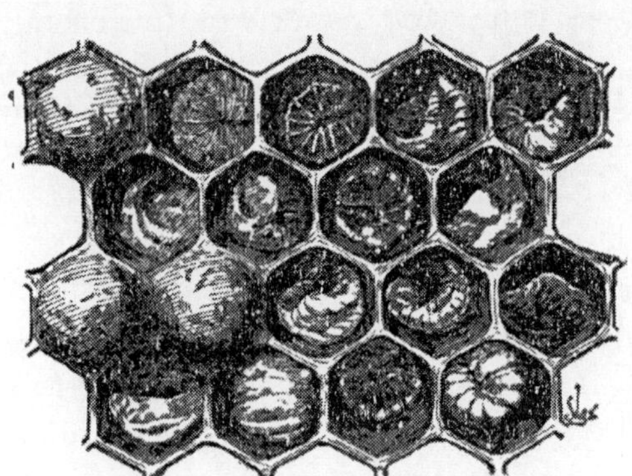

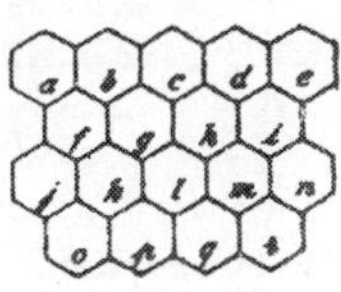

Fig. 172.—European foulbrood: *a, j, k,* normal sealed cells; *b, c. d, e, g, i, l, m, p, q,* larvæ affected by disease; *r,* normal larva at age attacked by disease; *f, h, n, o,* dried-down larvæ or scales. Twice natural size.

Decaying larvæ which have died of this disease are usually not ropy as in American foulbrood but a slight ropiness is sometimes observed. There is usually little odor in European foulbrood, but sometimes in bad cases a sour odor is present, which reminds one of yeast fermentation. This disease attacks drones and queen larvæ almost as quickly as those of the workers.

European foulbrood is more destructive during the spring and early summer than at other times, often entirely disappearing in late summer and autumn or in a heavy honeyflow. Italian bees seem better able to resist the ravages of this disease than any other race. The disease at times spreads with startling rapidity and is most destructive. Where it is prevalent a considerably larger percentage of colonies is affected than is usual for American foulbrood. This disease is variable in its symptoms and other manifestations and is often a puzzle to the beekeeper. The cause of European foulbrood is *Bacillus pluton.*[1]

Sacbrood

In this disease the larva dies about the time of sealing. It usually lies on its back with the head turned upward. The color varies, but is frequently light yellow or brown and the head is often almost black. The body is swollen and the contents watery and the head may be quite hard. There is no ropiness. Sacbrood is usually not the cause of any serious loss in the apiary and, as a rule, no treatment is necessary. The most serious aspect of this disease is that it is often mistaken for European or American foulbrood and the colony is treated accordingly. The cause is a filterable virus.

Methods of spread

All three of the brood diseases are infectious and to some extent doubtless spread in similar ways, but there is still much mystery about the spread of European foulbrood and sacbrood. In the absence of more definite knowledge on this phase of the investigation on these diseases, the beekeeper will usually find it desirable to take those precautions which are known to be important for preventing the spread of American foulbrood, with the exception that honey from a colony having European foulbrood may be used with

[1] See Lockhead, A. G., 1928. The etiology of European foulbrood of bees. Science, N. S. LXVII, No 1728, pp. 159-160.

safety, as will later appear. Especially for American foulbrood, the following precautions are necessary:

(1) Do not allow weak colonies to be robbed out.

(2) Never feed honey purchased on the open market.

(3) If possible keep all honey from diseased apiaries out of the neighborhood.

(4) In introducing purchased queens, transfer them to clean cages and destroy the old cage, candy and accompanying workers.

(5) Colonies of bees should never be purchased unless it is certain that they are free from disease.

(6) The purchase of old combs and second-hand supplies is dangerous unless it is certain that they come from healthy apiaries.

Treatment of American foulbrood

The treatment of this disease consists primarily in the elimination or removal of the cause, a microscopic bacterium. In treating a colony, therefore, the aim is to remove and to destroy all the virus causing the disease. It should be remembered that the effort is not to save the larvæ that are already dead or dying but to stop further devastation by removing all material capable of transmitting the cause of the trouble. In all of the operations great pains should be taken not to spread the disease through carelessness. After handling a diseased colony, the hands of the operator should be washed with water to remove any honey that may be on them. It does not pay to treat colonies that are considerably weakened by disease, and in case only one or two cases appear in a large apiary, the cheapest and safest plan is to burn them. In case there are several weak colonies to be treated, they should be united to make strong colonies before or during treatment.

Shaking treatment

The treatment consists essentially in the removal of all infected material from the colony and in compelling the colony to take a fresh start by building new combs and by gathering fresh stores. This is done by shaking the adult bees from the old combs into a clean hive on clean frames.

The shaking treatment should be given during a honey-flow, so that other bees in the apiary will not be inclined to rob. If this is not possible the operation may be performed under a tent made of mosquito-netting or a wire-

FIG. 173.—Apparatus for the shaking treatment: *A*, hive containing diseased colony (formerly in position of *B*); *B*, clean hive; *C*, empty hive to receive combs after shaking; *D*, hive cover used as runway; *E*, frames removed from *B* to give room for shaking; *F*, queen- and drone-trap; *G*, cover for clean hive, *B*.

cloth cage. The best time is in the middle of a clear day when a large number of bees are in the field.

All implements that will be needed, such as queen- and drone-trap, hive-tool and lighted smoker, should be in readiness before the operation is begun. A complete clean hive with frames is provided, as well as a tightly closed hive-body in which to put the contaminated combs after shaking. An extra hive-cover or some similar apparatus should be provided to serve as a runway for the bees as they enter the new hive. The new frames should contain strips of comb-foundation from one-fourth to one inch wide. Full sheets may also be used, or if combs built on full sheets of foundation are desired they may be built later.

The old hive containing the diseased colony (Fig. 173, *A*) is now lifted to one side out of the flight of returning field bees and the clean hive (*B*) set exactly in its place. The cover (*G*) is now taken off and a few frames (*E*) removed from the center of the hive. If unspaced frames are used, those remaining in the hive should be pushed tightly to either side of the hive, thus making a barrier beyond which the bees cannot crawl as they move to the top of the hive after shaking. This largely prevents them from getting on the outside of the hive. If self-spacing frames are used, a few thin boards laid on the top-bars on either side will accomplish the same result. The runway (*D*) is put in place in front of the entrance. The old hive is now opened for the first time. The frames are removed one at a time, lowered part way into the new hive and, with a quick downward shake, the bees are dislodged. The frames are then put into the extra hive-body (*C*) and immediately covered to prevent robbing. After all the frames are shaken the bees remaining on the sides of the old hive (*A*) are shaken out.

If honey is coming in freely, so that thin honey is shaken out of the combs, the runway (*D*) should be covered with newspapers and the bees shaken in front of the new hive (*B*), leaving all frames in place and the cover on. After the operation the soiled newspapers should be destroyed. In shaking in front of the entrance the first one or two frames should be so shaken that the bees are thrown against the entrance, where they can locate the hive quickly. Then they fan their wings and the others follow them into the hive. If this is not done the bees may wander about and get under the hive or in some other undesirable place.

After the bees are mostly in the new hive, a queen- and drone-trap (*F*) or a strip of perforated zinc is placed over the entrance to prevent the colony from deserting the hive.

The old combs are now quickly removed. If several colonies are being treated at one time it may pay to stack several hive-bodies containing contaminated combs over a weak diseased colony to allow most of the healthy brood to emerge, thereby strengthening the weak colony. After ten or twelve days this colony is treated in turn and all the combs are rendered into wax.

It is now possible safely to disinfect contaminated combs by the use of a solution devised by J. C. Hutzelman consisting of four parts ethyl alcohol and one part of a 37 per cent formaldehyde solution, this being commonly known as Hutzelman's solution. Sturtevant[1] finds a solution of four parts of water to one part formaldehyde fully as effective, provided absolutely every cell is uncapped. Several beekeepers have tried to use soap as a spreader for the water solution, some of them reporting good results. This is used because the water-formaldehyde solution does not enter the cells readily. With whatever solution is used for disinfection, it is best to soak the combs for forty-eight hours tc insure complete disinfection. Combs which have never contained brood (super combs) may be disinfected in twenty-four hours, possibly even less, but it pays the beekeeper to err on the safe side by leaving the combs in a sufficiently long time.

Disinfection of combs is not profitable unless there is a large number. For smaller numbers, it is probably most profitable simply to burn the combs, but they may be rendered into wax, the wax being entirely safe for use in making comb-foundation or other purposes. An apiary of any size should have included in its equipment a wax-press (Fig. 142) for removing wax from old combs.

After the contaminated combs are removed they should be kept carefully covered, so that no bees can reach them until they are either melted or burned. This should not be delayed very long or the combs may be ruined by wax-moths. The refuse or slumgum remaining after the wax is removed should be burned as it is usually not sterilized in the rendering of the wax. Contaminated combs should never be placed in a solar wax-extractor for fear of spreading the disease.

[1] Sturtevant, A. P., 1926. The sterilization of American foulbrood combs. Cir. 284, U. S. Dept. Agr., 28 pp.

The hive which has contained the diseased colony should be cleaned thoroughly of all wax and honey, and it is desirable that it be disinfected carefully by burning out the inside with a gasoline blue-flame torch (Fig. 174). If this piece of apparatus is not available, several hive-bodies may be piled together on a hive bottom and some gasoline or kerosene poured on the sides and on some straw or excelsior placed at the bottom of the pile. This is then ignited and after burning for a few seconds a close-fitting hive-cover is placed on top of the pile to extinguish the flames. The inside of the hive-bodies should be charred to a light brown. The careful cleaning and disinfection of frames always costs considerably more in labor than would new frames, but these also may be cleaned carefully and used again. Frames may be cleaned by boiling in water for about half an hour, but this frequently causes them to warp badly. The disinfection of hives and frames with chemicals is not recommended, but by the use of a lye solution all propolis and wax may be removed quickly without injury to the frames. The lye solution is a disinfectant.

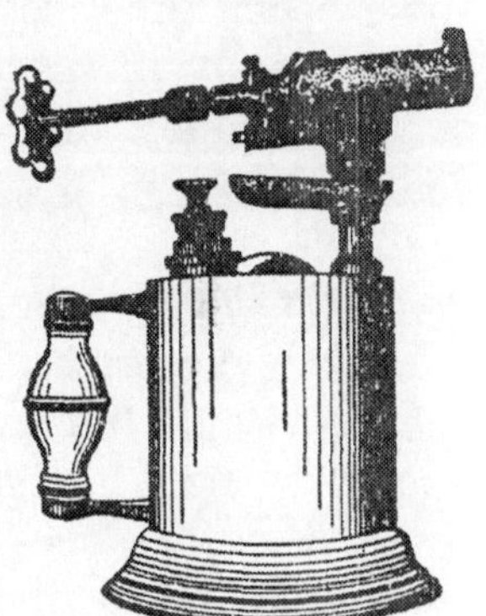

Fig. 174.—Gasoline torch.

Some beekeepers prefer to shake the bees first on to frames containing strips of foundation as above described and in four days to shake the colony a second time on to full sheets of foundation, destroying all comb built after the first treatment. This insures better combs than the use of strips of foundation, but it is a severe drain on the strength of the colony. Since it is desirable to have combs built on full sheets, the best policy is to replace any irregular combs with full sheets of foundation or good combs later in the season.

If the treatment just described is given at the beginning

of a good honey-flow, it is practically equivalent to artificial swarming (p. 297) and may result in an actual increase in the surplus honey, especially in the case of comb-honey-production. The wax rendered from the combs will sell for enough to pay for the comb-foundation if full sheets of foundation are employed. If treatment must be given at some other time, so that the colony must be fed, the cost is materially increased. In feeding, it is best to use sugar sirup or honey that is known to have come from healthy colonies.

Fall treatment

If it is necessary to treat a colony so late in the fall that it would be impossible for the bees to prepare for winter without assistance, the treatment may be modified by shaking the bees on to combs entirely full of honey so that there is no place for any brood to be reared. This will usually be satisfactory only after brood-rearing has entirely ceased. Unless a colony is quite strong it does not pay to treat in the fall, but it should be destroyed or united with another colony. In case a diseased colony dies outdoors in the winter, there is danger that other bees may have opportunity to rob the hive before the beekeeper can close the entrance. In case bees are wintered in the cellar it is more advisable to risk wintering before treatment, for if the colony does die the hive will not be robbed.

Treatment of European foulbrood

This disease attacks weak colonies or those that are not building up properly. The main attack is in late spring or early summer, and the disease is rare at other seasons, unless it is not cleaned up by the bees during the earlier honey-flows. The first brood of the year is rarely attacked but the disease sometimes spreads with great rapidity in colonies that are short of spring food or that are poorly protected. Italian bees are usually better able to ward off this disease than are black bees and it is recommended that this race be kept in regions where European foulbrood prevails. When this disease was first differentiated from American foulbrood, the usual control was by the shaking treatment, but this makes weak colonies still weaker and is therefore about the worst method for a colony having European foulbrood.

The brood dead of European foulbrood does not adhere to the cells and may be removed without difficulty by the bees, provided the colony is adequately strong to clean the hive and combs thoroughly. Under such conditions healthy brood may then be reared by the bees in cells which formerly contained diseased brood. It is also known that the honey stored by the bees during the time that this disease is in the hive does not long retain the causal bacteria in living condition. With such a combination of circumstances, the treatment of this disease must differ materially from that used with the other foulbrood.

In brief, the best means of controlling European foulbrood is to keep all colonies strong by methods of good beekeeping, under which conditions the disease does not appear. In the event that some colonies contract the disease, then the proper treatment is to permit the bees to clean up as rapidly as possible by good beekeeping methods and then to keep the colonies strong thereafter. To aid the bees in cleaning up, it is a good plan to cage the queen for a few days so that no new brood will be available to continue the disease, the time of queenlessness depending on the severity of the disease. Since queens which permit their colonies to contract this disease are often poor, some beekeepers insist on giving a young vigorous queen at the end of the broodless period, usually a wise practice. Generally the disease may also be controlled by heavy feeding. Another method often used is to place the queen on clean combs in the lower hive-body and then put all diseased brood over a queen-excluder. Beekeepers who are troubled by this disease are urged to study the bulletin on its control prepared by the author, which may be secured without charge from the Department of Agriculture.

European foulbrood is peculiarly distributed in the United States, occurring as a rule only in regions where the heavy honey-flow comes rather late in the season. The buckwheat and willowherb areas are especially troubled, indicating the necessity for an improvement in beekeeping methods to the end that all colonies may become strong at that season of the year when this disease makes its attack. In the type of region indicated, this is some time before the honey-flow, and it is often a good practice for the beekeeper to safeguard his bees from this disease by building them up rapidly, and after the danger has passed, the colonies may often be divided so that he has two colonies ready for the later honey-flow instead of one. Good beekeeping, by whatever system it is practiced, is the prevention and control of European foulbrood.

DISEASES OF ADULT BEES

These diseases are still imperfectly known and not much can be recommended in the way of treatment. Diagnosis is especially difficult since the behavior of the diseased bees is much the same for all the known adult diseases, so that it is often desirable for the beekeeper to have a diagnosis made by sending bees to the Bureau of Entomology, Washington, D. C., where the work will be done without charge.

Dysentery

This condition is manifest chiefly in late winter and is caused by improper food. It is, therefore, discussed in the chapter on wintering.

Nosema disease

In 1909 Zander [1] showed that a protozoon, named by him *Nosema apis,* is found abundantly in the mid-intestine of

[1] Zander, E., 1909. Tierische Parasiten als Krankheitserreger bei der Biene, München.

adult bees and he associated this organism in a causal relationship with the death of many thousands of colonies annually. Since this announcement was made, many other investigators have worked with this organism. It was at one time claimed that this protozoon is the cause of the Isle of Wight disease prevailing in Great Britain, but this is now known not to be the case. This organism is widely distributed throughout the world and occurs in the United States sporadically but by no means constantly. In Europe it is claimed that the organism causes heavy losses, whereas the experience in America suggests that it occurs rarely except in colonies that are depleted from some other cause such as dysentery. Because of the extreme difficulty of getting exact information on this organism in its relation to losses of bees, beekeepers can at present be advised only to use every precaution to keep their colonies strong and in good condition, especially during the winter season. Good wintering methods and especially the providing of a proper food supply seem to be the best means of combating this trouble which is fortunately rarely serious in America. For a discussion of the intricacies of this problem, the reader is referred to a paper by the author.[1]

Isle of Wight disease

This disease has for some years caused great losses in Great Britain and is now known to occur in various continental countries of Europe. It is caused by the invasion of a mite, *Acarapis woodi,* into the tracheal trunks of the thorax, this being the first disease of an insect to be attributed to such a cause. The discovery of the cause of this disease by Rennie and his associates has led to much investigation for a suitable method of treatment, but apparently nothing reliable has been found so far. After Rennie's announcement of the cause, a careful search was instituted

[1] Phillips, E. F., 1926. Eine Fehlerquelle im Studium der Krankheiten der erwachsenen Bienen. Archiv für Bienenkunde, VI, pp. 193-206.

in North America and so far no cases of this disease have been discovered,[1] so that for the present it need not cause worry on the part of American beekeepers. In August, 1922, Congress passed a law prohibiting the importation of adult bees except under supervisison of the Department of Agriculture, in the hope that this serious disease may not enter. The available information regarding this disease from other countries will be found in the circulars to which references are given.

Paralysis

Under this name beekeepers seemingly place practically all the diseases of adult bees which they observe. Symptoms attributed to paralysis are also given for poisoning and the more one reads of the symptoms and treatments suggested, the more hopeless it appears when one is asked to recommend treatment. Until more is known it is unsafe to give advice.

Spring dwindling

This name has also apparently been given to various conditions. To avoid confusion it should be applied only to the loss of bees in the spring due to the fact that the adults have been weakened by poor wintering and die faster than they can be replaced by emerging brood. This is, therefore, discussed in the chapter on wintering.

ENEMIES OF BEES

Most books on beekeeping devote considerable attention to the enemies of bees, of which there are several. Since they are relatively unimportant, however, the discussion will here be confined to the two species of wax-moth. These do no damage to strong healthy colonies of bees properly

[1] Phillips, E. F., 1922. The occurrence of diseases of adult bees. Circ. 218, U. S. Dept. Agr., 16 pp., 2 figs.

Phillips, E. F., 1923. The occurrence of diseases of adult bees. II. Circ. 287, U. S. Dept. Agr., 34 pp.

cared for, and if seen in the hive they indicate weakness. This weakness may be due to queenlessness or lack of stores, but the most common cause is probably a brood disease. Beekeepers frequently attribute the loss from disease to some other cause and wax-moths are most frequently blamed for the losses observed.

Fig. 175.—Wax-moth in natural position at rest.

The wax-moth (Galleria mellonella)

The larvæ of this moth (Figs. 175, 176, 177) destroy combs by burrowing through them, constructing tunnels of silk as they go (Fig. 178). These tunnels are spotted with excreta. The larvæ (Fig. 179) feed on pollen, cocoons and other materials in the combs. The eggs are laid in crevices in the hive

Fig. 176.—Wax-moth, male. Enlarged.

or in any narrow space (Fig. 180) and seemingly in most localities there are probably few hives that do not harbor some eggs. If combs are removed from the bees and sealed up, it will frequently be found that they become riddled by the tunnels of these larvæ, presumably developed from eggs already present on the combs or frames. After

Fig. 177.—Wax-moth, female. Enlarged.

feeding, the larvæ pupate, first spinning silken webs around themselves. Previous to pupation (Figs. 181, 182) they sometimes burrow a little way into the hive wall, this being specially noticeable in the redwood hives in the West. The life history of this moth has recently been described by Paddock.[1] Although repeatedly introduced, the wax-moth is rarely found in Colorado. Except for special regions, as

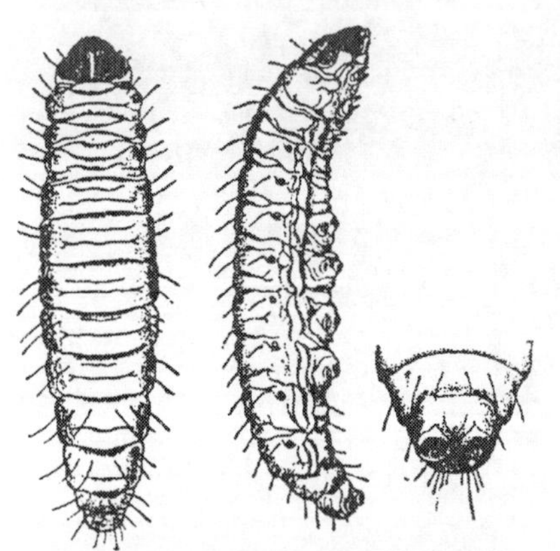

Fig. 179.—Larva of wax-moth.

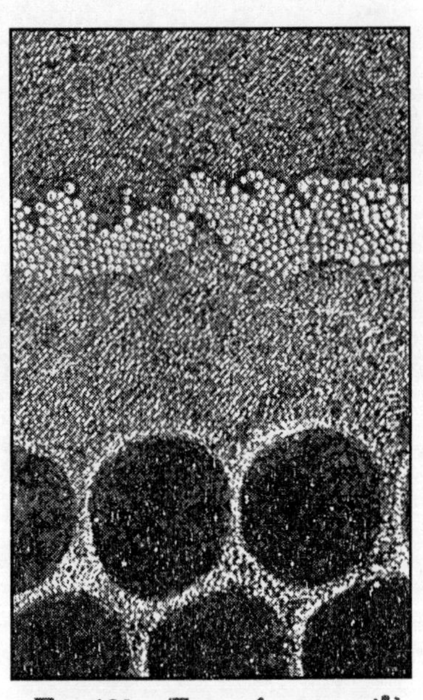

Fig. 180.—Eggs of wax-moth laid on top-bar of frame.

[1] Paddock, F. B., 1913. The life history and control of the bee-moth or wax-moth. In Bull. 158 "Investigations pertaining to Texas beekeeping." Tex. Agr. Exp. Sta.

the one just mentioned, this moth is present wherever bees are kept and is also destructive to the combs of the giant bee (*Apis dorsata*). The female moths can often be seen flying in the apiary in early evening and attempting to enter the hives.

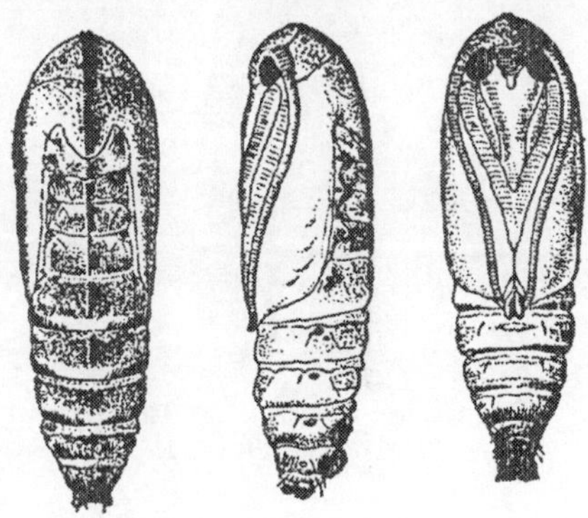

FIG. 181.—Pupa of wax-moth.

The lesser wax-moth (Achroia grissella)

This moth (Figs. 183-187) is less widely distributed in the United States than the previous species. The larvæ tunnel through combs in much the same way as those of the larger species. The eggs are laid singly on the side wall of cells.

Remedies

To destroy the moth larvæ and pupæ in combs not in use, the latter should be placed in hives tiered one above the other and on top an empty hive or super. On

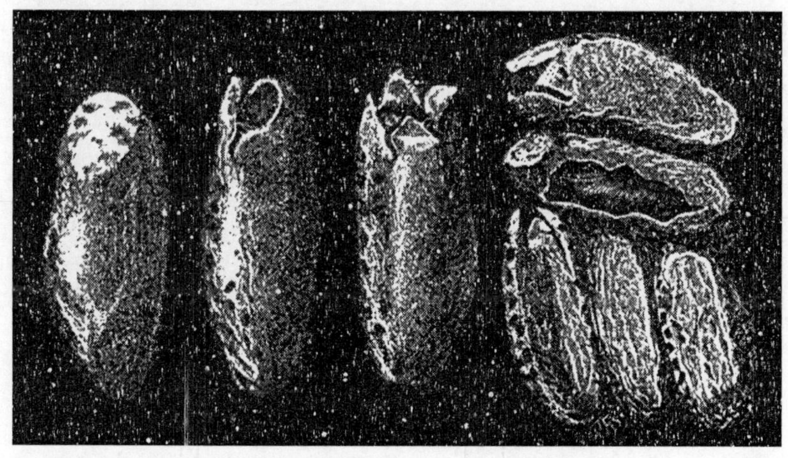

FIG. 182.—Cocoons of wax-moth.

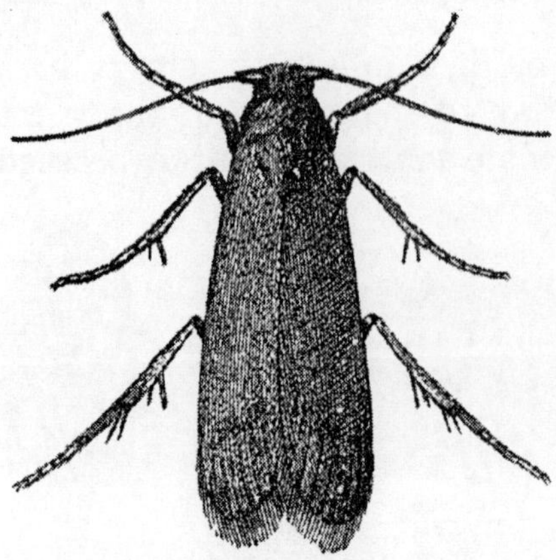

Fig. 183.—Lesser wax-moth in natural position.

the top-bars of the uppermost frames should be placed a saucer into which bisulfide of carbon is poured. The gas caused by the evaporation of the liquid is heavier than air and settles down through the combs. Care should be exercised not to allow the fumes to reach a flame, as the gas is highly inflammable. The eggs of the wax-moth are usually not destroyed by fumigation so the operation should be repeated at intervals of two or three weeks until all the eggs have hatched. Sulfur fumes may also be used.

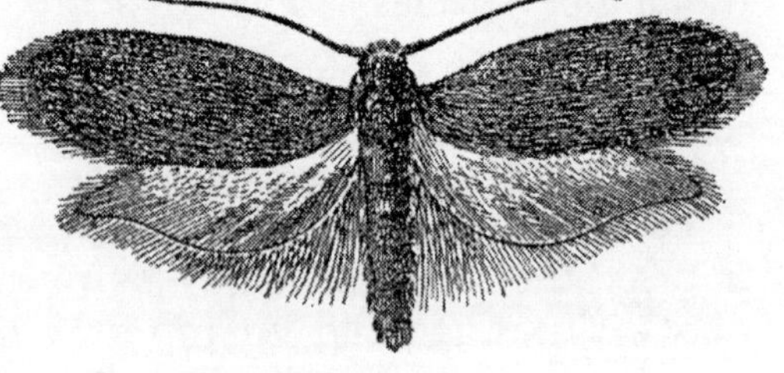

Fig. 184.—Lesser wax-moth, male.

Other enemies

Among other animals which may be mentioned as enemies of bees, several are parasitic or predaceous, or destroy the combs. Toads, various species of birds, mice, rats and other small mammals (especially in winter),

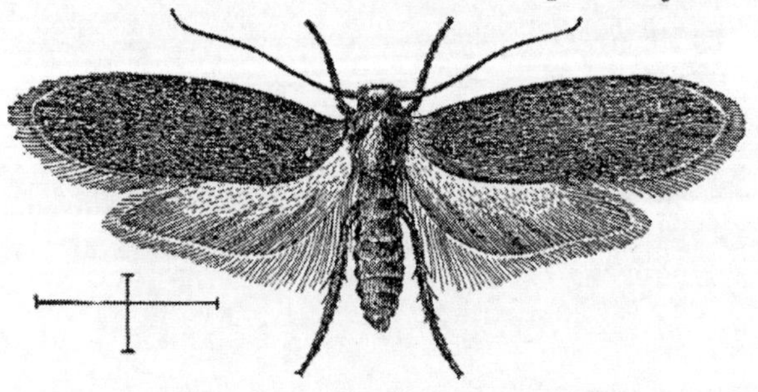

Fig. 185.—Lesser wax-moth, female.

certain spiders and mites, dragon-flies (especially in Florida where they destroy queens while mating), various Hemiptera which suck the blood of adult bees, the death-head moth (repeatedly mentioned in Europe), Mediterranean flour-moth (eating pollen in stored combs), a dipterous parasite[1] (the bee-louse, *Braula coeca*) sometimes found on imported queens, blister-beetle (Meloe) and other beetles feeding on pollen or combs, wasps and hornets (Vespa) and ants, especially in tropics

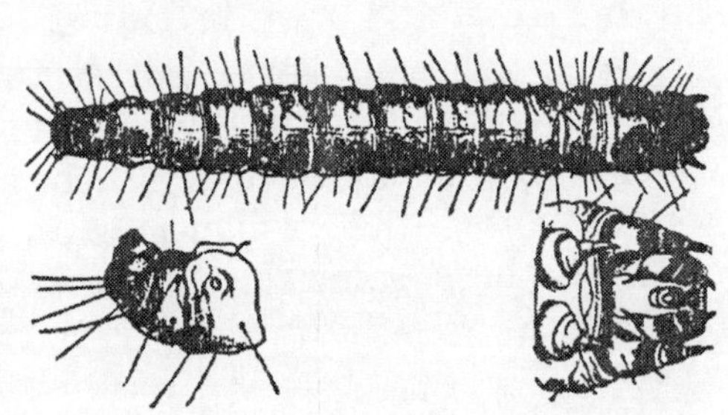

Fig. 186.—Lesser wax-moth, larva.

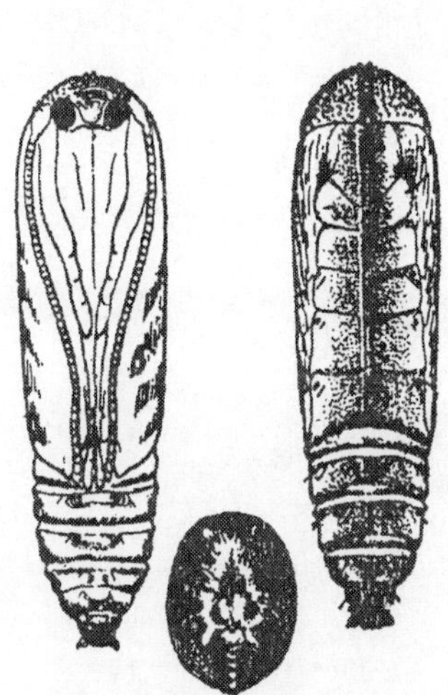

Fig. 187.—Lesser wax-moth, pupa.

Fig. 188.—Hive-stand to keep off ants. The band around the post is tree tanglefoot.

and semi-tropics, are the chief offenders. Dragon-flies are so destructive to queens as to make queen-rearing unprofit-

[1] This enemy is now established in parts of Maryland and Pennsylvania but so far has done no great damage. See, Phillips, E. F., 1925. The bee-louse, *Braula coeca,* in the United States. Circ. 334, U. S. Dept. of Agr., 11 pp.

able in some places. Various devices have been suggested for circumventing ants, among which is the hive-stand shown in Fig. 188, used in Hawaii. Around the post which serves as a base, a strip of tree tanglefoot is painted and this is renewed at intervals. There are several plants which trap bees and destroy them and, as mentioned under honey-plants, the pollen-masses of certain milkweeds adhere to bees, sometimes making them incapable of flight.

CHAPTER XXIII

THE REARING OF QUEENS

UNLESS the queen at the head of a colony is a good one it is useless to expect that colony to be productive. It, therefore, becomes necessary for the progressive beekeeper to pay considerable attention to the rearing of queens which fulfill the requirements for commercial success. The chief requirements are prolificness, vigor of offspring and purity of race. While ability in egg-laying is a character which is inherited, it is also influenced by the age of the queen and by the care she received during her development. Quietness in winter, reduction in swarming and gentleness are other desirable characters.

COMMERCIAL QUEEN-REARING

Queen-rearing has become a prominent specialty in American beekeeping and there are numerous beekeepers who devote almost their entire energies to rearing queens of various races for sale. To these specialists, beekeepers have in the past looked for the greatest advancement in the breeding of better stock, but it is becoming more and more evident that this work should not be left entirely to commercial breeders. In any event it is usually not economical for the extensive beekeeper to purchase all of his queens. Queens that have been shipped through the mails, especially those that have previously been laying heavily, are frequently injured to the extent that they never again fully show their former prolificness. Even if this were not the case, the cost of queens is almost always greater than is warranted by the time saved the honey-producer in not rearing them. This should not be interpreted as an intimation that American queen breeders charge excessive prices, for such is emphatically not the case, as is shown by the fact that so many queen breeders are compelled to abandon the work in a year or two as financially unprofitable. From data furnished the author by numerous commercial breeders, it is evident that many would make more money if they devoted their time to honey-production. However, each queen costs relatively much less in time and honey in requeening perhaps half the colonies in an apiary in a season than it does when one rears a large number of queens in making it a commercial business.

REQUEENING

The giving of a young queen to each colony at stated times is coming to be the approved practice of some of the best commercial honey-producers. After two seasons in a large colony in temperate regions (about one year in the tropics), the larger number of queens are incapable of laying the large number of eggs a day that were laid earlier. There are many individual exceptions, and if a beekeeper can give each colony considerable attention he may get good results from a large percentage of his older queens. The extensive commercial honey-producer cannot spend much time on each colony and he must work by averages. If, therefore, older queens are less prolific and if the cost of requeening does not exceed the increased profits due to the giving of young queens, he is prudent to requeen. Before deciding this he should count the cost and should especially see to it that he is reducing his queen-rearing to a system so that no time is wasted in this work. As honey-production becomes more intensive and as queen-rearing methods become more economical of time, an increasing number of extensive beekeepers are finding it profitable to requeen each colony systematically each season and, of course, to replace queens earlier if any prove defective.

Conditions under which queens are reared

There are three circumstances under which bees build queen-cells naturally and in artificial queen-rearing it is necessary to bring about or to utilize some one of these conditions. (1) The most common condition is that found in the preparation for swarming (p. 70). (2) If a colony becomes queenless and if suitable larvæ are present, queens will be reared. (3) If a queen becomes inefficient the workers will rear young queens to supersede her. It is believed that the best queens are those reared under the swarming impulse and in supersedure.

Saving natural queen-cells

During the swarming season the beekeeper can often obtain a number of fine queen-cells without any cost in time by taking queen-cells from colonies preparing to swarm, provided the parent queens are of satisfactory stock. By placing these in colonies to be requeened, after the removal of the condemned queens, requeening takes place naturally and without further manipulation. Making a colony queenless early in a honey-flow, like that from clover in the North, costs less perhaps than a period of queenlessness at any other time, in that the eggs laid then are not of value as future honey-gatherers. Furthermore, this may often be done in connection with dequeening to control swarming. By keeping a watch for opportunities to utilize good natural queen-cells, time may be saved by reducing the amount of artificial queen-rearing.

Having natural cells built

The Miller method.—C. C. Miller advocates the following method: The breeding queen is kept in a two-frame nucleus so that all comb built will be of worker-cells.

Beginning at about the time queen-cells are being built for swarming, on the same day each week a frame is inserted in place of one of the combs in the nucleus containing the breeding queen. This new frame contains two small starters of foundation about 4 by 1 inches, placed 4 inches from each end. If the nucleus is fairly populous, in a week this frame will contain considerable comb and the cells will contain eggs and young larvæ. It is now taken away and another frame with starters substituted. The new comb is now trimmed so that the cells at the edge containing eggs are cut away, leaving young larvæ on the border of the comb. It is then inserted in the middle of a strong colony which has begun to build queen-cells in preparation for swarming, all former queen-cells being destroyed and the queen removed. In ten days the comb containing queen-cells from eggs of the breeding queen is removed and the cells given to nuclei from which the queens are mated. They may, if desired, be left in a nursery cage to emerge.

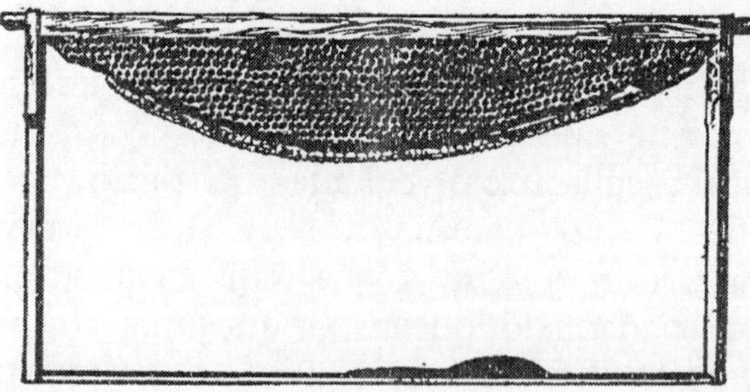

Fig. 189.—Comb cut for starting queen-cells by the Alley method. A strip of partly drawn comb-foundation is here used to hold the eggs chosen for queen-rearing.

The Alley method.—For convenience, a method described by Alley has much to commend it. A strip of comb is cut out, just wide enough to contain one complete row of cells containing eggs. This is then cut down by removing about two-thirds of the side walls on one side. With a match or small stick, one in every two or two in every three eggs are destroyed, leaving the cells empty. The strip of comb is now fastened to the lower edge of a comb cut as represented in Fig. 189, the eggs remaining being pointed downward. This prepared frame is now given to a queenless colony from which all young unsealed brood has been removed. The workers remodel the cells which contain the eggs, making them into queen-cells.

The Hopkins method.—Another method has been recommended by Hopkins [1] for getting queen-cells in quantity. A new comb is given to a breeding queen to be filled with eggs, after which it is removed, and with a sharp knife three out of every four rows of cells across the comb are cut away to the midrib, leaving every fourth row intact. Two of every three eggs are then destroyed as described previously, as well as any eggs accidentally left between the rows. This comb is now laid face down over the brood-chamber of a queenless colony, being raised above the top-bars of the hive by means of an empty frame or a specially constructed collar. The sealed queen-cells are shown in Fig. 190. To protect the developing queens from cold, the horizontal frame should be covered with a light mat. To prevent sagging, the comb may be supported by wires wound around the frame between the rows of cells. It is possible that when so many cells are built some queens are not good.

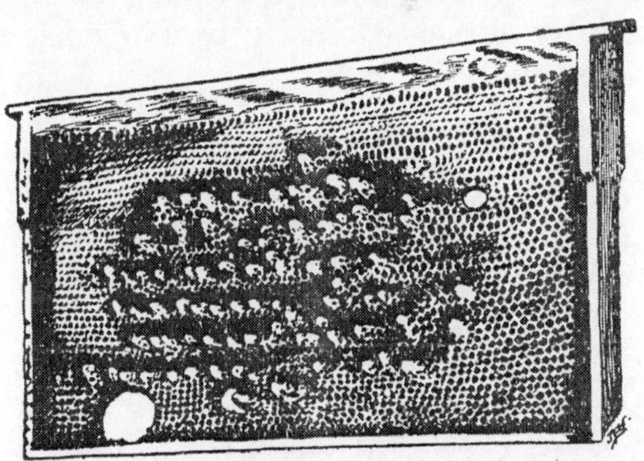

FIG. 190.—Queen-cells reared by the Hopkins method.

With any of these methods the queen-cells may be cut out and protected with a West spiral wire cell protector and

[1] Hopkins, I, 1911. The illustrated Australasian bee manual. Wellington, N. Z. See also various journal articles by this author.

given to a colony or small nucleus, or they may be placed in a nursery cage for the queens to emerge.

Queen-cells on artificial bases

To have the queen-cells in more convenient shape for handling, artificial cell-cups have been devised. Doolittle [1] made cups by dipping a smooth stick with rounded end into melted wax and removing the adhering wax. The usual method is to use wooden cell-bases. A short cylinder of wood is hollowed out on one end and lined with wax, the cavity being the size of a queen-cell base. The opposite end of the cylinder has a nail point in it so that the cell-cup may be attached readily to a wooden strip or, better, the cylinder is flanged and hangs through a hole in the supporting bar (Fig. 192).[2]

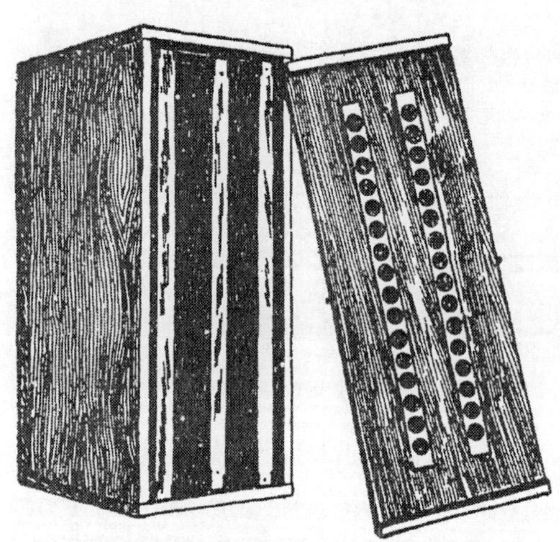

FIG. 191.—Swarm-box for starting queen-cells, showing position of frames and inner side of lid, with wooden cells in place, ready for bees.

Transferring larvæ

Having made the necessary cups they are inverted, and the usual practice is to wipe the inside of the cell with a little royal jelly procured from another queen-cell. Young larvæ are now carefully lifted from the worker-cells and placed in the artificial cell-cups, being taken of course from the colony of the queen selected as best for breeding. The supplied cells are hung in a colony prepared

[1] Doolittle, G. M., 1889. Scientific queen rearing. Chicago: also later editions.

[2] See the various booklets by E. L. Pratt (pseudonym Swarthmore).

for cell-building. The larvæ chosen should be as young as they can be obtained, preferably not more than one day from the egg. Older larvæ may be used but the resulting queens will probably be less valuable.

Swarm-box

A method for getting queen-cells started which is in some respects preferable to putting them in a queenless colony is the use of the swarm-box (Fig. 191). A special box, with wire screen bottom to provide adequate ventilation, is made large enough to hold five full frames, but only three are used, there being left alternating spaces the width of a frame. The frames should be abundantly supplied with pollen and honey and it is best to have one an empty comb into which water is poured. The top of the box is removable and has two slots cut in it into which are fitted two cell-bars which allow the queen-cells to hang over the spaces between the frames. When the box is prepared with the frames fastened in place and the slots filled with the empty cell-bars (or plain strips of wood), bees are shaken into the box sufficient to fill it more completely than bees are usually found in a hive, care being taken that a queen is not put into the swarm-box. This should usually be done about ten o'clock in the morning when the field bees are mostly away from the hive, thus providing a surplus of young bees. In about six hours the empty artificial cell-bases are removed one at a time and a worker larva transferred to each one, the hole meanwhile being closed by an extra cup. When this is completed the top of the box is covered snugly to keep the cells warm and the swarm-box is put away in a dark cool place. Usually by the next morning most of the cell-cups will have been built down and queen development will have begun. Considerable variation in the success of this method has been reported and there are numerous phases of this question on which more light is needed. Some strains of bees seem to be poor for this purpose. On the whole, however, when directions are carefully followed, a good number of fine queen-cells will usually be obtained. The method commends itself because of the saving of time and it is used by many commercial queen breeders.

Having cells built out

After cells have been started by any of the methods given, they may be put in the upper story of a normal colony, protected by perforated zinc to keep the queen from destroying the cells. During the time that the queen larvæ are taking food they should be kept in a strong colony so that they will be fed abundantly. If there is no honey-flow, it is necessary to give the colony some sugar sirup or honey daily to keep it in prime condition. The cells will be well cared for in strong queenless colonies, but to keep colonies queenless so long is expensive. It is a well recognized fact that if a colony is divided by perforated zinc, the portion away from the queen is in condition to build and care for queen-cells and may be considered as virtually queenless.

Nursery cages

Before the queens are ready to emerge, about ten days from the time of transferring the larvæ, each cell may be put in some sort of nursery cage (Fig. 192), so that as the

FIG. 192.—Pratt nursery. Two cells are removed to show construction. Six such nursery cages fit in a Langstroth frame.

queens emerge they will not kill each other or destroy other cells. As a rule, individual cages for each queen-cell are best. If colonies are ready to receive them the best method is to put each queen-cell in a colony so that there will be no necessity for introducing adult queens.

Mating hives

In case it is desired to have the queens mated before introducing them to full colonies or if queens are being raised for sale, the queen-cells or virgin queens (as most convenient) may be put in small colonies, usually known

Fig. 193.—Queen mating hives. This type is used in the apiary of the Bureau of Entomology. The frames are supported by tins which may be removed and used to fasten three frames together to form a large frame of Langstroth dimensions. A feeder is provided either at the front (right) or back (left) of the hive. These small hives are unnecessarily complex.

as nuclei. Two types of mating boxes are illustrated (Figs. 193, 194), but it is usually most satisfactory not to use too small a mating box. Many beekeepers prefer to use full Langstroth frames in boxes built to hold about three frames.

Classification of queens

When a queen has mated (usually in five or eight days) and has begun to deposit eggs she is ready to use and is known in the queen trade as untested. At this time it

Fig. 194.—"Baby nucleus" hive devised by Pratt. An introducing cage is in place between the frames.

cannot be determined whether she has mated with a drone of her own race, but if she is kept for a little over three weeks (until her progeny emerges) the color of the workers is taken as an indication of the purity or impurity of her mating. If apparently purely mated she is known in the trade as a tested queen. Further observations may cause her to be classed as select tested or finally as a breeding queen.

Mailing cages

If queens are to be shipped they are usually put in a queen mailing cage (Fig. 195) with some workers and an adequate supply of food, usually a soft paste or candy made by kneading together confectioner's (not powdered) sugar and honey without heating. Queens are frequently mailed across the continent from Europe in these cages and have been shipped successfully to New Zealand. Usually a trip of over ten days results in considerable loss.

Fig. 195.—Queen mailing cage. The right-hand hole is filled with candy which is then covered with a circle of comb-foundation or waxed paper. The cork at the end is removed when used for an introducing cage.

Introducing cages

The queen mailing cage is also used as an introducing cage or special cages may be utilized for this purpose. Cages are so constructed that the queen is separated from the workers in the hive that is to receive her by soft candy. The workers gradually eat this out and in the meantime the queen acquires the colony odor so that when the candy is eaten away she walks out without excitement and is accepted. This is the most common method of introducing queens. Some beekeepers dip the queen in honey and place her in the colony. The workers promptly remove the honey and usually accept the queen. Others fill the hive with smoke and close the entrance after letting the queen run in. Whatever is done the queen should acquire the colony odor so that the workers will not attack her as they normally do strange queens. Young virgin queens are more readily accepted than mated queens. Colonies that have been queenless for a considerable time are usually difficult to requeen and this is especially true if in the meantime some of the workers have begun to lay eggs (p. 200). In introducing a queen it is necessary that the colony be queenless or the strange queen will be killed.

IMPROVEMENT OF STOCK

In addition to the manipulations of queen-rearing there are some fundamental principles which should be considered. It should be the policy not only to provide queens as needed but steadily to keep improving the stock. For this work beekeepers usually depend on the specialists in queen-rearing but it is desirable that each beekeeper keep the ideal of bettering his stock constantly before him. The breeding of Italian queens for additional yellow on the abdomen, resulting in the so-called five-banded bees, clearly demonstrates that changes can be made by applying the principles of breeding to queen-rearing. While the merits of these bees is a subject of dispute, the success in this line of endeavor should encourage the beekeeper to believe that as striking things are possible in other lines of bee-breeding.

It is evident that certain characteristics which the beekeeper wishes to develop and some which he wishes to reduce or destroy must be inherited. Exceptional prolificness, gentleness, excessive swarming, protracted breeding and their opposites are characteristic of various races and strains of bees but not of the entire species. This leads to the belief that the bee-breeder may hope to modify his bees along these lines by proper care in selecting his breeding material. The actual results of practical beekeepers also show that improvement may be made, as indicated by increased crops.

Study of breeding needed

It is not practical in this place to enter on an elaborate discussion of the methods and results of modern breeding. To what characters of bees Mendelian inheritance is operative has not been shown by the work so far done although color is doubtless so inherited. Bee-breeding has not been subject to the researches of the theoretical breeders but investigation of this character is greatly to be desired. Certain fundamental facts should be mentioned, however, and they are chosen here because they have been misunderstood by beekeepers writing for bee-journals. The fact that a queen is poorly developed because of inadequate care does not make her undesirable as a breeder and, conversely, prolificness induced by extra care and manipulation does not make a queen more valuable for breeding, because characters acquired during the life of the individual are not inherited.

Selection of drones

As great care should be exercised in choosing the drones as is employed in selecting the breeding queen, but most beekeepers fail to give this subject adequate consideration. In general the drone (father) is just as influential in deciding the character of the offspring as is the queen (mother). Drones may be selected by allowing them to fly only from the colony or colonies which are up to the breeding standard. Drone production in these colonies may be increased by providing drone-comb. Drone-rearing in other colonies may be restricted by giving only worker-comb or the undesirable drones may be trapped by a queen- and drone-trap

(Fig. 31). While the beekeeper cannot choose the individual drone with which a queen mates,[1] he can increase the chances of desirable matings by providing plenty of drones of good stock and restricting undesirable drones. When the workers begin to drive drones from the hives they may be protected by putting them in a queenless colony, where they will not be molested.

Desirability of pure races

Above all, the desirability of pure races should be emphasized. It is a common belief that hybrids (usually crosses of Italians and blacks) are good honey-gatherers. Crosses of other races are also recommended. The first cross is often desirable from the standpoint of honey-gathering but it is better to breed from pure stock only, for the offspring of a hybrid queen is exceptionally variable and it is rather a matter of chance if good stock results. Presumably the desirable characteristics of certain crosses might be fixed by judicious and intelligent selection, but this is a problem for a professional breeder and not for the honey-producer or even for the commercial queen breeder.

Danger from inbreeding

This has been much over-estimated in the discussions of breeding in the bee-journals. Inbreeding may accentuate undesirable characters but it may likewise help to fix desirable characters, and it has been used with good results in other lines of breeding. The commercial honey-producer need have little fear of harmful results, for if any signs of degeneracy are observed it is easy at any time to introduce new blood.

[1] A great advance in the possibilities for better breeding of bees has recently been made by the discovery of a method whereby mating of queens may be controlled. See: Watson, Lloyd, R., 1927. Controlled Mating of Queen Bees, Hamilton, Ill.: Amer. Bee Journ., 50 pp., 11 figs. The method devised by Dr. Watson is not yet such that it can be used by breeders generally, but it marks a great step forward in making breeding work possible. The method is the instrumental insemination of queens by an apparatus devised by this author.

CHAPTER XXIV

MISCELLANEOUS INFORMATION

Beekeeping does not consist solely in caring for bees and in using or selling their products. The activities of the beekeeper are expressed in various allied fields and, since these are things about which the beekeeper wants and should have information, it is proposed in this brief closing chapter to give a few unrelated notes which may be helpful, but which do not properly find a place in the previous chapters.

LITERATURE ON BEES AND BEEKEEPING

In the centuries during which man has been interested in the honeybee, hundreds and perhaps thousands of books have been written on this subject. No other insect, and perhaps no other animal except man, has been so voluminously discussed. Many of these books are now of interest chiefly to the collector of old books, for recent investigations have naturally left many far behind. Even to list the books on beekeeping would require a book the size of this one, so this interesting task must be set aside. The beekeeper will find it to his advantage to read almost every one of the books now offered to the American beekeeper.

In addition to works issued in book form, there is an extensive literature on bees in scientific journals, unfortunately not readily accessible to most beekeepers. References have been made to many of these papers in the preceding pages. Some of the journals devoted to beekeeping have contained articles of lasting practical value but unfortunately these journals are too often read and at once cast aside. The Bureau of Entomology has a working bibliography, arranged by authors and subject, which is far from complete but which, nevertheless, is helpful and is probably the most extensive so far attempted for beekeeping literature. It contains perhaps 25,000 to 30,000 titles and is constantly growing.

There are several journals in America devoted exclusively to beekeeping, and a still larger number appear regularly in foreign countries, all of which are of value to the beekeeper. It is extremely unfortunate that abstracts of the more important scientific and practical articles from other countries cannot be made available to American beekeepers.

Until rather recent time, no effort has been made to collect the world's beekeeping literature, but now several institutions are undertaking this important work. The Bureau of Entomology has an excellent library in this field, unfortunately not readily accessible to others. A few years ago there was established at the University of Wisconsin a memorial Library to the beloved American beekeeper, C. C. Miller, so that the good work begun by him during his life may be continued. More recently there has been established at Cornell University a library which already contains some of the treasures of beekeeping and which is constantly growing. In the Cornell Beekeeping Library will be found the personal journal kept by Father L. L. Langstroth for forty-five years, containing his notes and comments, the greatest treasure in beekeeping literature. Books and journals may be obtained by beekeepers in any part of the country from either the Miller or the Cornell Library through any public library, so that these are by no means local helps. A few other institutions are making similar but so far less extensive efforts to make collections of such literature.

LEADERS IN BEEKEEPING

Space will not permit mention of all who have contributed to the advancement of beekeeping, but every beekeeper should make an effort to learn something of the men who have made the industry what it is today. After completing this book the author finds that adequate mention is not made of some of the most important works of the past, chiefly because in giving relatively few references to the literature it is essential that choice be made of papers and books that are most readily accessible. This is obviously unfair to the outstanding leaders of the past. The great leader in America was Langstroth, the inventor of the movable frame-hive. Quinby, Root, Miller, Doolittle and others did their share in making valued improvements and in spreading the news of better methods, and it is eminently fitting that beekeepers should render unto these men the credit to which they are entiled. Going even further back, Huber, the blind Swiss naturalist, did work which forms the very foundation of beekeeping, and his writings are still worthy of serious study. The special libraries of beekeeping literature contain information about all these men, and it is especially fitting that memorials to Miller, Langstroth, Quinby and Root have been established in these several libraries. It would be impossible properly to weigh the contributions of more recent workers in this field, but the important papers of most of them have been mentioned in earlier pages. It is a matter of some regret that the American literature on beekeeping does not contain books recording the work of these earlier leaders. It is also appropriate to mention the regrettable fact that a history of American beekeeping has not yet been prepared.

ORGANIZATIONS OF BEEKEEPERS

There are in the United States a considerable number of societies of beekeepers, organized for their mutual advancement. There is a national organization, state societies in almost all the states and many county or regional associations. During the period of the War, these societies were extremely active, but recently there has been a decline in interest which is regrettable. This decrease is doubtless due to the present difficulties with the honey market, which is perhaps a transient condition. Every real bee-enthusiast will wish to take his part in making these societies more helpful.

In addition to the organizations which deal especially with educational and social affairs, some associations are directing their efforts toward a betterment of honey markets. These are usually cooperative organizations of beekeepers. While efforts have been and are being made to create such associations in the East, the more successful ones have been located in western states, where the honey-producer is a long distance from the consuming public.

Information regarding these societies may usually be obtained from the Bee Culture Laboratory, Bureau of Entomology, Washington, D. C. A few of the societies now issue official organs which are helpful.

LAWS

It is not proposed to discuss in this place the legal rights of the beekeeper or the legal status of the bee. The American Honey Producers' League has made a compilation of the laws in this field. Some of the associations of beekeepers offer protection to their members in case of legal complications.

The special laws in which beekeepers are most interested are those which provide for the inspection of apiaries for the control of bee diseases. This work falls on the several states, there being no federal law on this subject. The number of states having such laws has increased until now almost all the important beekeeping states have some provisions for apiary inspection. Information concerning the inspection laws of any of the states may be obtained from state officials or from the Bureau of Entomology.

The Federal Government has passed a law prohibiting the importation of adult bees into the United States, except under the direction of the Department of Agriculture for certain specific reasons, in an effort to prevent the introduction of certain diseases of bees which occur in Europe but which are not known to exist in the United States. Canada has similar provisions. The details of this law may be obtained from the Department of Agriculture, Washington, D. C.

The Federal Food and Drugs Act, enacted June 30, 1906, has been one of the greatest benefits to beekeeping of any law yet passed. On this as a basis, the several states have enacted similar laws. The essential feature of this law is that the label shall tell the exact truth about the contents of the package. Only in cases in which the contents may actually be injurious does this law specify the nature of the materials to be used, so that it rests with the purchaser to decide what he shall buy after the truth is told him. This law has been amended to make it necessary that the net weight of the contents shall appear on the label. Recently efforts have been made to nullify parts of this law by amendments which would permit the use of certain inferior products without declaration on the label, but the beekeepers of the country have firmly insisted that the law shall not be destroyed. Their battle is perhaps not yet fully won.

Some states have laws which prohibit the spraying of fruit-trees while in bloom, the purpose of these being to protect bees from the applied poisons. A law to control wide-spread applications of poisonous dusts has been advocated by many beekeepers, but none has been enacted at the time of the publication of this book. Such a protection to beekeeping is badly needed.

EDUCATIONAL WORK IN BEEKEEPING

The advance of past years in beekeeping has come chiefly through an exchange of ideas and results of observations through the bee-journals and books, but more recently it has occurred through the distribution of bulletins from federal and state laboratories devoted to beekeeping. The distribution of literature alone is inadequate, and to remedy this defect extension in beekeeping was begun in 1916 by the Bureau of Entomology. This work is now entirely in the hands of the several states and well qualified extension specialists are now employed in many states. Their number should be increased. In several states the extension services issue monthly news letters which are highly beneficial. Several agricultural colleges are now offering courses in beekeeping and at least two universities are offering graduate work in this field. These various lines of research, extension and teaching are being conducted with the greatest possible degree of cooperation among the several states. If beekeeping is to advance in the United States and Canada, it must be through the application of better scientific methods in production and marketing, and it thus becomes the duty of each beekeeper to do all that he can to advance such education. The federal and state laboratories have already issued a considerable number of valuable bulletins, some of which have been mentioned in earlier pages. At present it is only through such agencies that scientific work on beekeeping is widely conducted, but it is to be hoped that other institutions not directly connected with state activities may be induced to increase their efforts to learn more about the honeybee. Gratifying results in this line have come from cooperative efforts between the regular bee-culture laboratories and some of the other institutions.

If any one fault may be found with the attitude of the American beekeeper it is in his failure to appreciate the excellent work for the advancement of beekeeping in other countries. Beekeepers of all countries are coming to realize that many of their problems are not limited by artificial lines of political divisions and several efforts are being made to bring about a unity in effort in the various countries. The Apis Club with headquarters in Great Britain and the International Apicultural Congresses are efforts in this line and are worthy of increased support. Until these efforts are more widely supported, the individual beekeeper will find it vastly to his advantage to read the bee-journals of other countries, especially those which deal more largely with the scientific aspects of beekeeping.

SUPPLIES FOR BEEKEEPING

It has been shown in earlier chapters that it is quite necessary that hives and other apiary supplies be accurately made, and for this reason it is usually desirable that a beekeeper buy his equipment from some manufacturer, unless he is a skilled wood-worker. The American beekeepers are fortunate in that the supply business is adequate. There are a number of extensive establishments, and most of them have agencies or branches in various sections from which supplies may be obtained on short notice. The manufacturers will gladly send catalogues and give information concerning agencies. The addresses of manufacturers may be obtained from advertisements in the bee-journals.

MARKETING HELPS

One of the great problems of the commercial beekeeper is to obtain accurate information regarding honey markets. In 1914 the Bureau of Crop Estimates (now the Bureau of Agricultural Economics) of the Department of Agriculture, Washington, D. C., inaugurated a system of reports on crop conditions, but through lack of support from beekeepers these have recently been abandoned. The same Bureau has, however, undertaken to get another type of information of even greater value, these being the semimonthly reports on the chief honey markets of the country. To these are added valuable information on honey-plant conditions and other data from producing areas. Data on exports and imports are also included. These reports are sent without charge to beekeepers in any part of the United

States and are the most reliable source of market information available. Strangely enough, some beekeepers have objected to giving the desired information to the Bureau, on the ground that it gave more data to dealers than to producers. It must be remembered that dealers have sources of information which the producer cannot obtain, so that the producers gain far more from such reports than do any others. No beekeeper who sells honey should fail to obtain these reports and it is likewise his duty to give all information desired. The bee-journals either reprint this information or give additional data from other sources.

THE USES OF HONEY

This subject might well be the title of a separate chapter. While the production and marketing of honey does not include its uses, this is a subject on which beekeepers should have more information. They and their families should set a good example to their customers by using honey freely in their homes, which will be a vast improvement over the inferior jams and jellies so widely sold and infinitely superior to the cheap and often dangerous sirups which are so widely advertised.

The chief use of honey at present is as a spread for bread, for which purpose it may be utilized in any form. If this use alone were more prevalent in American households, there would be no worry about the sale of the honey crop. Honey is often recommended in older books on beekeeping for almost every human ailment, but in these days of more enlightenment in medical affairs, such uses can be advised only on recommendation of a properly qualified physician. In certain intestinal disorders, honey is often advised to the exclusion of all other forms of sweets.

The use of honey in cooking and baking is declining, largely through the advertisement of cheaper and inferior sirups. In home cooking and baking there are many ways in which honey may be employed advantageously, and recipes may be found in a bulletin issued by the Department of Agriculture.[1]

Fruits preserved in honey have long been relished for their superior flavor, and the famous Bar le duc preserves are made with honey. Honey is also used in some of the finest confections, but many modern confectionery manufacturers avoid it because of the sweetness of honey. They find it more profitable financially to use sirups that are less sweet, so that the public will be more prone to eat too much candy. This is a regrettable and probably dangerous tendency in the manufacture of confectionery.

An excellent vinegar is made of honey, and the beekeeper who desires to manufacture such a product will find it necessary to consult the regulations of the Prohibition Division of the Treasury Department before embarking on such methods. This is obviously due to the fact that the first stage in vinegar manufacture is one in which alcohol is produced, which leads to extensive uses of honey for alcoholic drinks in other lands. Honey is now used in making anti-freeze mixtures for automobile radiators, a mixture which sometimes gets beekeepers into rather serious troubles with their motors and one which at present cannot be recommended strongly. Honey is used in many manufacturing processes for which gylcerine was formerly thought necessary.

The American people lead the world in the use of sugar, the average annual sugar consumption now being far greater than the interests of health would dictate. This fact is now coming to be widely recognized and campaigns for better dietaries are being pushed. In the relief from excessive sugar consumption, one of the best methods is to substitute honey for sugar and cheap and unsweet sirups, and this seems the most probable means of advanc-

[1] Hunt, Caroline L., and Atwater, Helen W., 1915. Honey and its uses in the home. Farmers' Bull., 653, U. S. Dept. Agr., 26 pp.

ing the sales of this delectable product. In order to take advantage of this forthcoming change, beekeepers will find it desirable to study honey to learn its many virtues.

THE BUREAU OF ENTOMOLOGY

At the time that the first edition of this book was issued, the author was in charge of the Bee Culture Laboratory of this Bureau. Since that time he has changed his work to another location, making it possible for him to speak his mind more freely regarding this institution. Since the various states are enlarging their work for the advancement of beekeeping, it is obviously the function of the Bureau largely to limit its work to research in the various problems which confront the beekeeper and to present its work of a practical nature largely through publications, leaving to the several states the effort to carry this knowledge to beekeepers through extension.

The work of the Bureau in the past has beyond question ranked high scientifically and the most important investigations for the advancement of the beekeeper in the United States have emanated from this institution. Scientific investigations of the highest class have been recorded on the structure, development and behavior of bees, from which detailed practical methods have been devised. The work on bee diseases has been outstanding. The study on wintering has perhaps been the line of effort which gave most speedy practical results. At present many important problems are being attacked and the Bureau deserves full support from beekeepers.

The work of the Bee Culture Laboratory is recorded in bulletins issued by the Department of Agriculture and occasionally in outside publications. It is greatly to be regretted that the publication policies of the Department, made necessary by shortage of funds, have allowed some of the most important bulletins to be out of print. The interested beekeeper can obtain on application to the

Bureau a list of all available publications, with directions for obtaining them. Many of these publications have been mentioned in previous pages and will be helpful.

Other Bureaus of the Department have also issued bulletins or circulars which are helpful, largely through the influence of men connected with the Bureau of Entomology. These may be obtained in a similar way and information about them secured from the Bureau of Entomology.

The Bureau also renders direct service by diagnosing samples of suspected disease without charge and at present determines the grade of honey samples. Inquiries on beekeeping questions are always answered freely.

APPENDIX

EXPLANATION OF SYMBOLS USED IN THE ANATOMICAL ILLUSTRATIONS

SINCE nearly all of the illustrations of anatomical parts are from the work of Snodgrass it may be best to give the list of symbols and alphabetical lettering prepared by him and given on pp. 141–147 of his paper. These will aid in identifying parts which are labeled in the illustrations, used in this book to illustrate certain portions only.

1. SYMBOLS

A, anal vein; *1A*, first anal, *2A*, second anal, etc.

AcGl, accessory gland of male reproductive organs.

AGl, acid gland of sting, opening into poison sac (*PsnSc*).

AGlD, duct of acid gland of sting.

An, anus.

ANP, anterior wing process of notum.

ANR, anterior marginal ridge of notum.

Ant, antenna.

AntL, antennal lobe of brain.

AntNv, antennal nerve.

Ao, aorta.

Ap, apodeme, any internal chitinous process of body-wall.

Aph, anterior phragma of any tergum, prephragma.

Ax, the axillaries or articular sclerites of the wing base, designated individually as *1Ax*, *2Ax*, *3Ax*, and *4Ax*.

ax, accessory axillary sclerites of irregular occurrence in connection with the principal axillaries (*Ax*).

AxC, axillary cord, or ligament-like thickening of posterior edge of basal membrane of wing, attached to posterior angle of scutellum.

AxM, axillary membrane, the thin membrane of wing base, containing the axillary sclerites and forming in some cases the lobes called alulæ.

B,	bulb (bulb of penis or of sheath of sting).
BC,	body-cavity.
bc,	any particular part of body cavity such as that prolonged into the mouth parts, legs or pieces of the sting.
BCpx,	bursa copulatrix.
BGl,	alkaline gland of sting.
BM,	basement membrane.
Br,	brain.
1Br,	protocerebrum.
2Br,	deutocerebrum.
3Br,	tritocerebrum.
Brb,	barb.
BW,	body-wall.
C,	costa, first vein of wing.
Cb,	pollen basket or corbiculum on hind tibia of worker.
CC,	crystalline cone of compound eye.
Cd,	cardo.
Cer,	cercus.
CL,	crystalline lens of compound eye.
Cl, Cls,	cell, cells.
Cla,	claw.
Clp,	clypeus.
Clsp,	clasping lobes of ninth segment of male, perhaps equivalent to the four gonapophyses of ninth segment of female.
1Clsp,	upper or outer clasper.
2Clsp,	lower or inner clasper.
Com,	commissure (of either nervous or tracheal system).
Cor,	cornea.
Ctl,	cuticle, the chitinous layer of the epidermis.
Cu,	cubitus, fifth vein of generalized wing.
Cv,	cross-vein.
Cx,	coxa.
CxP,	pleural coxal process.
Dct,	duct.
DDph,	dorsal diaphragm.
Dph,	diaphragm.
DphCls,	diaphragm cells.
Dphmb,	membrane of diaphragm.
DphMcl,	muscle fibers of diaphragm.
E,	compound eye.
EAp,	apodeme of extensor muscle.
EjD,	ejaculatory duct.
Em,	lateral emargination of notum.
EMcl,	extensor muscle.

Emp,	empodium.
Enz,	digestive vesicles formed by ventricular epithelium.
Ep,	epicranium.
Ephy,	epipharynx.
Epm,	epimerum.
Eps,	episternum.
Epth,	epithelium.
F,	femur.
Fl,	flagellum.
For,	foramen magnum.
Ft,	front.
FtCom,	frontal commissure.
FtGng,	frontal ganglion.
FtNv,	frontal nerve.
Fu,	furca or median entosternal apodeme of thoracic sterna.
G,	gonapophysis.
Ga,	galea.
Ge,	gena.
Gl,	gland.
1Gl,	large pharyngeal gland in anterior part of head of worker.
2Gl,	salivary gland in posterior part of head.
3Gl,	thoracic salivary gland.
4Gl,	small median gland below pharyngeal plate (*s*).
Gls,	glossa.
Gng,	ganglion.
Gu,	gula.
H,	head.
Hk,	hooks on front edge of hind wing.
Hphy,	hypopharynx.
Hr,	hair.
hr,	surface disk of "auditory" organ of antenna, probably modified base of sensory hair.
HS,	honey stomach.
Ht,	heart.
ht,	individual chamber of heart.
HtCls,	pericardial cells.
HtTraSc,	pericardial tracheal sac.
Int,	intima, the chitinous lining of any internal organ.
IT,	tergum of first abdominal segment, the *median segment*, or *propodeum*, incorporated into thorax.
L,	leg.
Lb,	labium.
Lbl,	labellum.
LbNv,	labial nerve.

LbPlp, labial palpus.
Lc, lacinia.
Lct, lancet of sting, equivalent to first gonapophysis (*1G*).
Lg, ligula.
LGl, "lubricating" gland of sting (not shown in figures).
Lin, median lobe of lingua or hypopharynx.
Lm, labrum.
LMcl, longitudinal muscles.
lmcl, ventral longitudinal muscles of thorax.
LmNv, labral nerve.
Lr, lorum.
LTra, trachea of leg.
Lum, lumen, the cavity of any hollow organ, whether the glossa, sting, alimentary canal, or gland.
M, media, fourth vein of wing. M_1–M_4, first to fourth branches of media.
m, median plate or plates of wing base.
Mal, Malpighian tubules.
Mb, intersegmental membrane.
mb, membrane.
m-cu, medio-cubital cross-vein.
MD, disklike muscle apodeme.
Md, mandible.
1MdGl, outer saclike mandibular gland.
2MdGl, inner racemose mandibular gland.
MdNv, mandibular nerve.
Mes, mesathorax, designated by figure 2 placed after and below any thoracic symbol.
Met, metathorax, designated by figure 3 placed after and below any thoracic symbol.
Mi, the chitinous plates of the neck collectively, the "microthorax," individually designated *mi*.
mi, cervical (microthoracic) sclerites.
m-m, median cross-vein.
Mps, mouth parts or trophi.
Mt, mentum.
Mth, mouth.
Mx, maxilla.
MxPlp, maxillary palpus.
MxNv, maxillary nerve.
N, notum.
Nu, nucleus.
Nv, nerve.
O, ocellus.
Ob, oblong plate.

Oc, occiput.
Œ, œsophagus.
ŒCom, circumœsophageal commissures.
Om, ommatidium.
OpL, optic lobe.
Ost, ostium or lateral aperture of heart.
Ov, ovary.
ov, ovariole, individual ovarian tube.
OvD, oviduct.
OvO, opening of vagina or median oviduct.
P, paraptera, small pleural plates below base of wing, typically two episternal paraptera or preparaptera (*1P* and *2P*) before pleural wing process (*WP*), and two epimeral paraptera or postparaptera (*3P* and *4P*) behind wing process.
1P, 2P, episternal paraptera, preparaptera.
3P, 4P, epimeral paraptera, postparaptera.
PA, arm of pleural ridge.
Pcl, postclypeus.
PD, muscle disk of episternal paraptera, giving insertion to pronator muscle (not present in the bee).
Pd, peduncle.
Pen, penis.
PenB, bulb of penis.
Peps, preepisternum.
Pge, postgena.
Pgl, paraglossa.
Pgu, pregula.
Ph, phragma.
Phy, pharynx.
Pl, pleurum,
pl, subdivision of pleurum.
Plf, palpifer, palpus-carrying lobe of maxilla.
Plg, palpiger, palpus-carrying lobe of labium.
Plp, palpus.
Pmb, peritrophic membrane.
PMcl pronator muscle.
PN postnotum or pseudonotum, the second or postalar tergal plate of the wing-bearing segments of most insects, the "postscutellum" of higher orders.
pn, small rod connecting postscutellum (postnotum *PN*) with upper edge of epimerum, probably a detached piece of the former.
PNP, posterior notal wing process.
PNR, posterior marginal ridge of notum.

Pph, posterior phragma or postphragma of any tergum, carried by the second notal plate or postnotum (*PN*), the "postscutellum" of higher forms.
PR, internal pleural ridge, the entopleurum, marked externally by pleural suture (*PS*).
Prb, proboscis.
PrbFs, fossa of proboscis.
PS, pleural suture, external line separating episternum and epimerum, marking site of internal pleural ridge.
Ps, presternum.
Psc, prescutum.
Pscl, postscutellum (postnotum).
Psl, poststernellum.
PsnC, poison canal of sting.
PsnSc, poison sac of sting into which opens the acid gland (*AGl*).
Pt, sensory pit.
Ptr, peritreme, spiracle-bearing sclerite.
Pvent, proventriculus.
PventVlv, proventricular tube or valve in ventriculus.
Qd, quadrate plate of sting.
R, radius, third vein of generalized wing. R_1–R_5, first to fifth branches of radius. R_s radial sector.
RAp, apodeme of flexor muscle.
Rd, posterior extension or reduplication of any tergal or sternal plate overlapping plate following it.
Rect, rectum, the large intestine of insects.
RGl, rectal glands.
r-m, radio-medial cross-vein.
RMcl, flexor muscle of mandible or wing.
1RMcl, dorsal retractor muscle of ligula.
2RMcl, ventral retractor muscle of ligula.
R_s, radial sector, or second branch of radius at first forking.
S, sternum.
SalD, salivary duct.
SalDO, external opening of salivary duct.
Sc, subcosta, second vein of generalized wing.
Scl, scutellum.
Scp, scape.
Sct. scutum.
Sga, subgalea.
Sh, sheath of sting, equivalent to the second gonapophyses (*2G*) or middle pair on ninth abdominal segment.
ShA, basal arm of sheath of sting.
ShB, bulb of sheath of sting or ovipositor.
ShS, shaft of sheath of sting.

SInt, small intestine.
Sl, sternellum.
Slin, superlingua, embryonic lateral lobes of hypopharynx, true appendages of fifth head segment.
Smt, submentum.
SœGng, subœsophageal ganglion.
Sp, spiracle.
Spm, spermatheca.
SpmGl, spermathecal gland.
St, stipes.
StgNv, stomatogastric nerve.
Stn, sting.
StnPlp, palpuslike appendages of the sting, equivalent to the third gonapophyses (*3G*) or the outer pair on ninth abdominal segment.
T, tergum.
IT, first abdominal tergum, the propodeum, incorporated into thorax.
IIT, second abdominal tergum.
Tar, tarsus.
Tb, tibia.
Ten, large tentorial arms of head, the mesocephalic pillars.
ten, slender tentorial arch over foramen magnum.
Tes, testes.
Tg, tegula.
TMcl, transverse muscle.
Tn, trochantin (not separated from sternum in bee).
TnC, coxal condyle of trochantin.
Tr, trochanter.
Tra, trachea.
TraCom, transverse ventral tracheal commissures of abdomen.
TraSc, tracheal sac.
Tri, triangular plate of sting.
Vag, vagina.
VDef, vas deferens.
VDph, ventral diaphragm.
Vent, ventriculus.
VentVlv, ventricular fold or valve in small intestine.
Ves, vesicula seminalis.
Vlv, valve of sting carried by lancet.
VMcl, large vertical muscles of thorax.
VNR, internal, median V-shaped notal ridge, the "entodorsum."
Vx, vertex.
W, wing.

W_2Nv, mesothoracic wing nerve.
W_3Nv, metathoracic wing nerve.
WP, wing process of pleurum.

2. ALPHABETICAL LETTERING

a, clypeal suture.
b, anterior tentorial pit, in clypeal suture.
c, posterior tentorial pit, in occiput beside foramen magnum.
d, thickened posterior edge of lateral wall of fossa of proboscis.
e, process at upper end of *d* articulating with cardo of maxilla and forming maxillary suspensorium.
f, internal median keel of vertex in cranium of drone.
g, suspensorial ligaments of anterior end of œsophagus.
h, pharyngeal rod.
i, convolutions of dorsal blood vessel.
j, anterior articular knob of mandible.
k, ventral groove of glossa.
l, ventral groove of maxillary rod.
m, median plates of wing base.
n, basal hooks of glossa.
o, median ventral plate of ligula.
p, dorsal plates of anterior end of mentum, supporting ligula.
q, inner wall of canal of glossa.
r, chitinous rod of glossa.
s, pharyngeal plate, on anterior part of floor of pharynx.
t, salivary pouch opening on dorsal side of base of ligula, receiving common duct of salivary glands (*SalD*).
u, oblique muscles inserted upon dorsal side of salivary pouch of ligula.
v, transverse or V-shaped suture on surface of mesonotum or metanotum, formed by the internal V-shaped ridge or "entodorsum" (*VNR*).
w, lateral lobe of pronotum projecting posteriorly over the first spiracle.
x, thoracic plate lying laterad of anterior part of sternum, often regarded as a part of presternum.
y, accessory sclerite of fourth axillary (*4Ax*) of front wing, affording insertion for slender muscle (*cc*) attached below to common apodeme of mesosternum and metasternum.
z, coxal condyles of mesothoracic and metathoracic sterna,

probably really the coxal condyles of trochantins (*TnC*) fused entirely with the sterna and episterna in each segment.

aa, muscle arising from inner wall of mesothoracic pleurum and inserted upon outer end of corresponding scutellum, probably accessory in function to the great vertical muscles (*VMcl*) between the mesothoracic sternum and scutum.

bb, coxo-axillary muscle, extending from upper end of coxa to third parapterum (*3P*).

cc, muscle inserted upon accessory sclerite (*y*) of fourth axillary (*4Ax*) from common entosternum of mesothorax and metathorax.

dd, notch of antenna cleaner on first tarsal joint (*1Tar*) of front leg.

ee, spine of antenna cleaner situated on distal end of tibia (*Tb*).

ff, so-called "wax shears" or "wax pincers."

gg, transverse chitinous band of empodium (*Emp*), which compresses its two lobes when not in use and spreads out by muscular effort.

hh, dorsal plate supporting empodium.

ii, ventral plate supporting empodium.

jj, dorsal groove of lancet interlocking with ventral ridge of sheath of sting.

kk, sting chamber within end of seventh abdominal segment, lodging sting whose accessory plates are derived from eighth and ninth segments.

ll, reservoir of thoracic salivary gland.

mm, receptacular chitinous pouches on ventral side of pharyngeal plate (*s*) receiving ducts of large lateral pharyngeal glands of head (*1Gl*).

nn, "stomach-mouth" at summit of proventricular projection within honey stomach (*HS*).

oo, pores on lancets and shaft of sting sheath opening to exterior from prolongation of body-cavity (*bc*) contained in each.

pp, gelatinous layer secreted upon inner surface of ventricular epithelium.

qq, food contents of alimentary canal.

rr, cells of ventricular epithelium apparently forming the internal gelatinous layer.

ss, cartilaginous mass on inner surface of dorsal wall of bulb of penis (*PenB*).

tt. dorsal plates of bulb of penis.

uu, fimbriated dorsal lobes of penis at base of bulb.
vv, ventral scalariform row of plates on tube of penis.
ww, dorsal basal plates of penis.
xx, ventral basal plates of penis.
yy, basal pouch of penis.
zz, copulatory sacs of penis.

INDEX

NOTE: The names of honey-plants given in the Annotated List of Honey-Plants (pp. 397 to 420) are not included in this alphabetical index since they are given in alphabetical order in the list.